Submarine Slope Systems:
Processes and Products

Special Publication reviewing procedures

The Society makes every effort to ensure that the scientific and production quality of its books matches that of its journals. Since 1997, all book proposals have been refereed by specialist reviewers as well as by the Society's Books Editorial Committee. If the referees identify weaknesses in the proposal, these must be addressed before the proposal is accepted.

Once the book is accepted, the Society has a team of Book Editors (listed above) who ensure that the volume editors follow strict guidelines on refereeing and quality control. We insist that individual papers can only be accepted after satisfactory review by two independent referees. The questions on the review forms are similar to those for *Journal of the Geological Society*. The referees' forms and comments must be available to the Society's Book Editors on request.

Although many of the books result from meetings, the editors are expected to commission papers that were not presented at the meeting to ensure that the book provides a balanced coverage of the subject. Being accepted for presentation at the meeting does not guarantee inclusion in the book.

Geological Society Special Publications are included in the ISI Index of Scientific Book Contents, but they do not have an impact factor, the latter being applicable only to journals.

More information about submitting a proposal and producing a Special Publication can be found on the Society's web site: www.geolsoc.org.uk.

It is recommended that reference to all or part of this book should be made in one of the following ways:

HODGSON, D.M. & FLINT, S.S. (eds) 2005. *Submarine Slope Systems: Processes and Products.* Geological Society, London, Special Publications, **244.**

UNDERWOOD, M.B. & FERGUSSON, C.L. 2005. Late Cenozoic evolution of the Nankai trench–slope system: evidence from sand petrography and clay mineralogy. *In*: HODGSON, D.M. & FLINT, S.S. (eds). *Submarine Slope Systems: Processes and Products.* Geological Society, London, Special Publications, **244,** 113–129.

GEOLOGICAL SOCIETY SPECIAL PUBLICATION NO. 244

Submarine Slope Systems: Processes and Products

EDITED BY

DAVID M. HODGSON

and

STEPHEN S. FLINT

Stratigraphy Group, Department of Earth and Ocean Sciences, University of Liverpool, UK

2005

Published by

The Geological Society

London

THE GEOLOGICAL SOCIETY

The Geological Society of London (GSL) was founded in 1807. It is the oldest national geological society in the world and the largest in Europe. It was incorporated under Royal Charter in 1825 and is Registered Charity 210161.

The Society is the UK national learned and professional society for geology with a worldwide Fellowship (FGS) of 9000. The Society has the power to confer Chartered status on suitably qualified Fellows, and about 2000 of the Fellowship carry the title (CGeol). Chartered Geologists may also obtain the equivalent European title, European Geologist (EurGeol). One fifth of the Society's fellowship resides outside the UK. To find out more about the Society, log on to www.geolsoc.org.uk.

The Geological Society Publishing House (Bath, UK) produces the Society's international journals and books, and acts as European distributor for selected publications of the American Association of Petroleum Geologists (AAPG), the American Geological Institute (AGI), the Indonesian Petroleum Association (IPA), the Geological Society of America (GSA), the Society for Sedimentary Geology (SEPM) and the Geologists' Association (GA). Joint marketing agreements ensure that GSL Fellows may purchase these societies' publications at a discount. The Society's online bookshop (accessible from www.geolsoc.org.uk) offers secure book purchasing with your credit or debit card.

To find out about joining the Society and benefiting from substantial discounts on publications of GSL and other societies worldwide, consult www.geolsoc.org.uk, or contact the Fellowship Department at: The Geological Society, Burlington House, Piccadilly, London W1J 0BG: Tel. +44 (0)20 7434 9944; Fax +44 (0)20 7439 8975; E-mail: enquiries@geolsoc.org.uk.

For information about the Society's meetings, consult *Events* on www.geolsoc.org.uk. To find out more about the Society's Corporate Affiliates Scheme, write to enquiries@geolsoc.org.uk.

Published by The Geological Society from:
The Geological Society Publishing House
Unit 7, Brassmill Enterprise Centre
Brassmill Lane
Bath BA1 3JN, UK

Orders: Tel. +44 (0)1225 445046
Fax +44 (0)1225 442836

Online bookshop: www.geolsoc.org.uk/bookshop

British Library Cataloguing in Publication Data
A catalogue record for this book is available from the British Library.

ISBN 1-86239-177-7

Typeset by Servis Filmsetting, Manchester, UK
Printed by The Alden Press, Oxford, UK

Distributors

USA
AAPG Bookstore
PO Box 979
Tulsa
OK 74101-0979
USA
Orders: Tel. + 1 918 584-2555
Fax +1 918 560-2652
E-mail bookstore@aapg.org

India
Affiliated East-West Press Private Ltd
Marketing Division
G-1/16 Ansari Road, Darya Ganj
New Delhi 110 002
India
Orders: Tel. +91 11 2327-9113/2326-4180
Fax +91 11 2326-0538
E-mail affiliat@vsnl.com

Japan
Kanda Book Trading Company
Cityhouse Tama 204
Tsurumaki 1-3-10
Tama-shi, Tokyo 206-0034
Japan
Orders: Tel. +81 (0)423 57-7650
Fax +81 (0)423 57-7651
Email geokanda@ma.kcom.ne.jp

Contents

Submarine slope systems: processes and products

STEPHEN S. FLINT & DAVID M. HODGSON

Stratigraphy Group, Department of Earth and Ocean Sciences, University of Liverpool, 4 Brownlow Street, Liverpool L69 3GP, UK (e-mail: flint@liverpool.ac.uk)

Abstract: Understanding of the processes operating on submarine slopes, the preserved depositional products and post-depositional modifications to sediment body geometries through instability and remobilization requires integration of data from modern slopes with information derived from seismic and outcrop studies of ancient slope successions. Although local factors are important, key generic concepts that aid in predicting submarine slope processes and products include: (1) shelf accommodation/lateral sediment supply variations on sediment delivery; (2) the spatial/temporal distribution of characteristic styles/intensities of sediment instability and remobilization; and (3) a generalized model for the stratigraphic development of slope channel complexes, slope fans and the temporal relationships between these major components of slope stratigraphy.

Key remaining problems include bridging the gap between the timescales sampled by Recent to late Quaternary studies and those represented by ancient slope successions. Moreover, present-day highstand conditions may not provide a good analogue for lowstand slope settings. Future research efforts will also concentrate on better calibration of seismic facies to rock facies and linking of physical and numerical (process and forward) modelling techniques at different scales to observational datasets. The future lies in integration of these complementary research directions.

Our understanding of the erosion, bypass, deposition and remobilization processes that operate on submarine slopes and the stratigraphic record of these 'processes and products' has increased enormously over the last decade. The main driving forces have been the continued development and deployment of state-of-the-art seabed sonar and other imaging systems in Quaternary slope and basin floor settings (e.g. Klaucke *et al.* 2000; Babonneau *et al.* 2002; Kenyon *et al.* 2002; Habgood *et al.* 2003; Klaucke *et al.* 2004) and the acquisition, processing and interpretation of excellent quality 3D seismic data in the exploration for and development of new slope-hosted hydrocarbon reserves (e.g. Booth *et al.* 2003; Prather 2003).

In April 2003, the international conference *Submarine Slope Systems* was convened at the University of Liverpool, UK, with the aim of bringing together the latest ideas from these two research areas, together with studies of exposed ancient slope successions (Fig. 1). The intention was to present, in a single meeting, information and interpretations from these traditionally disparate research areas, to explore commonalities and to identify truly generic themes that run though the different datasets. Several key themes emerged, most of which are captured in the papers included in this volume. This short paper discusses these generic issues and offers some view on the way forward towards improved predictive models for submarine slope systems in space and time. The key themes (Fig. 2) are:

1. delivery systems: mechanisms by which sediment is transferred over the shelf edge and onto and through the slope;
2. stratigraphy of submarine slope systems: how the evidence of erosion, bypass, deposition and remobilization are preserved and understanding their spatial-temporal controls;
3. canyons and channels: formation, geometries and fills; conduits for down-slope bypass and later storage of sediment;
4. instability and remobilization: post-depositional remobilization pre-requisites, processes, products and stratigraphic prediction.

Delivery systems

Over the last few years considerable attention has been focused on the sedimentary responses to stepped relative sea level fall and the downward-stepping geometries of shelf and shelf-edge deposits produced within late highstand and falling stage systems tracts (e.g. Posamentier & Morris 2000; Porębski & Steel 2003). Studies of ancient shelf edge successions show that these deltaic deposits can extend onto the upper slope in certain cases (e.g. Mayall *et al.* 1992; Mellere *et al.* 2002; Plink-Björklund & Steel 2002). Along-margin changes in sediment supply affect the style of shelf-edge deposits and Quaternary examples from the Gulf of Cadiz (Figs 1 & 2) are provided by **Lobo *et al.*** In this case, linear sediment sources and a high degree of reworking resulted in simple shelf margin wedges while more lobate wedges developed as a response to point sources of sediment and uneven rates of shelf break progradation.

Ongoing studies of large-scale outcrops of slope

From: Hodgson, D.M. & Flint, S.S. (eds) 2005. *Submarine Slope Systems: Processes and Products*. Geological Society, London, Special Publications, **244**, 1–6. 0305–8719/$15.00

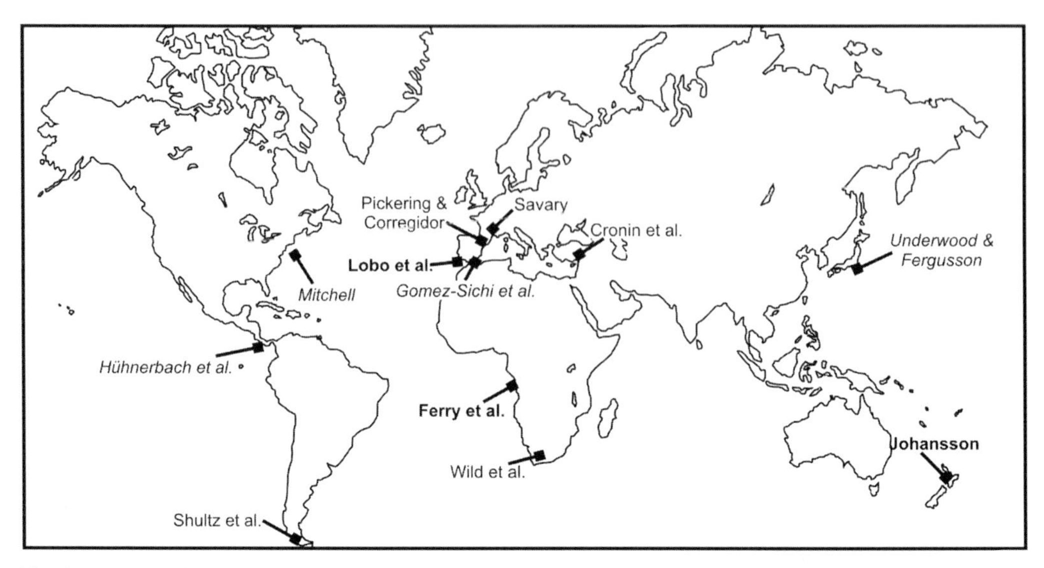

Fig. 1. Locations of submarine slope systems covered by the papers in this publication. Author names in bold have used primarily subsurface datasets, italics used modern datasets, and normal font indicates outcrop datasets of ancient slope successions.

and basin floor successions from different basins are revealing generic similarities between the stratigraphy of the deep-water deposits. For example, Permian basin floor and slope deposits of the Delaware Basin, Texas and the Karoo Basin, South Africa, show similar thicknesses, geometries and stacking patterns in interpreted fourth and fifth order sequences; however the Delaware basin had a steep, static carbonate margin, whereas the Karoo basin margin is inferred to have been a progradational, delta-fed type. (Beaubouef *et al.* 1999; Johnson *et al.* 2001; Gardner *et al.* 2003; Hodgson *et al.* 2005). It appears, therefore, that deep-water system architecture at the scales of tens to a few hundred metres vertically by tens of kilometres laterally by 1–2 Ma in duration is not strongly controlled by large-scale variations in basin margin/sediment delivery system (Hadler-Jacobsen *et al.* 2005). However, the delivery system (delta type) and shelf dimensions (width and gradient) are important controls on the sediment grain-size range and volume that reaches the shelf edge, and these input parameters have an important control on the sandbody architecture (sizes of levees, depth of erosion) and gravity flow processes.

Stratigraphy

Outcrop and subsurface datasets from deep-water systems of all ages indicate a clear hierarchy of cycles and generally, workers agree that most of the sheet-dominant deposits (basin floor fans, intraslope fans, slope fan/sheet complexes) are composite bodies. Commonly, seismically mappable bodies are 50–300 m thick, 200–2000 sq km in extent, (dependent on confinement) and represent components of falling stage and lowstand systems tracts (depending on profile position) of third or fourth order sequences. Within these seismic volumes, well- and outcrop-based studies reveal that these 'lowstands' are composite sequence sets (Mitchum & Van Wagoner 1991), with each high frequency (fifth or sixth order) nested sequence being dominated by its lowstand component. In slope channel complexes a comparable hierarchy is evident (e.g. Campion *et al.* 2000) with channel complex sets (commonly third or fourth order) being built of channel complexes (typically fourth or fifth order), which themselves are comprised of sixth order individual and composite channels. Many slope successions contain both channel complexes and sheet deposits, which, traditionally, have been viewed as genetically related channel-overbank strata. Careful studies of examples at outcrop and the increasingly high-resolution of 3D seismic data have indicated that so-called overbank deposits may in fact be combinations of older frontal splays (genetically unrelated to the channel complexes) and true overbank deposits related to late stage spill from the channels. ***Wild et al.*** discuss these relationships, using examples from the Karoo basin of South Africa (Figs 1 & 2), and highlight the potential for using zones of deformation in off-axis positions as indicators of periods of incision and bypass. Within this type of framework, there is commonly variability in the fill styles

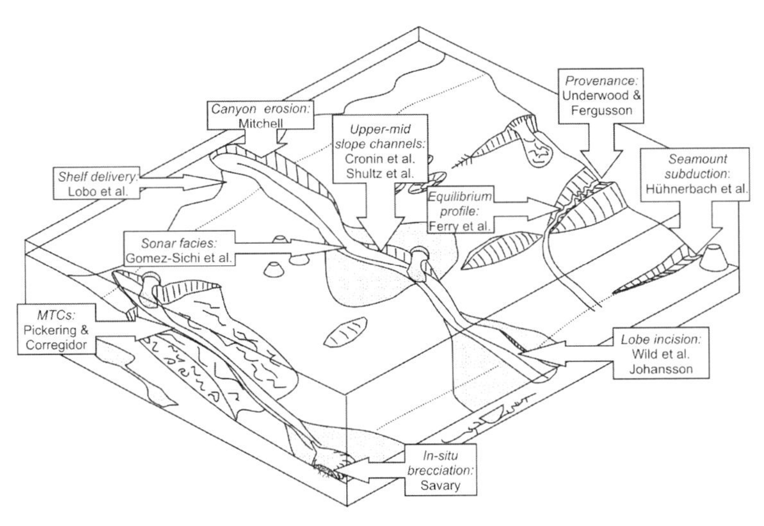

Fig. 2. The range of slope profile positions, processes and products covered by papers within this publication.

of slope channels, which may reflect changing availability of different sediment grade, changing gradient and variation in profile position. Examples of variable channel geometries and fills are described for the first time from the Tres Pasos Formation of the Magallanes Basin, southern Chile (Figs 1 & 2) by **Shultz *et al.*** In this example, fills are commonly heterolithic, with multiple, complex internal onlap surfaces. Application of outcrop datasets to solve subsurface correlation problems can be aided by employing industry datasets. **Johansson** takes this approach by calibrating Formation Microimager (FMI) logs to nearby outcrop and analysing bed dip data in the Taranaki Basin, New Zealand in order to understand lateral and stratigraphic changes in facies, and channel-fill styles from an incised slope fan setting (Figs 1 & 2).

Deep-water stratigraphy is controlled by variations in sediment supply, which can usually be understood in terms of accommodation history on the feeder shelf. Positions and geometries of the deep-water deposits are strongly controlled by topography and gradient, different combinations of which favour intraslope ponding, lateral confinement, etc. Slope gradient is a dynamic property, continually responding to inherited features such as intraslope grabens (**Ferry *et al.***), salt and shale diapirism (e.g. Prather 2000) and faulting (e.g. Ravnås & Steel 1998; Hodgson & Haughton 2004). A distinction can be drawn between passive topography and active topography. **Pickering & Corregidor**, for example, highlight how passive topography, formed by deposition of different types of mass transport complex, affected the routing of subsequent sediment-laden gravity flows and the geometry of resultant deposits (Figs 1 & 2). Eventually, the rugose seabed will be 'healed' such that younger deposits are not confined by this topography.

Active topography is created either constantly or episodically, such that the degree of depocentre confinement is related to the relative difference between the rate of deposition and the rate of seabed deformation (e.g. Grecula *et al.* 2003; Sixsmith *et al.* 2004). Active topography can be maintained for long periods, resulting in thick successions of confined turbidites. In fore-arc basins and accretionary settings, additional large-scale changes in basin accommodation result from changes in plate convergence parameters. Variations in sediment provenance have been used by **Underwood & Ferguson** to track changes in slope drainage patterns from transverse to axial in the Tertiary stratigraphy of the Nankai trench-slope system of Japan (Figs 1 & 2).

Canyons and channels

Processes of erosion, bypass and deposition are reasonably well understood but the temporal relationships between deposition and (partial) re-evacuation are not always clear. Much of our understanding of canyons comes from seabed sonar datasets from present-day examples and via imaging of ancient canyon systems from seismic reflection data. It is critical, therefore, that assessment of sediment facies distributions that rely on acoustic measurements are interpreted accurately. **Gómez Sichi *et al.*** demonstrate the potential for using textural analyses in order to quantify the second-order statistics of sonar imagery, using new datasets acquired from the Almería Canyon offshore SE Spain (Figs 1 & 2). This canyon is a 57 km long meandering conduit for present-day sediment transfer from the shelf edge to the Alborán Sea seabed at 1700 m water depth. In some systems, canyon erosion via the passage of multiple turbidity currents produces degradational morphologies that share many attributes with subaerial landscape produced by surface runoff. **Mitchell** adapts modern geomorphological techniques of predicting large-scale landscape characteristics and applies them to submarine canyon systems eroded by sediment gravity flows (Figs 1 & 2).

Excellent examples of the fills of Tertiary canyon systems are provided by **Cronin *et al.*** and **Ferry *et al.*** The exposed Eocene Nohut palaeocanyon/channel complex in eastern Turkey (Figs 1 & 2) is over 250 m thick and contains a tripartite composite fill of clastic and reworked carbonate deposits (**Cronin *et al.***). These and many other slope canyon/major channel complexes are comprised of a complex, basal incision surface overlain by a mass transport complex (MTC). Sandy, bedded deposits overlie the MTC, with a general tendency for increasingly meandering internal channel-fills in the upper section. A similar channel-fill succession is reported from offshore West Africa (Mayall & Stewart 2000). However the high-resolution internal fill style also reflects sequence hierarchy and the type of sediment available at the shelf edge. The Turkish channel complexes, for example, contain a strong carbonate component. **Ferry *et al.*** demonstrate how the evolution of the late Miocene Lower Congo channel system was strongly controlled by changing gradients in a slope setting (Figs 1 & 2). Areas of increasing gradient are subjected to erosional processes whereas zones of decreased gradient are depositional, such that the submarine slope is trying to work toward an equilibrium profile (Pirmez *et al.* 2000). Changes in longitudinal slope gradient correlate with variations in the sinuosity, the width and depth of basal incision, the presence of splay and levee deposits, the location of vertical aggradation zones and channel avulsion.

Instability and remobilization

Submarine slopes are a primary site for a spectrum of instability processes that range from major features such as the generation and deposition of mass flow complexes and the subsurface emplacement of injectite complexes, through to much more subtle phenomena such as *in-situ* dewatering and downslope creep. In all cases the original fabric of the sediment is modified and in most cases the original depositional geometry is also changed. This means that in hydrocarbon reservoir situations, the reservoir quality and horizontal to vertical permeability ratio is also modified.

Examples of large-scale sediment instability and remobilization processes driven by the subduction of several seamounts at the Costa Rica margin (Figs 1 & 2) are described by **Hühnerbach *et al.*** Deformed and uplifted areas of the continental slope that formed as the seamounts were subducted, collapse through landslide (debris-flow) processes as support for the uplifted area is withdrawn. The zone of collapse migrates landward resulting in up to 55 km-long parallel-sided depressions.

As discussed above, mass transport complexes are typical of the early stages of deep-water sequences and have an important role in development of passive topography with which later turbidity currents interact (**Pickering & Corregidor**). Slope creep processes result in fluid escape and development of a homogeneous fabric; creep sand bodies commonly have homogenized siltstone caps and the bodies are elongate along strike of the local slope (**Wild *et al.***). Another mechanism for initiating post-depositional deformation is via the *in-situ* brecciation of the seabed by hydraulic microfracturing during the passage and emplacement of turbidity currents. This mechanism is discussed in the case of Cretaceous calcareous turbidites of SE France by **Savary** and provides an interesting alternative deformation process (Figs 1 & 2).

Increasingly reported from subsurface and ancient settings are examples of large-scale sand remobilization after burial: a post-depositional deformational style broadly referred to as injectites. It is important to understand the prerequisites and mechanisms needed for sand remobilization and their resulting geometries and distribution because these post-depositional bodies can change reservoir character, connectivity and porosity/permeability (Lonergan *et al.* 2000). The prevailing view is that when sand is remobilized then the path of the sand will be horizontal and/or upwards following a decreasing pressure gradient. However, examples of downward sand injection have been reported from the Vocantian Basin, France (Pairze & Fries 2003), the Magallanes Basin, Chile (Shultz 2004), and the Karoo Basin, South Africa (van der Merve, *pers. comm.*).

Future work on slope instability and remobilization processes will help geoscientists appreciate the prerequisites needed to induce deformation and instability and aid the stratigraphic prediction and distribution of different types of slope instability features.

Summary

The papers in this Special Publication provide a snapshot of different aspects on the theme of processes and deposits associated with submarine slopes, both modern and ancient. In common with other recent work, they suggest that, although local factors (type/volume of sediment being supplied, active versus passive topography, relative sea level history, etc.) are important, a series of exportable, generic concepts can be used to predict and understand these systems. These concepts include the role of shelf accommodation/lateral sediment supply variations on sediment delivery, the spatial/temporal distribution of characteristic styles/intensities of sediment instability and remobilization, and a generalized model for the stratigraphic development of slope channel complexes, slope fans and the temporal relationships between these major components of slope stratigraphy.

Key remaining problems include bridging the gap between the timescales sampled by Recent/late Quaternary studies and those represented by ancient slope successions. No doubt, the resolution of surveys on present day slope systems will increase, as will our understanding of slope development and current configuration. However, the caveat that present-day highstand conditions do not provide a good analogue for lowstand slope settings must be remembered. Future research efforts will also concentrate on better calibration of seismic facies to rock facies, which will further close the gap between subsurface and outcrop-based geoscientists. For example, estimating volumes of sediment bypassed versus accreted to the slope, the true 3D distribution of (remnant) facies and the controls on connectivity between channels and overbank deposits are all issues that require integrated research approaches. Physical and numerical (process and forward) modelling techniques are currently being used to investigate a range of scales, from the dynamics of individual flows to multiple large-scale events. This work will help geoscientists understand how sediment is transported via turbidity currents and debris-flows. The future lies in integration of these complementary research directions.

The SLOPE 2003 conference from which this publication arose was co-supported by the Geological Society and the IAS, and co-convened by Tim Garfield of ExxonMobil, Houston. We would like to thank the following companies for their generous financial sponsorship of the meeting: Badley Ashton, BHP-Billiton, BP, Britannia, ExxonMobil, Norsk Hydro, Statoil, Schlumberger and Total. In addition, we would like to acknowledge the help of all the reviewers of the manuscripts, who helped to sharpen the clarity and content of the papers.

References

Babonneau, N., Savoye, B., Cremer, M. & Klein, B. 2002. Morphology and architecture of the present canyon and channel system of the Zaire deep-sea fan. *Marine and Petroleum Geology*, **19**, 445–467.

Beaubouef, R.T., Rossen, C., Zelt, F.B., Sullivan, M.D., Mohrig, D.C. & Jennette, D.C. 1999. Deep-water sandstones, Brushy Canyon Formation, West Texas. *AAPG Continuing Education Course Note Series #40*, The American Association of Petroleum Geologists, Tulsa.

Booth, J.R., Dean, M.C., DuVernay, III, A.E. & Styzen, M.J. 2003. Paleo-bathymetric controls on the stratigraphic architecture and reservoir development of confined fans in the Auger Basin: central Gulf of Mexico slope. *Marine and Petroleum Geology*, **20**, 563–586.

Campion, K.M., Sprague, A.R., Mohrig, D., Lovell, R.W., Drzewiecki, P.A., Sullivan, M.D., Ardill, J.A., Jensen, G.N. & Sickafoose, D.K. 2000. Outcrop expression of confined channel complexes. *In:* Weimar, P., Slatt, R.M., Coleman, J., et al. (eds) *Deep-water reservoirs of the world*. Gulf Coast Section SEPM (CD-ROM), 127–150.

Gardner, M.H., Borer, J.A., Melick, J.J., Mavilla, N., Dechesne, M. & Wagerle, R.N. 2003. Stratigraphic process-response model for submarine channels and related features from studies of Permian Brushy Canyon outcrops, West Texas. *Marine and Petroleum Geology*, **20**, 757–787.

Grecula, M., Flint, S., Wickens, H. Dev & Potts, G.J. 2003. Partial ponding of turbidite systems in a basin with subtle growth-fold topography: Laingsburg-Karoo, South Africa. *Journal of Sedimentary Research*, **73**, 603–620.

Habgood, E.L., Kenyon, N.H., Masson, D.G., Akhmetzhanov, A., Weaver, P.P.E., Gardner, J. & Mulder, T. 2003. Deep-water sediment wave fields, bottom current sand channels and gravity flow channel-lobe systems: Gulf of Cadiz, NE Atlantic. *Sedimentology*, **50**, 483–510.

Hadler-Jacobsen, F., Johannessen, E.P., Ashton, N., Henriksen, S., Johnson, S.D. & Kristensen, J.B. 2005. Submarine fan morphology and lithology distribution, a predictable function of sediment delivery, gross shelf-to-basin relief, slope gradient and basin topography. *In*: Dore, A.G. & Vining, B.A. (eds) *Petroleum Geology: North West Europe and Global Perspectives*. Proceedings of the 6th Petroleum Geology Conference: Geological Society, London, 1121–1145.

Hodgson, D.M. & Haughton, P.D.W. 2004. Impact of syn-depositional faulting on gravity current behaviour and deep-water stratigraphy: Tabernas-Sorbas Basin, SE Spain. *In*: Lomas, S.A. & Joseph, P. (eds) *Confined Turbidite Systems*. Geological Society, London, Special Publications, **222**, 135–158.

Hodgson, D.M., Flint, S., Hodgetts, D., Drinkwater, N.J., Johannessen, E.P. & Luthi, S.M. 2005. Stratigraphic evolution of fine-grained submarine fan systems, Tanqua Depocentre, Karoo Basin South Africa. *Journal of Sedimentary Research* (in press).

Johnson, S.D., Flint, S., Hinds, D. & Wickens, H. Dev. 2001. Anatomy of basin floor to slope turbidite systems, Tanqua Karoo, South Africa: sedimentology, sequence stratigraphy and implications for subsurface prediction. *Sedimentology*, **48**, 987–1023.

Kenyon, N.H., Klaucke, I., Millington, J. & Ivanov, M.K. 2002. Sandy submarine canyon-mouth lobes on the western margin of Corsica and Sardinia, Mediterranean Sea. *Marine Geology*, **184**, 69–84.

KLAUCKE, I., SAVOYE, B. & COCHONAT, P. 2000. Patterns and processes of sediment dispersal on the continental slope off Nice, SE France. *Marine Geology*, **162**, 405–422.

KLAUCKE, I., MASSON, D.G., KENYON, N.H. & GARDNER, J.V. 2004. Sedimentary processes of the lower Monterey Fan channel and channel-mouth lobe. *Marine Geology*, **206**, 181–198.

LONERGAN, L., LEE, N., JOHNSON, H.D., CARTWRIGHT, J.A. & JOLLY, R.J.H. 2000. Remobilization and injection in deepwater depositional systems: implications for reservoir architecture and prediction. *In:* WEIMAR, P., SLATT, R.M., COLEMAN, J., ROSEN, N.C., NELSON, H., BOUMA, A.H., STYZEN, M.J. & LAWRENCE, D.T. (eds) *Deep-water reservoirs of the world*, GCSSEPM Foundation 20th Annual Research Conference (CD-ROM), 515–532.

MAYALL, M. & STEWART, I. 2000. The architecture of turbidite slope channels. *In:* WEIMAR, P., SLATT, R.M., COLEMAN, J., ROSEN, N.C., NELSON, H., BOUMA, A.H., STYZEN, M.J. & LAWRENCE, D.T. (eds) *Deep-water reservoirs of the world*, GCSSEPM Foundation 20th Annual Research Conference, 304–317.

MAYALL, M.J., YEILDING, C.A., OLDROYD, J.D., PULHAM, A.J. & SAKURAI, S. 1992. Facies in a shelf-edge delta — an example from the subsurface of the Gulf of Mexico, Middle Pleistocene, Mississippi Canyon, Block 109. *American Association of Petroleum Geologists Bulletin*, **76**, 435–448.

MELLERE, D., PLINK-BJÖRKLUND, P. & STEEL, R. 2002. Anatomy of shelf deltas at the edge of a prograding Eocene shelf margin, Spitsbergen. *Sedimentology*, **49**, 1181–1206.

MITCHUM, R.M. & VAN WAGONER, J.C. 1991. High-frequency sequences and their stacking patterns: sequence stratigraphic evidence of high-frequency eustatic cycles. *Sedimentary Geology*, **70**, 131–160.

PAIRZE, O. & FRIES, G. 2003. The Vocontian clastic dykes and sills: a geometric model. *In*: VAN RENSBERGEN, P., HILLIS, R.R., MALTMAN, A.J. & MORLEY, C.K. (eds) *Subsurface Sediment Mobilization*. Geological Society, London, Special Publications, **216**, 51–71.

PLINK-BJÖRKLUND, P. & STEEL, R. 2002. Sea-level fall below the shelf edge, without basin-floor fans. *Geology*, **30**, 115–118.

PORĘBSKI, S.J. & STEEL, R.J. 2003. Shelf-margin deltas: their stratigraphic significance and relation to deep-water sands. *Earth Science Reviews*, **62**, 283–326.

POSAMENTIER, H.W. & MORRIS, W.R. 2000. Aspects of the stratal architecture of forced regressive deposits. *In*: HUNT, D. & GAWTHORPE, R.L. (eds) *Sedimentary Responses to Forced Regressions*. Geological Society, London, Special Publications, **172**, 19–46.

PRATHER, B.E. 2000. Calibration and visualisation of depositional process models for above-grade slopes; a case study from the Gulf of Mexico. *Marine and Petroleum Geology*, **17**, 419–438.

PRATHER, B.E. 2003. Controls on reservoir distribution, architecture and stratigraphic trapping in slope settings. *Marine and Petroleum Geology*, **20**, 529–545.

PIRMEZ, C., BEAUBOUEF, R.T., FRIEDMANN, S.J. & MOHRIG, D.C. 2000. Equilibrium profile and baselevel in submarine channels: examples from Late Pleistocene systems and Implications for the architecture of deep water reservoirs. *In:* WEIMAR, P., SLATT, R.M., COLEMAN, J., ROSEN, N.C., NELSON, H., BOUMA, A.H., STYZEN, M.J. & LAWRENCE, D.T. (eds) *Deep-water reservoirs of the world*, GCSSEPM Foundation 20th Annual Research Conference, 782–805.

RAVNÅS, R. & STEEL, R.J. 1998. Architecture of marine rift-basin successions. *American Association of Petroleum Geologists Bulletin*, **82**, 110–146.

SHULTZ, M.R. 2004. Stratigraphic architecture of two deep-water depositional systems: The Tres Pasos Formation, Chilean Patagonia, and the Stevens Sandstone, Elk Hills, California. Unpubl. Ph.D. thesis, Stanford University, 307pp.

SIXSMITH, P.J., FLINT, S., WICKENS, H. DEV. & JOHNSON, S.D. 2004. Anatomy and stratigraphic development of a basin floor turbidite system in the Laingsburg Formation, main Karoo basin, South Africa. *Journal of Sedimentary Research*, **74**, 239–254.

Late Quaternary shelf-margin wedges and upper slope progradation in the Gulf of Cadiz margin (SW Iberian Peninsula)

F.J. LOBO[1,2], J.M.A. DIAS[1], F.J. HERNÁNDEZ-MOLINA[3], R. GONZÁLEZ[1], L.M. FERNÁNDEZ-SALAS[4] & V. DÍAZ DEL RÍO[4]

[1] *CIACOMAR-CIMA, Universidade do Algarve, Avenida 16 de Junho s/n, 8700–311 Olhão, Portugal*

[2] *Present address: Instituto Andaluz de Ciencias de la Tierra, CSIC-Univ. Granada, Facultad de Ciencias, Campus de Fuentenueva, s/n. 18002 Granada, Spain (e-mail: pacolobo@ugr.es)*

[3] *Departamento de Geociencias Marinas y Ordenación del Territorio, Facultad de Ciencias, Universidad de Vigo, 36200 Vigo, Spain*

[4] *Instituto Español de Oceanografía (IEO), Centro Oceanográfico de Málaga, Puerto Pesquero s/n, 29640 Fuengirola, Spain*

Abstract: The distribution patterns and internal geometries of recent shelf-margin wedges off the Guadiana River, Gulf of Cadiz margin, were studied in order to discern the effects of varying trends of falling sea-level and lowstand on upper slope progradation. A seismic-sequence stratigraphic analysis was conducted, based on the interpretation of a dense grid of high-resolution seismic profiles.

Five major shelf-margin wedges deposited during late Quaternary sea-level fall and lowstand periods were documented. Most of the studied shelf-margin wedges produce upbuilt-outbuilt upper slopes. The analysis of their internal geometries reveals two distinct types of configuration: the four older shelf-margin wedges are mainly composed of forced regressive deposits developed during stepped sea-level falls. The scarceness of lowstand deposits suggests abrupt sea-level fall to rise transitions; and the most recent shelf-margin wedge shows both forced regressive deposits and lowstand deposits significantly preserved. This architecture probably resulted from the occurrence of a long-lived sea-level lowstand after a prolonged period of gentle sea-level fall.

Two types of shelf-margin wedges have been recognized: wedges with elongate parallel depocentres, laterally constant thickness and uniform seaward shelf-break migration, related to linear source supply and high lateral sediment redistribution during gently falling sea level; and wedges with (multi) lobate depocentres with laterally variable thickness, leading to uneven shelf-break migration during periods of faster sea-level fall, due to delta lobe switching and significant shelf valley incision.

Shelf-edge and upper slope wedge-shaped deposits of temperate regions commonly record a high variety of sedimentary processes, as they occur at the seaward limits of continental margins where subaerial processes and marine depositional events leave a direct imprint (Vanney & Stanley 1983). Sedimentary environments at the shelf edge and upper slope are diagnostic for elucidating local eustatic/tectonic history (Field *et al.* 1983). The shelf edge is considered a key environment in which to determine the influence of sea-level changes on shelf-margin sedimentation. Although the relationship between late Quaternary shelf-margin wedges and periods of sea-level fall and lowstand is well documented, the influence of different trends of sea-level change on the distribution patterns and facies geometries of shelf-margin deposits is less well understood (Kolla *et al.* 2000; Plink-Björklund & Steel 2002; Porębski & Steel 2003). One of the most challenging problems is the distinction between forced regressive (or early lowstand) and lowstand facies (Porębski & Steel 2003).

In spite of the stratigraphic significance of shelf-margin wedges, most studies on continental margins focus either on shelf or on deep-water slope deposits. This general trend is also applicable to the Gulf of Cadiz margin (SW Iberian Peninsula), where the transition between these domains is poorly understood. Thus, previous stratigraphic studies have dealt with shelf sequences (Somoza *et al.* 1997; Rodero *et al.* 1999; Hernández-Molina *et al.* 2000; Lobo *et al.* 2002), whereas the study of slope sedimentation has focused on contourite deposition controlled by an intense contour current, the Mediterranean Outflow Water or MOW (e.g. Faugères *et al.* 1984; Stow *et al.* 1986; Nelson *et al.* 1993; Llave *et al.* 2001; Habgood *et al.* 2003; Hernández-Molina *et al.* 2003). However, the influence of this contour current over the

From: Hodgson, D.M. & Flint, S.S. (eds) 2005. *Submarine Slope Systems: Processes and Products*. Geological Society, London, Special Publications, **244**, 7–25. 0305–8719/$15.00

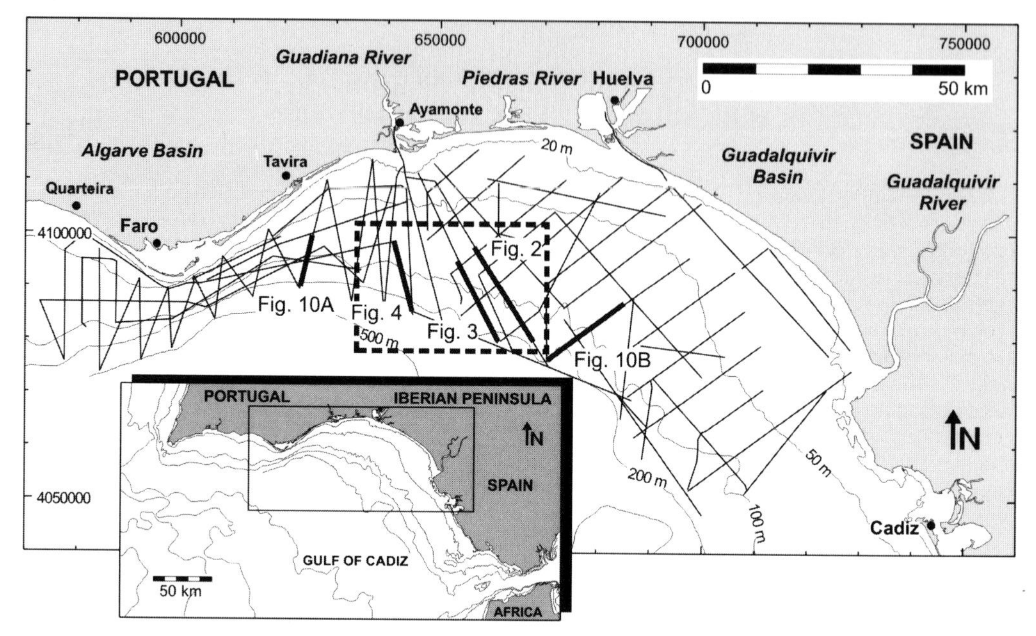

Fig. 1. Geographical location of the Gulf of Cadiz margin and position of high-resolution seismic lines used in this work. The study area is highlighted with a black dashed box.

upper slope is variable; in most places the upper slope is not significantly affected by this water mass, and sedimentary processes are controlled by the deposition of shelf-margin deltas.

The aims of this paper are: (1) to characterize the geometry and investigate the development and preservation of the most recent regressive shelf-margin wedges off the Guadiana River, Gulf of Cadiz, which received abundant sediment supply during lowstand periods; (2) to interpret the geometry of shelf break/upper slope seismic facies from a sequence stratigraphic perspective, in order to discern the influence of distinct trends of falling sea-level and lowstand; and (3) to define growth patterns and estimate the potential growth of the upper slope.

The Gulf of Cadiz margin

Physiography of the shelf break and upper slope

The shelf break in the Gulf of Cadiz margin is located at water depths ranging between 100–140 m (Hernández-Molina *et al.* 2003). A deepening trend can be observed between the Portuguese and the Spanish margin, from 100 m off Faro, to 140–150 m off the Guadiana River (Vanney & Mougenot 1981), where it shows a convex-up profile. These depth changes are related to changes in width of the continental shelf. The shelf has a minimum width of 5 km off Faro, increasing to 20–25 km off the Guadiana River (Fig. 1).

The upper slope extends between 150 and 400 m water depth, showing an average width of 10 km and gradients ranging between 2–3° (Nelson *et al.* 1993; Hernández-Molina *et al.* 2003). The present-day upper slope off the Guadiana River is not affected by submarine canyons or other valley-shaped features, probably because of strong lateral sediment transport during the Plio-Quaternary (Llave *et al.* 2001; Hernández-Molina *et al.* 2003).

Fluvial supply and oceanographic agents

The Guadiana River is one of the main fluvial sources draining into the Gulf of Cadiz margin. Its drainage basin has an extent of 68 000 km^2 and the average annual water discharge has been estimated at 5500 km^3 (Van Geen *et al.* 1997). Other nearby fluvial sources, such as the Piedras River, are much less significant.

The littoral zone is affected by two main surface wave trains, W–SW (68%) and SE (25%). The higher occurrence of westerly waves determines an eastward-directed littoral drift. Flow patterns on the outer margin are dominated by an anticyclonic circulation, causing the eastward and southeastward deflection of sediment bodies (Nelson *et al.* 1999). The influence of MOW is restricted to water deeper than 300 m. This contour current flows northwestwards in close proximity to the seafloor (Nelson *et al.* 1999).

Late Quaternary evolution

Sedimentation on the Gulf of Cadiz margin during the late Quaternary has been controlled by periods of forced regression. Since the last interglacial, shelf wedges have accumulated during periods of sea-level fall and lowstand. Each wedge is composed of a forced regressive wedge systems tract (FRWST) and a lowstand systems tract (LST) (Hernández-Molina *et al.* 2000). However, the relative significance of each deposit in every sea-level cycle and its regional distribution pattern has not yet been studied in detail. The occasional identification of backstepping units has been used as evidence for preserved transgressive systems tract (TST) to highstand systems tract (HST) complexes on the Gulf of Cadiz margin (Lobo *et al.* 2002).

Methodology

The database comprises about 1700 km of high-resolution seismic profiles collected on the Gulf of Cadiz margin during the last ten years. Two systems were used, a sub-bottom profiler (3.5 kHz) with a 100 ms recording interval and a Uniboom system (Geopulse™: 280 Jul, shot delay of 500 ms, recording scale of 200 ms). These records were collected during three oceanographic surveys: Golca-93, Fado-9611 and Wadiana 2000. The seismic grid covers the continental shelf and upper slope of a sector of the northern Gulf of Cadiz margin stretching between Quarteira (Portugal) and the Guadalquivir River mouth (Spain). However, for the purposes of this study, we concentrated on an area on the outer margin off the Guadiana River, where the recent shelf-margin wedges are particularly well developed (Fig. 1). Positioning was achieved using a differential GPS.

The analysis of high-resolution seismic records was undertaken following standard seismic stratigraphy procedures, which involved the recognition of regionally mappable seismic discontinuities and units (Mitchum *et al.* 1977*a*) and the characterization of seismic facies inside individual units (Mitchum *et al.* 1977*b*), particularly with regard to their application to high-frequency sequences (Mitchum & Van Wagoner 1991). Isopach maps (in milliseconds) of individual shelf-margin wedges were constructed. An average velocity of 1650 m s^{-1} was used to provide estimates of time–depth conversion (e.g. 10 ms represent 8.25 m). Apparent inclinations of internal reflectors and seismic discontinuities were measured in all available profiles and appeared to be consistent. Those measurements are given as range of values or as maximum/minimum estimates, and are considered to be representative of the study area.

The seismic stratigraphic architectures were interpreted in terms of relative sea-level changes and a sequence stratigraphic interpretation was completed. A four-fold division of system tracts was considered, according to the relationship between sediment deposition and relative sea-level changes (Hunt & Tucker 1992; Helland-Hansen & Gjelberg 1994): (1) FRWSTs are deposited during falling relative sea levels; (2) LSTs are deposited during relative sea-level lowstands; (3) TSTs are deposited during rising relative sea levels; (4) HSTs are deposited during relative sea-level highstands. In addition, the chronostratigraphic scheme proposed by Hernández-Molina *et al.* (2000) and Lobo (2000) for the Gulf of Cadiz margin, adopted in this study, is based on the correlation between seismic units and late Quaternary sea-level curves, and with exposed highstand and shelf deposits with similar stratigraphic architectures.

Seismic stratigraphy of shelf-margin wedges off the Guadiana River

Shelf-margin wedges, aggradational–progradational complex and intercalated units: general remarks

The seismic architecture of the shelf-margin off the Guadiana River shows the progradational stacking of several wedges that can be correlated laterally (Figs 2, 3 & 4). These wedges overlie a sheet-like, aggradational seismic unit, which extends across the shelf and can be considered a regional stratigraphic marker (Hernández-Molina *et al.* 2000; Lobo 2000). Detailed analysis of seismic records reveals a more complex internal architecture of this seismic unit. Off the Guadiana River, this sheet-like unit pinches out towards the middle shelf, and is composed of two aggradational lower and upper members, and a progradational middle member (Fig. 4). Thus, this seismic unit is considered an aggradational–progradational complex (APC). The lower and upper aggradational members have sheet-like external shapes, whereas the middle progradational member has a wedge shape and oblique clinoforms.

The seismic architecture of deposits overlying the APC is characterized by five shelf-margin wedges off the Guadiana River (Figs 2 & 3). The shelf-margin wedges were designated from bottom to top as lower (LW), lower intermediate (LIW), middle (MW), upper intermediate (UIW) and upper wedge (UW) (Table 1). Locally, aggradational sheet-like units are

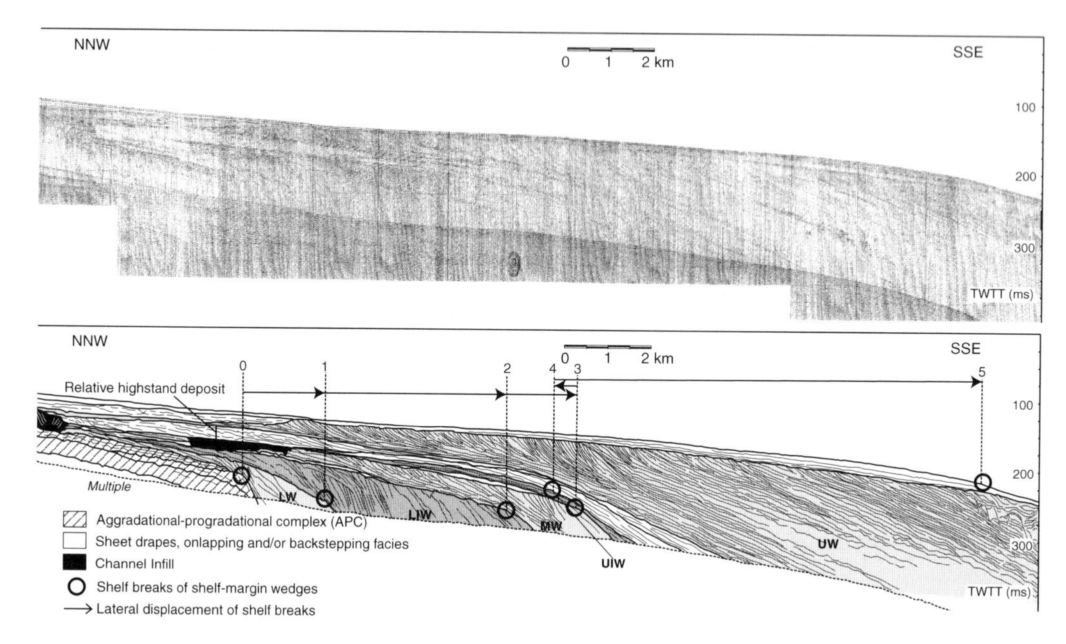

Fig. 2. Seismic section and interpretation from the outer margin off the Piedras River (see position in Fig. 1). Five shelf-margin wedges overlying an aggradational–progradational complex (APC) are identified: lower (LW), lower intermediate (LIW), middle (MW), upper intermediate (UIW) and upper wedge (UW). Shelf-break positions are indicated by numbers, from 0 (APC) to 5 (UW). The most significant seaward shelf-break migrations are associated with LIW and UW, whereas the poor development of UIW leads to landward shelf-break migration. MW is eroded at its top boundary by channel features. TWTT (ms), two-way travel time (milliseconds).

intercalated between these shelf-margin wedges. These sheet-like units in most cases consist of drapes or healing phases on the outer shelf and/or upper slope, and occur intercalated between LIW and MW (Fig. 4), and between MW and UIW (Fig. 2). In addition, a backstepping unit composed of two seismic sub-units, the older located on the outer shelf–upper slope and the younger on the middle shelf, is identified between UIW and UW. A detailed description of this backstepping unit is reported in Hernández-Molina *et al.* (2000) and Lobo *et al.* (2002).

Quaternary shelf-margin wedges off the Guadiana River

The thickness distribution of seismic units described here is only partially resolvable, as all of them are distally hindered by a seismic multiple signal. Therefore, the seaward pinch out of these wedges could not be determined.

Lower Wedge (LW). The lower boundary is characterized by seaward increasing gradients (Figs 2, 3 & 4). They are higher off and westward of the Guadiana River, where they increase from values around 0.5° in the proximal pinch out zone, to around 0.8° on the outer shelf. Close to the shelf break, gradients increase to 1–1.5°, and on the upper slope they are higher than 5° and in places up to 7–8°. Off the Piedras River, gradients are moderate (about 0.5°) on the outer shelf, but they increase close to the shelf break up to 1°. The upper slope shows values ranging between 4.5–6°.

Seismic facies are dominated by a parallel–oblique configuration on the outer shelf and upper slope (Figs 2, 3 & 4). Gradients range between 1–3.5° on the outer shelf, whereas on the upper slope the inclination of reflectors is about 4° between the Guadiana and Piedras rivers, increasing to values higher than 5–6° off and west of the Guadiana River.

The landward termination of the lower wedge is located at 20–22.5 km off the present coastline (Fig. 5). The unit has lateral continuity. To the east it is located below the multiple signal. Thickness is moderate, with maximum values located over the previous shelf break and on the upper slope. Two depocentres are distinguished: off the Guadiana River, with a thickness of more than 60 ms (about 50 m), and west of the Piedras River, where it can be more than 30 ms thick (Fig. 5). Seismic records off the Piedras River suggest that the main depocentre of this unit should be located further eastward. However, thickness values could not be determined,

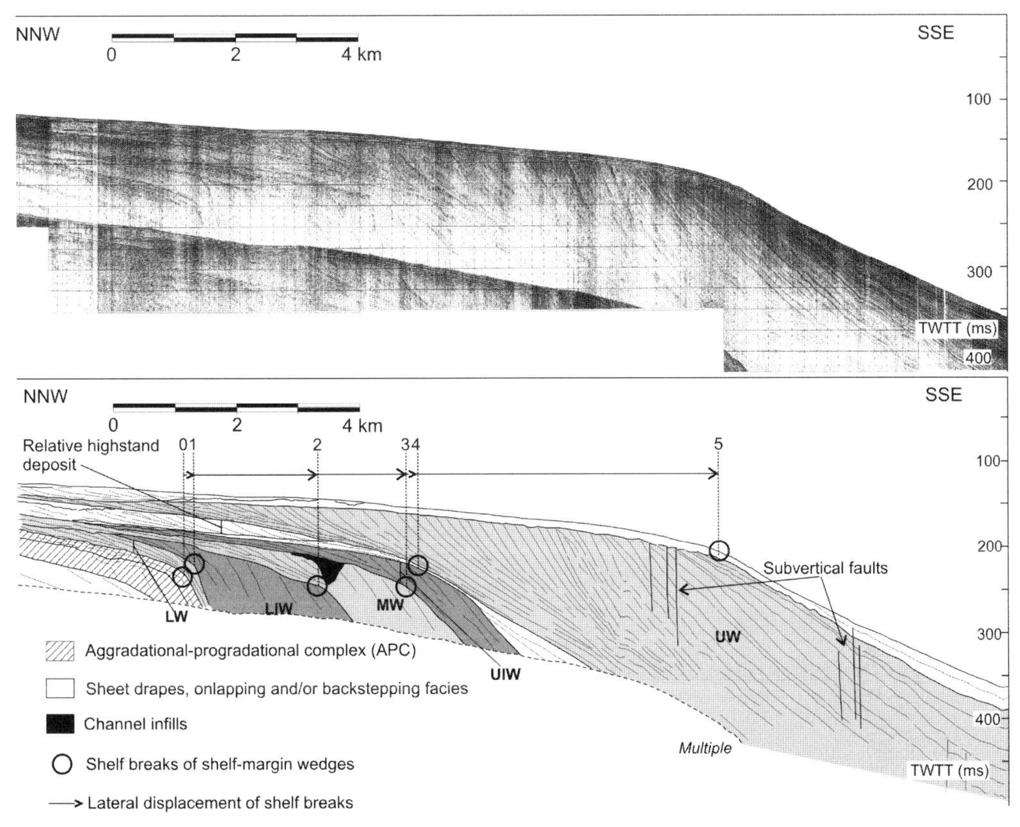

Fig. 3. Seismic section and interpretation from the outer margin between the Guadiana and Piedras rivers (see position in Fig. 1). The best developed shelf-margin wedge is upper wedge (UW), whereas lower intermediate (LIW) and middle wedge (MW) show moderate development. Lower (LW) and upper intermediate wedge (UIW) show poor development. Shelf-break positions are indicated by numbers, from 0 (APC) to 5 (UW). A distinct erosive valley is located overlying MW close to the shelf break. TWTT (ms), two-way travel time (milliseconds).

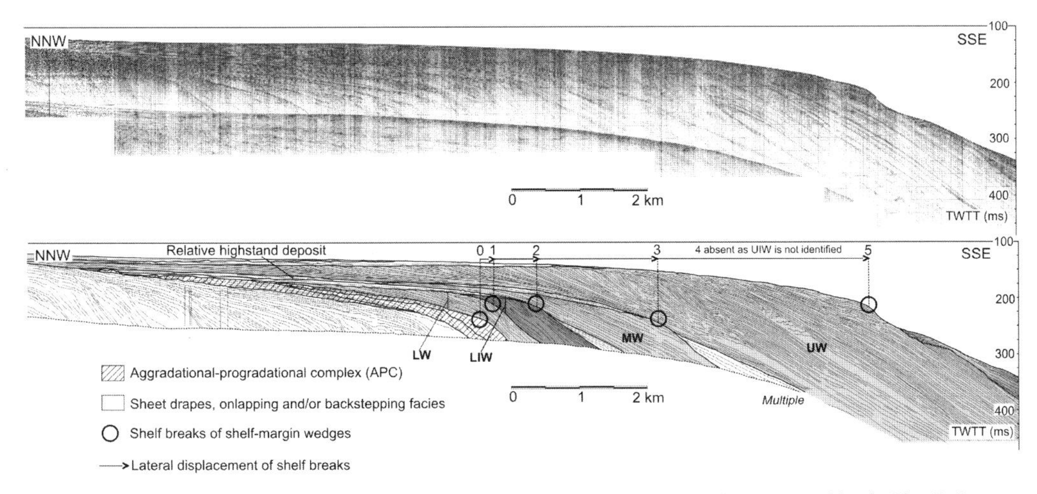

Fig. 4. Seismic section and interpretation from the outer margin off the Guadiana River (see position in Fig. 1). Lower (LW), lower intermediate (LIW) and middle wedge (MW) show moderate development in relation to highly developed upper wedge (UW). Upper intermediate wedge (UIW) is not identified in this area. Shelf-break positions are indicated by numbers, from 0 (APC) to 5 (UW). TWTT (ms), two-way travel time (milliseconds).

Table 1. *Correlation between shelf-margin wedges documented in this study with previous work on the Gulf of Cadiz shelf.*

This study	Somoza *et al.* 1997; Hernández-Molina *et al.* 2000	Lobo 2000
Aggradational–progradational complex	Seismic unit 4	Seismic unit 5
Lower wedge	Seismic unit 5	Seismic unit 7A
Lower intermediate wedge	Seismic unit 6	Seismic unit 7B
Middle wedge	Seismic unit 7	Seismic unit 9
Upper intermediate wedge	Seismic unit 8	Seismic unit 11
Upper wedge	Seismic units 10 + 11	Seismic unit 13

due to multiple signal masking. The thickness on the shelf-margin between depocentres is less than 20 ms.

The associated shelf break displays a pseudo-linear pattern, although two low-amplitude lobes are related to the two depocentres. The seaward shelf-break migration is small. Greater migration is related to the two depocentres, but is still lower than 1 km (Fig. 5).

Lower Intermediate Wedge (LIW). The lower boundary shows low gradients proximally, ranging between 0.5–0.7°, increasing to up to 1.5° towards the shelf break. Upper slope gradients are much higher off and west of the Guadiana River, with values of more than 7°, than off the Piedras River, where the values are below 3.5° (Figs 2, 3 & 4).

The wedge presents a parallel–oblique configuration, with gradients ranging between 1.5–2°. On the upper slope, seismic facies are dominated by inclined reflectors that mimic the upper slope surface (Figs 2, 3 & 4). These inclined reflectors mainly correspond to parallel–oblique configurations, due to the common occurrence of erosional truncation at the top boundary and the identification of downward downlap terminations. Locally, multiple convex-up, clinoform offlap breaks are identified (Fig. 2). The inclination of these progradational reflectors is higher than 4°, and in places higher than 6°. An aggradational configuration characterized by toplap, the absence of downlap terminations, and inclinations generally below 4° can be identified in some seaward locations, although these facies are poorly represented. The boundary between the progradational and aggradational facies is not well defined (Fig. 2).

The landward termination of this unit shows an undulating pattern and is located within 20–25 km of the present coastline (Fig. 6). This wedge shows a limited distribution over the outer shelf, as the landward termination is located close to the previous shelf break. The lateral continuity of this unit is high, and it extends below the multiple signal to the east. A seaward thickness increase determines a homogeneous, laterally continuous depocentre on the upper

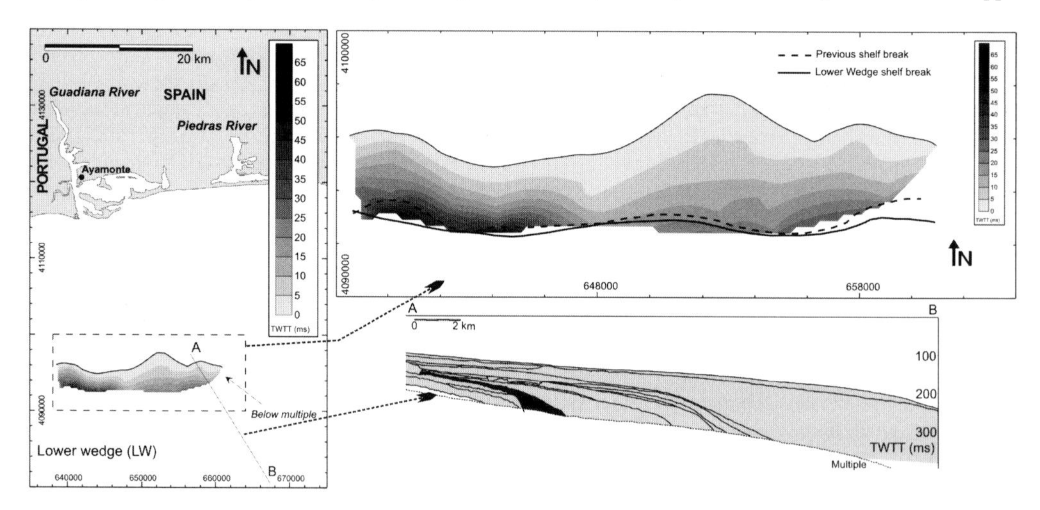

Fig. 5. Distribution pattern of lower wedge (LW) and associated shelf-break migration. TWTT (ms), two-way travel time (milliseconds).

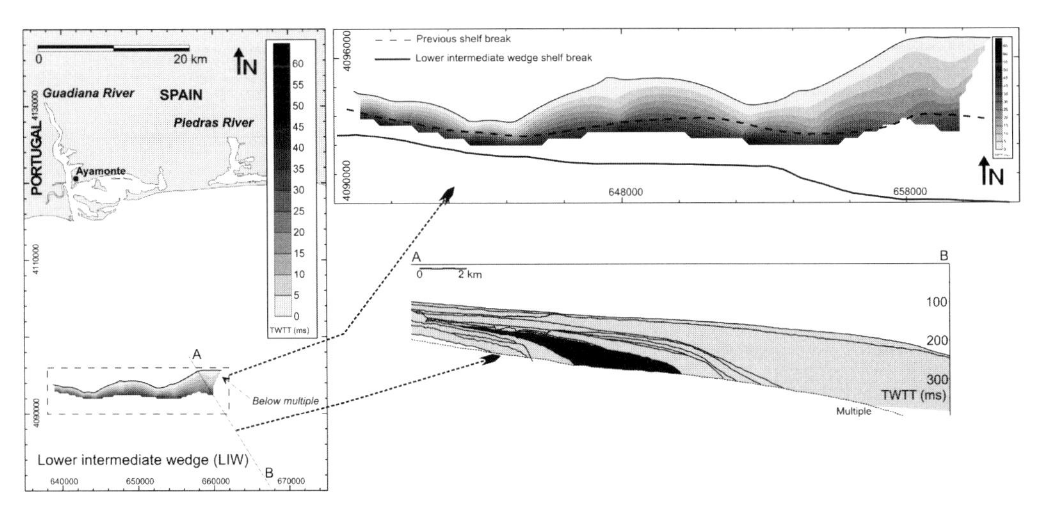

Fig. 6. Distribution pattern of lower intermediate wedge (LIW) and associated shelf-break migration. TWTT (ms), two-way travel time (milliseconds).

slope. This depocentre reaches maximum values of more than 60 ms (Fig. 6).

The associated shelf break is relatively straight, following an east–west orientation, although a small lobe seems to occur to the east. The amount of shelf-break progradation increases from the west (where it is less than 1 km) to the east (where it is up to 3 km; Fig. 6).

Middle Wedge (MW). The lower boundary is characterized by seaward increasing gradients (Figs 2, 3 & 4). On the shelf, it shows gradients below 0.5°, which increase to 1–1.5° close to the shelf break off the Guadiana River, and to values up to 1° off the Piedras River. On the upper slope, gradients decrease from 3.5–4.5° in the west, to less than 3° in the east.

Seismic facies are dominated by parallel–oblique configurations on the outer shelf, with gradients lower than 2°. Locally, tangential–oblique facies are preserved on the shelf off the Piedras River, where gradients of up to 3° in the foresets decrease to 1° in the bottomsets. The upper slope is dominated by inclined reflectors which mimic the previous upper slope surface, with gradients higher than 3° (Figs 2, 3 & 4). Most of these inclined reflectors represent progradational configurations; however, in places a poorly visible aggradational–divergent distal facies may be represented. Interesting stratigraphic features related to this wedge are significant valleys eroding the top boundary, located on the outer shelf close to the shelf break. Valley incision exceeds 20 ms (Fig. 3).

The landward pinch-out of this unit follows an irregular pattern, within 16–22 km of the present coastline (Fig. 7). The unit pinches out laterally to the west of the Guadiana River. It continues eastward of the study area, although with minor development. In the study area, upper slope depocentres seem to be laterally discontinuous, as maximum thickness is identified off the Guadiana River where this wedge may be more than 70 ms thick. Another depocentre is located to the west of the Piedras River, showing a thickness greater than 50 ms (Fig. 7).

The shelf break generated by this wedge shows a lobate pattern, as two lobes associated with the upper slope depocentres are identified. The amount of shelf-break migration is greater where the depocentres are more than 2 km thick, compared to less than 1 km in the inter-lobe area (Fig. 7).

Upper Intermediate Wedge (UIW). The lower boundary of this wedge shows a smooth profile. Proximal gradients up to 0.5° increase to 1° close to the shelf break, and up to 3° on the upper slope (Figs 2 & 3). The gradients decrease laterally from west to east. Parallel–oblique facies are common within this wedge. Inclinations on the outer shelf are lower than 1°, whereas on the upper slope inclinations as high as 3° are found (Figs 2 & 3).

The landward termination of this unit is relatively straight, and is located more than 25 km off the present coastline (Fig. 8). The regional distribution of this unit is restricted, as it pinches out laterally between the Guadiana and Piedras rivers (Fig. 4). The main depocentre is located on the upper slope, with a maximum thickness of more than 60 ms and lateral extension of about 8 km. Thickness on the upper slope decreases both west- and eastward (Fig. 8).

The shelf break generated by this wedge shows a

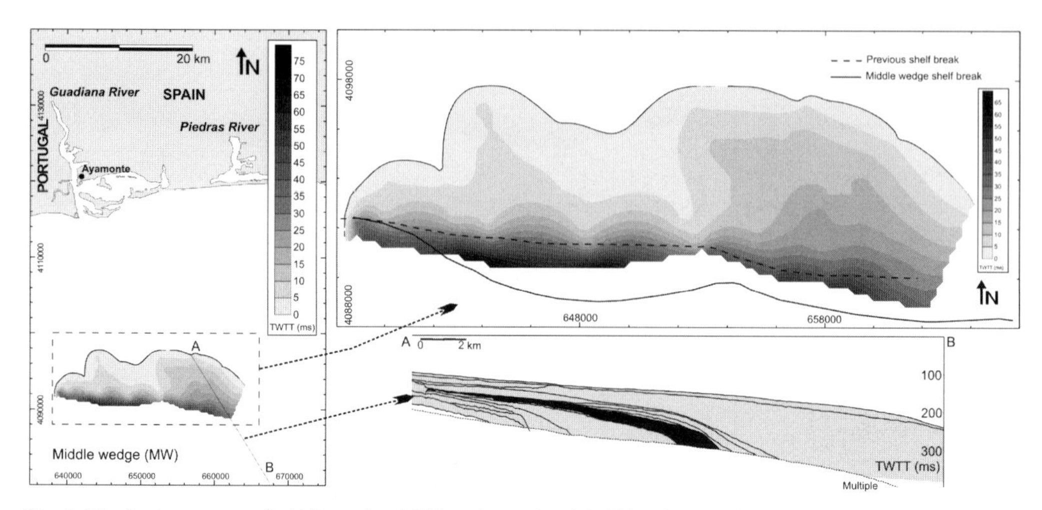

Fig. 7. Distribution pattern of middle wedge (MW) and associated shelf-break migration. TWTT (ms), two-way travel time (milliseconds).

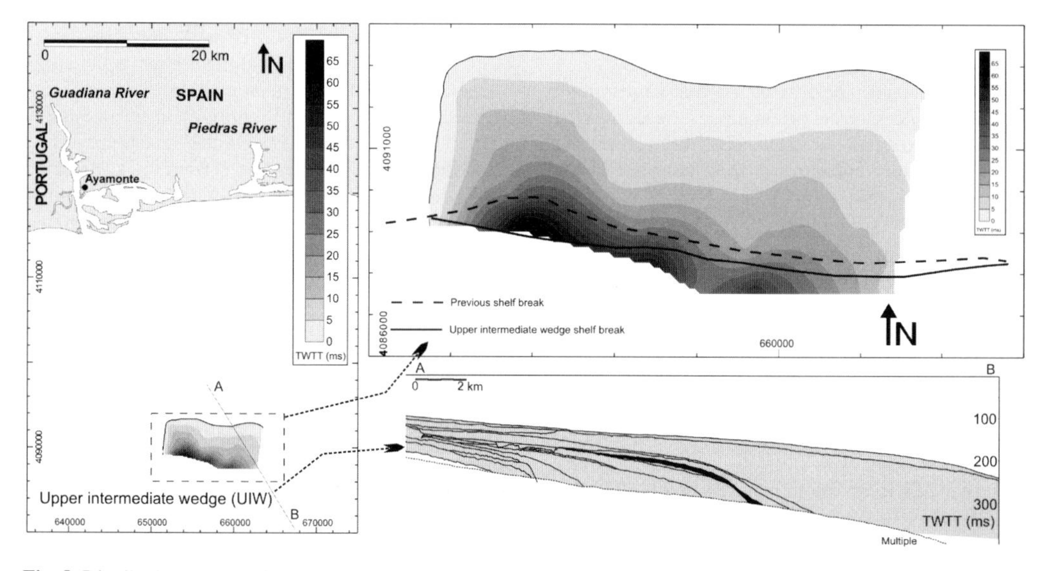

Fig. 8. Distribution pattern of upper intermediate wedge (UIW) and associated shelf-break migration. TWTT (ms), two-way travel time (milliseconds).

gentle lobate pattern, as the main migration (about 1 km) is related to the upper slope depocentre, whereas it laterally merges with the previous shelf break (Fig. 8).

Upper wedge (UW). The gradients of the lower boundary show two distinct patterns: (1) off the Guadiana River, a narrow band with gradients between 0.5–1° occurs where this unit pinches out. Seaward, the gradients decrease to 0.25–0.5°, and they increase close to the shelf break to values up to 1°. On the upper slope, gradients range between 2.5–3°. (2) Off the Piedras River, gradients are low proximally (less than 0.6°) but increase up to 1° towards the shelf break. The upper slope shows gradients up to 1.5° (Figs 2, 3 & 4).

This unit shows a seaward transition of facies (Figs 2, 3 & 4). Progradational facies occur on the shelf, where the top boundary is an erosional truncation. Parallel–oblique facies with inclinations lower than 0.5° are common on the middle shelf. On the outer shelf, the configuration may be parallel–oblique but with higher inclinations (1–1.5°) or tangential–oblique with foreset inclina-

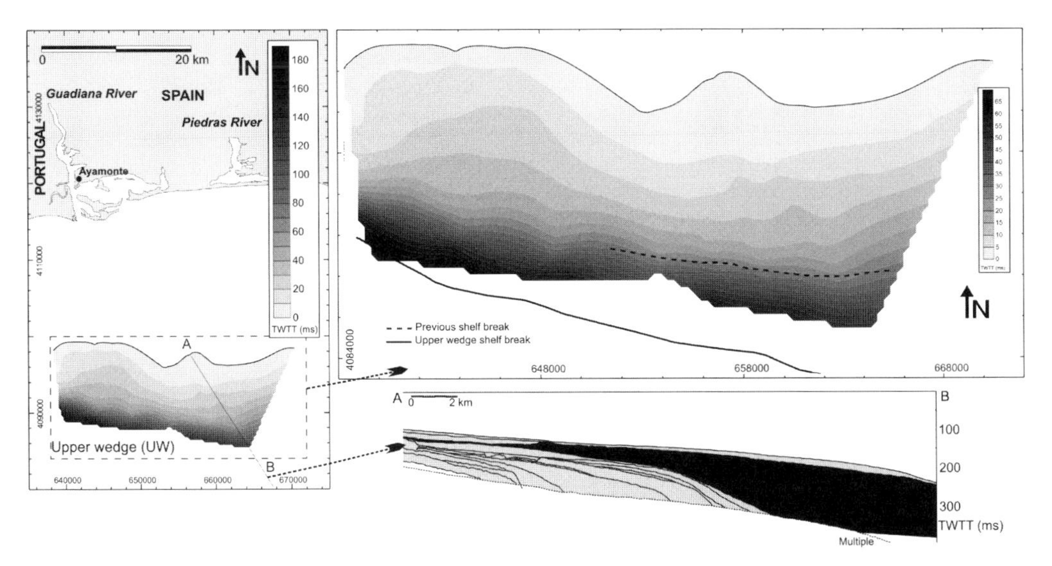

Fig. 9. Distribution pattern of upper wedge (UW) and associated shelf-break migration. TWTT (ms), two-way travel time (milliseconds).

tions of 1–4° that increase seawards. In contrast, progradational– aggradational facies occur on the upper slope, as seismic facies show intermediate characteristics between both configurations. Although the internal reflectors show inclinations ranging between 3–4° and generally increasing seaward, the upper boundary is a toplap surface, whereas the lower boundary shows concordant reflectors or even onlap. An updip erosional surface evolving downdip into a correlative conformity establishes the boundary between shelf progradational facies and upper slope progradational–aggradational facies (Fig. 4).

The landward termination of this wedge follows an east–west orientation and an undulating pattern, within 15–22 km of the present coastline (Fig. 9). This wedge shows a high lateral continuity, and is the thickest wedge. The main depocentre is elongated, laterally continuous and located on the upper slope, where thickness is higher than 140 ms in the study area; values of more than 180 ms have been detected locally (Fig. 9).

The shelf break generated by this wedge follows a straight pattern and a WNW–ESE orientation. The seaward migration of the shelf break is fairly constant and significant, reaching values of more than 4 km (Fig. 9).

Lateral development of late Quaternary shelf-margin wedges

The shelf-margin architecture in the shelf areas located to the west and east of the Guadiana Shelf shows a less pronounced development than most of the shelf-margin wedges (Fig. 10). On the western Algarve Shelf, only two shelf-margin wedges are identified above the APC (Fig. 10a). The lower unit could correspond to LW and/or to LIW, and is reduced in extent and thickness. It extends in cross-shelf section for less than 1 km, and the maximum thickness is about 25 ms. The upper unit is UW, and is characterized by a very reduced thickness (below 25 ms) in comparison with the Guadiana Shelf. On the eastern shelf, located off the Guadalquivir Basin, LW and LIW are obscured by the multiple signal, whereas MW and UIW show poor development, with maximum thickness below 20 ms. Only UW attains a considerable thickness (Fig. 10b). Therefore, the upper slope progradation induced by the formation of these marginal wedges was particularly significant off the Guadiana River.

Upper slope seismic facies as indicators of constructional processes

The observed shelf-margin deposits are characterized by convex arcuate profiles, resulting from the long-term effect of alternating deposition and erosion (Vanney & Stanley 1983). Most of them generated prograding shelf breaks, whose formation is favoured under the absence of upper slope canyons (Field *et al.* 1983; Mellere *et al.* 2002). Off the Guadiana River, the absence of submarine canyons combined with intense lateral sediment redistribution by shelf wind-driven currents and slope contour currents probably influenced the

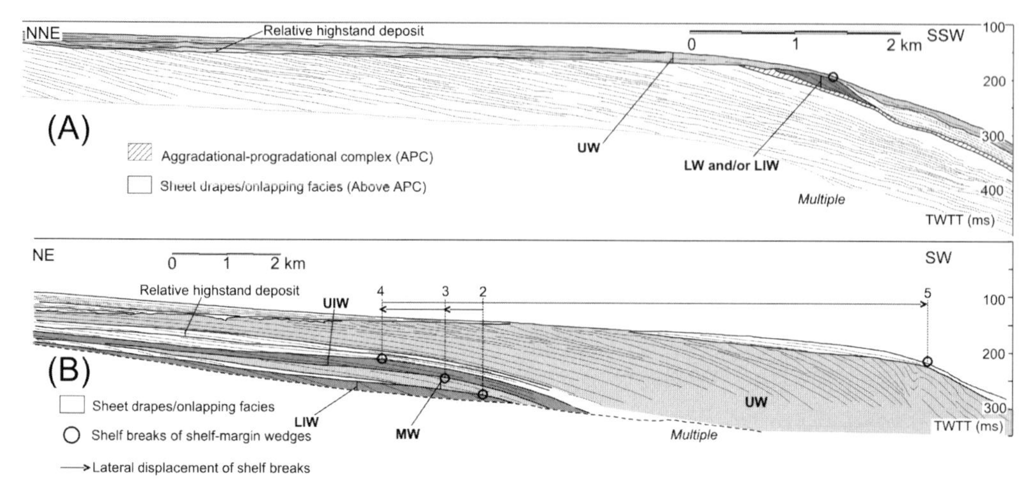

Fig. 10. Interpretative sections to the west and to the east of the study area (see position in Fig. 1). (**a**) Shelf-margin wedges show very poor development off Tavira, on the Portuguese margin; (**b**) Upper wedge (UW) shows higher development to the east of the study area. Middle (MW) and upper intermediate wedge (UIW) are very thin, whereas lower (LW) and lower intermediate wedge (LIW) are masked below the multiple. TWTT (ms), two-way travel time (milliseconds).

observed shelf-margin architecture. A classification of shelf-margin geometries identified in the study area is proposed, based on previous schemes dividing shelf-break types according to factors such as pattern and rate of sediment accumulation, dominant hydrodynamic regime, tilting and subsidence of the margin and eustatic sea-level changes (Field *et al.* 1983; Mougenot *et al.* 1983). We have considered not only the seismic facies of shelf-margin wedges, but also overlying sheet drapes or onlapping facies. Thus, the following upper slope types have been identified in the study area:

Type A: Starved-draped upper slope

This type has been related to low sedimentation rate, caused by shelf trapping and transport of sediments away from the shelf break by oceanic processes (Field *et al.* 1983). In the study area, it is characteristic of the APC, which causes the upward and landward shelf-break translation (Fig. 11). Shelf trapping and upper slope starvation were probably favoured by a rapid sea-level fall within a period of overall, high-amplitude sea-level rise, that caused a lack of fluvial sediment supply. The drape would be related to a subsequent sea-level rise.

Type B: Outbuilt upper slope

Deposition occurred on the upper slope, seaward of the shelf break (Fig. 11). This upper slope type has been related to high sedimentation rates (Field *et al.* 1983), controlled by high shelf sediment redistribution and/or shelf tilting (Field *et al.* 1983; Mougenot *et al.* 1983; Ercilla & Alonso 1996). In the study area, it is related to the Lower Intermediate Wedge (LIW). The outbuilding may be simple (Subtype B1), when it is exclusively composed of progradational facies, or composite, when onlapping facies also contribute distally (Subtype B2). In both cases, this upper slope type is dominated by progradational facies. The shelf break typically moves down- and seaward (about 1 km).

Type C: Progradational upbuilt-outbuilt upper slope

Shelf-margin deposits are represented by a shelf-to-slope progradational wedge building upward and outward (Fig. 11). The shelf break marks the transition between shelf progradation and upper slope divergent beds (Field *et al.* 1983) or oblique talus-like deposits (Mougenot *et al.* 1983). The formation of this type is related to very high sedimentation rates and enhanced subsidence in relation to the outbuilt type, favouring the formation of gently inclined slopes (Field *et al.* 1983; Mougenot *et al.* 1983; Ercilla & Alonso 1996).

In the study area, the shelf-break displacement varies according to the amount of progradation, which is linked to the proximity of fluvial sources. The upbuilt-outbuilt pattern may be simple (C1), when the upper slope outgrowth is exclusively formed by progradational clinoforms, as in the case of LW; or composite (C2), when aggradational

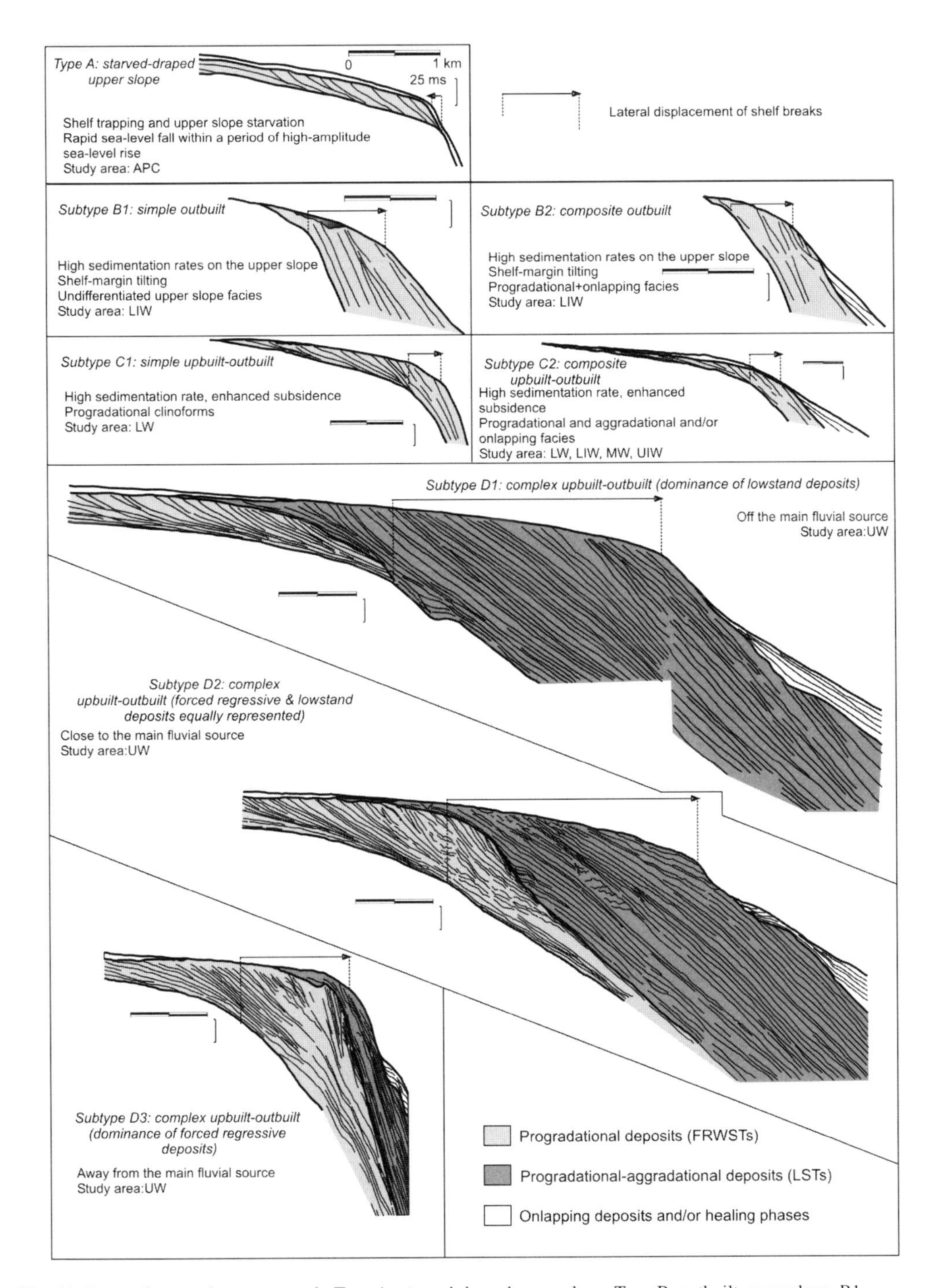

Fig. 11. Types of upper slope outgrowth: Type A, starved-draped upper slope; Type B, outbuilt upper slope. B1, progradational upper slope; B2, progradational-onlapped upper slope. Type C, progradational upbuilt-outbuilt upper slope. C1, progradational upper slope. C2, progradational-onlapped upper slope. Type D, complex upbuilt-outbuilt upper slope. D1, dominance of the progradational–aggradational upper slope wedge; D2, both the progradational shelf wedge and the progradational–aggradational upper slope wedge are well represented; D3, dominance of the progradational shelf wedge. APC, aggradational–progradational complex; LW, lower wedge; LIW, lower intermediate wedge; MW, middle wedge; UIW, upper intermediate wedge; UW, upper wedge.

and/or onlapping facies can contribute distally to the upper slope outgrowth, although progradational clinoforms are more significantly preserved (Fig. 11). This type has been found within LW, LIW, MW and UIW. Laterally, it evolves to types B and C1.

Type D: Complex upbuilt-outbuilt upper slope

This type produces a similar shelf-margin build-up to type C, but in this case progradational–aggradational upper slope seismic facies characterized by toplaps and bottom concordance and/or onlap are well represented (Fig. 11). This type was not defined in early shelf-break classifications, and is characterized by the Upper Wedge in the study area. Three subtypes have been differentiated (D1 to D3) according to the variable representation of progradational–aggradational upper slope facies (Fig. 11). The shelf break moves upward and seaward, and the displacement is higher where progradational–aggradational facies are significantly thicker in the proximity of fluvial sources, i.e. subtypes D1 and D2 (Fig. 11).

The record of relative sea-level changes

Geometrical relationships between and within the observed shelf-margin wedges are used to interpret relative sea-level changes. The relation between shelf-margin wedges and periods of falling sea-level and lowstands is well documented from numerous shelf margins (Ercilla *et al.* 1992, 1994*a*; Kolla *et al.* 2000). In contrast, sheet-like units consisting of drapes or healing phases on the outer shelf and/or upper slope and intercalated between shelf-margin wedges could be related to periods of relative sea-level rise, as reported in the Gulf of Mexico (Suter *et al.* 1987). The following stratigraphic criteria support the attribution of shelf-margin deposits to periods of sea-level fall and lowstand:

1. The dominance of low-angle, parallel–oblique reflectors on the shelf, evolving seaward to higher-angle reflectors on the upper slope, has been attributed in other deltaic settings to generation during periods of falling sea-level and lowstand (Suter & Berryhill 1985). Shelf facies are generally attributed to deposits generated during episodic sea-level falls (Sydow & Roberts 1994; Anderson *et al.* 1996), whereas upper slope sedimentation is especially favoured during lowstand and early rise conditions (Kindinger 1988; Anderson *et al.* 1996).
2. Thickness increase towards the upper slope is another indicator of their relationship with relative sea-level falls (Anderson *et al.* 1996).
3. Landward boundaries of shelf-margin wedges occur farther seaward than recent highstand deposits.
4. The most compelling evidence of the relationships between shelf-margin deposits and sea-level falls and lowstands is the common occurrence of erosional truncation at the top boundary and downward downlap terminations, as documented in numerous shelf settings (Yoo & Park 1997; Kolla *et al.* 2000). Erosional unconformities at the top boundaries are related to subaerial erosion during sea-level falls (Kindinger 1988; Anderson *et al.* 1996), which may cause the removal of sediments deposited during the early stages of forced regressions (Chiocci 2000).

Characterization of the internal structure of major shelf-margin wedges and their relation to sea-level trends is open to diverse interpretations. A basic interpretation considers continuous stratal patterns from the outer shelf to the upper slope, with seaward downlapping oblique clinoforms grading downward and seaward into low-angle, parallel reflections. Shelf-margin wedges are thus interpreted as prograding complexes of the LST, formed during periods of falling sea-level and lowstand (Piper & Perissoratis 1991; Ercilla *et al.* 1992, 1994*a*, *b*; Morton & Suter 1996; Chiocci *et al.* 1997; Yoo & Park 1997). However, other studies consider two main constructional phases of shelf-margin deltas, which show an overall configuration of progradation–aggradation (Kindinger 1988; Sydow & Roberts 1994; Torres *et al.* 1995; Anderson *et al.* 1996; Hiscott 2001) related to sea-level fall/lowstand conditions (Kolla *et al.* 2000):

1. Shelf phase (FRWST) dominated by deltaic progradation and characterized by successive seaward stacking of clinoform sets separated by downlap surfaces. Upper slope facies are composed of distal bottomsets of the FRWST.
2. Upper slope phase (LST), characterized by progradation of the shelf break due to the construction of a prograding wedge with a rising shelf-edge trajectory (Helland-Hansen & Gjelberg 1994). This phase is related to lowstand conditions and/or early rise. LSTs may eventually be draped or onlapped by healing phases of early TSTs (Kolla *et al.* 2000).

The two-fold scheme (FRWST versus LST) can be applied in the study area to wedge types B, C and D, characterized by significant upper slope progradation. Two contrasting internal geometries may be defined, capped at the distal terminations by drape units or onlapping deposits, interpreted as early rise healing phases. These geometries show different development of progradational–aggradational facies:

1 Shelf-margin wedges composed mainly of forced regressive deposits (FRWST) formed during sea-level falls (Fig. 12a). Types B and C (LW, LIW, MW and UIW) are dominated by this facies pattern. Lowstand deposits are not preserved or show poor development. Consequently, it is difficult to distinguish a forced regressive-lowstand boundary. The prevalence of forced regressive deposits in shelf-margin wedges has also been documented in Gulf of Mexico deltas, where intervals of aggradation are reduced (Kindinger 1988; Kolla *et al.* 2000), and in the Baram delta (Hiscott 2001). Indeed, most of the shelf-margin wedges that show continuous stratal patterns and which do not show distinct regressive to lowstand facies are probably equivalent to this internal geometry.

2 Shelf-margin wedges where both forced regressive (FRWST) and lowstand deposits (LST) contribute to the upper slope outgrowth. This facies pattern is represented by Type D (UW). The LST is represented by a progradational–aggradational wedge, which does not show seismic evidence indicative of significant sea-level fall. Thus, erosional truncation and downlap terminations characteristic of FRWSTs are substituted on the upper slope by toplap and concordant/onlap terminations. Internal downlap surfaces, also frequent within FRWSTs, are not observed within the LST. In addition, the shoreline trajectory path moves slightly upward or remains at the same level during deposition of the progradational–aggradational wedge, indicating normal regression during lowstand conditions (Helland-Hansen & Gjelberg 1994). The LST may account for more than 85% of progradation in zones of greater upper slope outgrowth (Fig. 12b). The boundary between shelf progradational facies (FRWST) and upper slope progradational–aggradational facies (LST) is identified in zones where the progradational–aggradational wedge shows greater development, and is represented by an erosional surface that grades downprofile to a concordance. This surface satisfies the definition of a sequence boundary *sensu* Vail *et al.* (1977) and Posamentier & Vail (1988). However, laterally the recognition of this boundary becomes uncertain. A similar geometry was observed within the most recent shelf-margin wedge in the Gulf of Mexico. In some places, clinoforms deposited during the lowstand are poorly developed, and the distinction of the sequence boundary is uncertain (Sydow & Roberts 1994). However, the dominant case is characterized by significant aggradation, although forced regressive deposits also occur (Kolla *et al.* 2000). This pattern is similar to the UW internal geometry in areas highly influenced by river sources.

The identification of these contrasting facies patterns is thought to indicate the influence of different durations of sea-level cycles, as the duration of lowstand probably influences sediment supply and therefore the thickness of LSTs (Piper & Perissoratis 1991; Torres *et al.* 1995; Chiocci 2000). Thus, wedges strongly dominated by FRWSTs would have been formed in response to sea-level cycles with short-lived lowstands (Fig. 12a). In contrast, the upper slope depositional geometry of the most recent sediment wedge shows well-developed FRWST and LST, probably indicating a longer lowstand interval (Fig. 12b).

Chronostratigraphic framework

The interpretation of additional geophysical information provided by this paper permits us to improve previous chronostratigraphic schemes (Somoza *et al.* 1997; Hernández-Molina *et al.* 2000; Lobo *et al.* 2002), which can be considered a basic working hypothesis (Fig. 13). As absolute age dates such as biostratigraphic data are missing, the chronostratigraphic framework was built by comparing relative sea-level changes interpreted from shelf-margin wedge geometries with well-known late Quaternary sea-level fluctuations (Shackleton 1987; Chappell *et al.* 1996).

The Aggradational–Progradational Complex (APC) permits us to constrain the correlation, as it indicates a major sea-level rise related to the 6/5 transition (Somoza *et al.* 1997; Hernández-Molina *et al.* 2000). The identification of a middle progradational member within a general aggradational trend is explained by the higher frequency sea-level fall that interrupts the overall rise (Fig. 13). Shelf-margin wedges composed mainly of forced regressive deposits (LW, LIW, MW and UIW) may have formed during the falling sea-level interval of sea-level cycles occurring between MISs 5 and 3 and characterized by abrupt sea-level fall-to-rise transitions. The backstepping unit located between UIW and UW has been interpreted as a TST-to-HST complex, which culminated with a highstand occurring during marine isotopic stage (MIS) 3 (Hernández-Molina *et al.* 2000; Lobo *et al.* 2002). UW was related to the sea-level fall and lowstand during MISs 3 and 2 (Somoza *et al.* 1997; Hernández-Molina *et al.* 2000). The high preservation of lowstand facies within UW could be the result of a different shape of the most recent sea-level cycle (MISs 3 and 2), in which the sea-level lowstand was relatively long-lived, as it lasted for

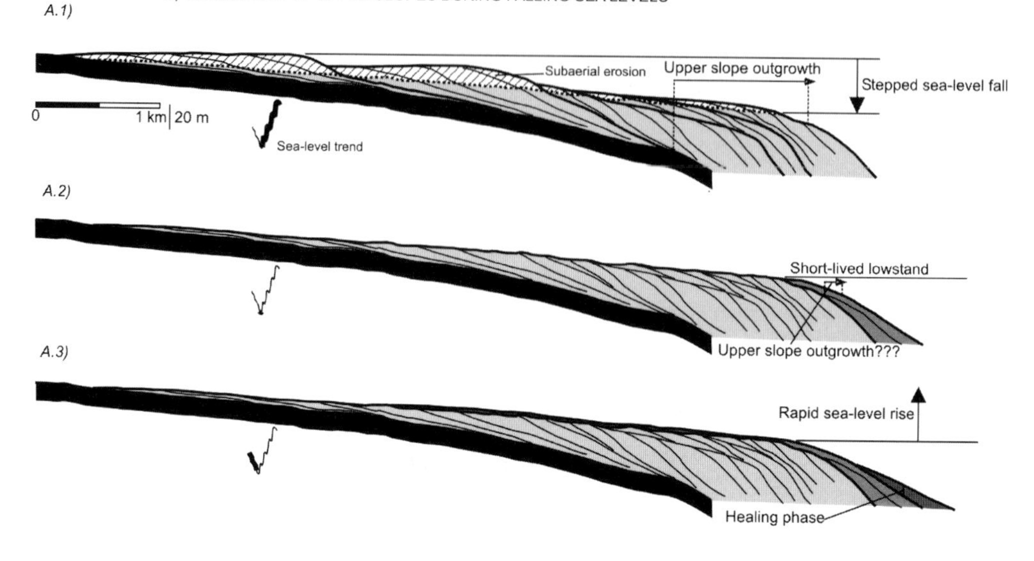

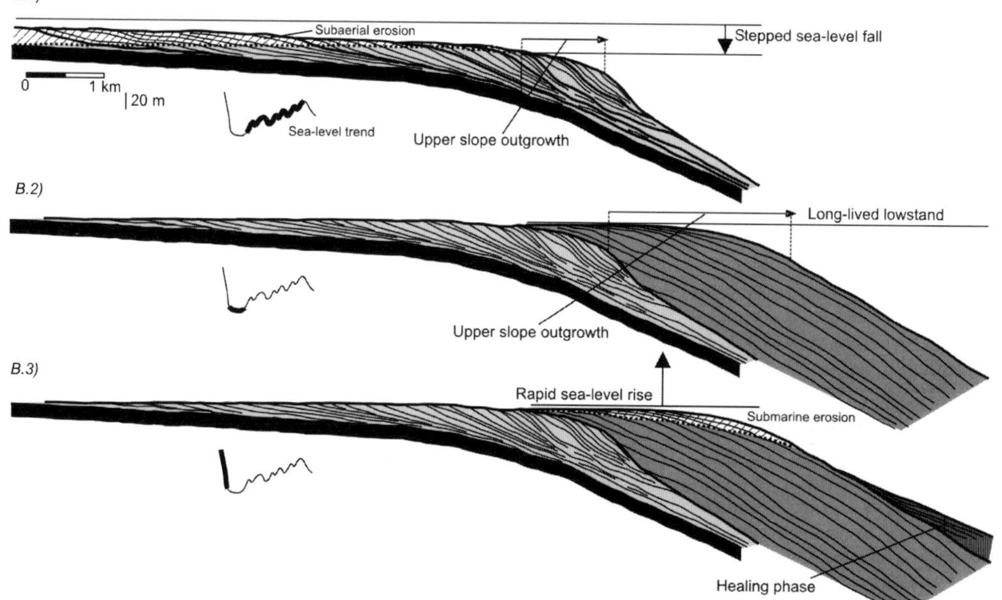

Fig. 12. Models of upper slope outgrowth identified in the study area. (**a**) Outgrowths of upper slopes during sea-level falls: (A.1) upper slope progradation through regressive wedge construction; (A.2) low or no development of lowstand wedges; (A.3) healing phase formation during subsequent sea-level rise. (**b**) Outgrowth of upper slopes during sea-level falls and lowstands: (B.1) moderate upper slope progradation through regressive wedge construction; (B.2) high upper slope outgrowth during long-lived lowstand; (B.3) healing phase formation during subsequent sea-level rise.

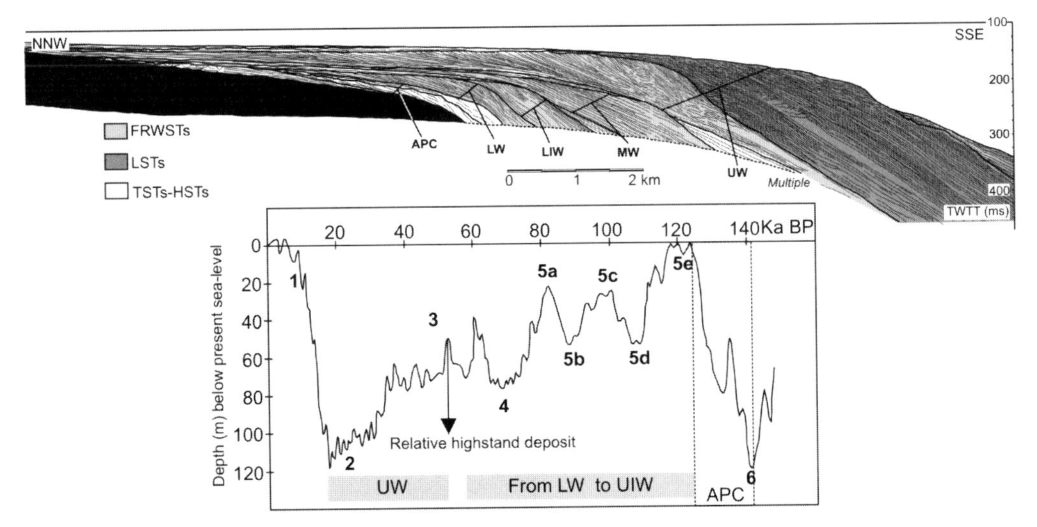

Fig. 13. Sequence stratigraphic interpretation of observed stratigraphic architecture and proposed chronostratigraphic framework, based on correlation of shelf-margin wedges with late Quaternary glacio-eustatic sea-level changes. Sea-level curve after Shackleton (1987). FRWST, forced regressive wedge systems tract; LST, lowstand systems tract; TST, transgressive systems tract; HST, highstand systems tract. TWTT (ms), two-way travel time (milliseconds).

more than 10 ka, and the maximum sea-level lowstand was considerably lower than in previous cycles, between 100–120 m below present-day level. Consequently, the generation of lowstand facies was strongly favoured during the Last Glacial Maximum. Our investigations also detected several previously undocumented sheet drapes intercalated between the major regressive wedges.

Styles of upper slope progradation

Distribution maps and shelf-break patterns of shelf-margin wedges show two distinct responses in the study area, determining different styles of shelf-edge build up and upper slope progradation.

Uniform progradation

Uniform progradation is characteristic of laterally continuous wedges whose upper slope depocentres show elongated distributions with laterally constant thickness (e.g. Fig. 9). The associated shelf break acquires a mostly straight, linear pattern, and the seaward shelf-break migration is significant along the length of the deposit, although it may vary laterally. The most typical example of this type of lateral accretion is in UW, although LIW also shows similar characteristics (Fig. 14).

The deltaic nature of these wedges is strongly suggested by the identification of incised valleys in inner to middle shelf areas (Somoza *et al.* 1997; Hernández-Molina *et al.* 2000; Lobo 2000). This type of shelf-margin progradation suggests linear sources associated with whole margin progradation, which is considered the dominant shelf-margin construction pattern (Suter & Berryhill 1985; Chiocci 1994, 2000; Yoo & Park 1997).

Elongate parallel patterns of depocentre distributions characteristic of uniform progradation indicate overall margin subsidence (Suter & Berryhill 1985; Porębski & Steel 2003). However, several authors also recognized the controlling effect of oceanographic conditions. Thus, such patterns may also be characteristic of high wave energy combined with abundant sediment supply (Suter & Berryhill 1985), or increased redistribution of sediments due to enhanced longshore current activity, as current enhancement during low sea-levels has been reported from various settings (Matteucci & Hine 1987; Yoo *et al.* 1996; Chiocci 2000). In the study area, the seaward advance of the shelf break was relatively regular, although increasing in rate eastward (Fig. 14). This pattern suggests a higher volume of eastward sediment distribution, and therefore enhanced action of littoral drift and shelf currents, similarly to the present-day sediment transport pattern. During cold periods, particularly during the last glaciation, the North Atlantic region showed an intensification of the westerly winds, and consequently enhancement of anticyclonic gyres (McIntyre *et al.* 1976). This process resulted from compression of the climatic belt due to the southward displacement of the polar front, and would have caused subpolar and transitional water masses

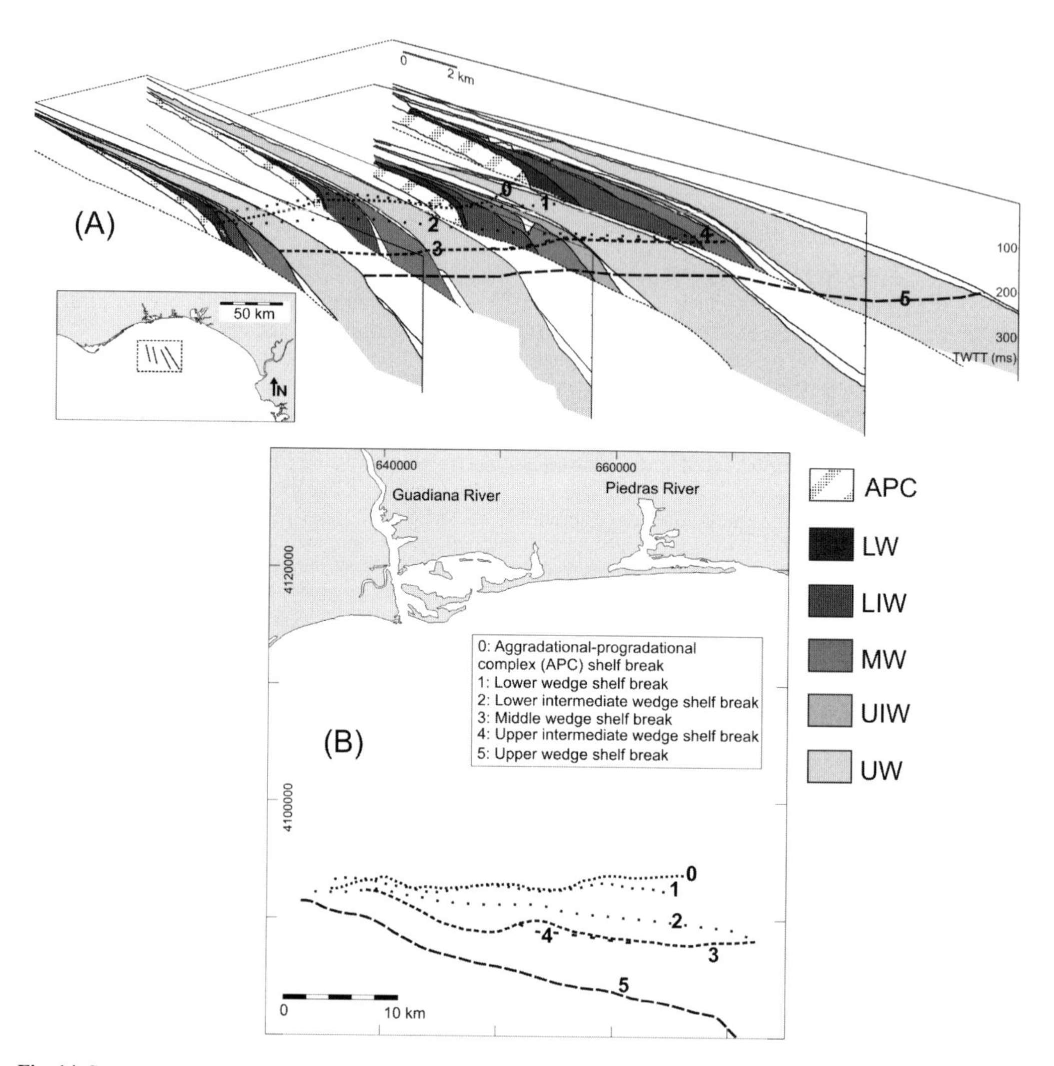

Fig. 14. Successive shelf-break migrations during deposition of shelf-margin wedges: (**a**) 3D view of shelf-margin wedges off the Guadiana River; (**b**) plan view of shelf breaks related to studied shelf-margin wedges. TWTT (ms), two-way travel time (milliseconds). APC, aggradational–progradational complex; LW, lower wedge; LIW, lower intermediate wedge; MW, middle wedge; UIW, upper intermediate wedge; UW, upper wedge.

to be squeezed into a narrow band. However, the geometry of water mass gyres differed only slightly from the present day, which is characterized by an anticyclonic gyre affecting the distal margin (Ochoa & Bray 1991; Nelson *et al.* 1999).

Sequence thickness at the shelf margin is commonly determined by the interplay between sea-level fluctuations and structural dynamics (Morton & Suter 1996). In this case, the influence of the sea-level fall trend should be emphasized. High efficiency of redistribution processes was probably favoured by long-lived, stepped sea-level falls, that were dominant during the late Quaternary, due to the asymmetric character of sea-level fluctuations (Chiocci *et al.* 1997; Hernández-Molina *et al.* 2000).

The Upper Wedge (UW) has been related to post-MIS 3 sea-level fall and lowstand and shows this type of shelf-margin progradation. Rates of sea-level fall during that period have been estimated at 1.4 m ka^{-1} (Shackleton 1987), causing the marked asymmetry observed in the sea-level cycles (Chiocci *et al.* 1997). It is reasonable to assume that formation of LIW was also related to a slow sea-level fall, although the seaward migration rate of UW was much higher. The prolonged period of sea-level fall/lowstand associated with the formation of UW lasted for about 35 ka, whereas previous falling sea-level/lowstand intervals were much shorter, ranging between 10–15 ka (Shackleton 1987; Chappell *et al.* 1996).

Laterally variable progradation

Laterally variable progradation is characteristic of wedges that pinch out or significantly thin laterally. The associated shelf break shows a (multi) lobate pattern, as lobes correspond broadly with depocentre location, and the seaward shelf-break migration pattern is very irregular. Progradation rate is highest in the lobes, and laterally the shelf break may remain stationary or even move landward, due to reduced rates of sediment supply. The most typical example of this type is MW, although LIW also shares similar characteristics (Fig. 14).

In contrast to uniform progradation, this pattern of upper slope progradation suggests point sources with variable sediment supply (Ercilla *et al.* 1994*b*) and moderate to low rates of sediment redistribution. In addition, MW shows the most compelling evidence of distal valley incision, as significant erosive valleys have been determined on the middle–outer shelf in the zone where the highest depocentre is located (Figs 2 & 3). This pattern of fluvial erosion may be due to loss of shelf accommodation during rapidly lowered sea levels (Morton & Suter 1996; Porębski & Steel 2003). MIS 4 sea-level fall rates are higher than $4\,m\,ka^{-1}$, a value considerably higher than the $1.4\,m\,ka^{-1}$ value reported for MIS 2 (Fig. 13). These relatively high rates of sea-level fall are not common during the Pleistocene (Chiocci *et al.* 1997), and could explain the relatively scarce occurrence of this type of margin outgrowth during that period.

Conclusions

The most recent late Quaternary shelf-margin wedges of deltaic origin recognized off the Guadiana River (Gulf of Cadiz margin) are characterized by convex arcuate profiles and prograding shelf breaks. Their formation has been favoured by the absence of upper slope canyons, and probably occurred during episodes of late Quaternary sea-level fall and/or lowstand. The bases of these deposits are defined by a major sea-level rise recorded by a dominantly aggradational sheet drape. The study of the internal geometry and distribution patterns of these marginal wedges provides significant information about the influence of different patterns of falling sea-level and lowstand on upper slope sedimentation.

Most of the identified shelf-margin wedges show an upbuilt-outbuilt upper slope growth pattern. Within upbuilt-outbuilt margins, two distinct internal geometries were observed. Shelf-margin wedges mainly composed of forced regressive deposits, formed during sea-level cycles with abrupt sea-level fall to rise transitions. Recognition of the regressive-lowstand boundary is uncertain within those wedges. Second, shelf-margin wedges where both forced regressive deposits and lowstand deposits are well represented. This pattern would be generated during longer duration sea-level lowstands. The boundary between forced regressive and lowstand deposits is recognized in areas of high lateral outgrowth as an updip erosional surface becoming concordant downslope, similarly to a classic sequence boundary.

Distribution patterns of shelf-margin wedges show two contrasting trends in the study area: (1) Elongated parallel depocentres, with constant lateral thickness and relatively uniform seaward shelf-break migration patterns. This pattern suggests linear sources and high amounts of lateral sediment redistribution, and was probably favoured by periods of long-term gently falling sea-levels. (2) (Multi) lobate depocentres, with laterally variable thickness and uneven rates of seaward shelf-break migration. This pattern suggests point sources and moderate to low sediment redistribution rates, probably as a result of delta lobe switching. This situation was probably favoured by a higher rate of sea-level fall.

The seismic database used in this study was collected through several oceanographic surveys (Golca, Fado and Wadi Ana), jointly organized between several institutions, including the Universities of Algarve and Cádiz, the Instituto Español de Oceanografía, the Instituto Geológico y Minero de España and the Disepla group. The research benefited from the following projects: Emerge (Odiana Program), PB-91-0622-C03/Golca and PB94-1090-CO3/Fado (Spanish Marine Science and Technology Program). F.J. Lobo was funded by a Marie Curie Individual Fellowship, under contract HPMF-CT-2001-01494 between the Universidade do Algarve and the European Commission. Helpful comments and suggestions that improved the manuscript were provided by P. Plink-Björklund (Göteborg University) and by R.B. Wynn (SOC). Special Publication editors Stephen Flint and David Hodgson are gratefully thanked, for their detailed editorial work. The participation of F. González, L. Godoy, M. García and J. Miranda in the Wadi Ana 2000 survey is particularly acknowledged.

References

Anderson, J.B., Abdulah, K., Sarzalejo, S., Siringan, F. & Thomas, M.A. 1996. Late Quaternary sedimentation and high-resolution sequence stratigraphy of the east Texas shelf. *In*: De Batist, M. & Jacobs, P. (eds) *Geology of Siliciclastic Shelf Seas*. Geological Society, London, Special Publications, **117**, 95–124.

CHAPPELL, J., OMURA, A., ESAT, T., MCCULLOCH, M., PANDOLFI, J., OTA, Y. & PILLANS, B. 1996. Reconciliation of Late Quaternary sea levels derived from coral terraces at Huon Peninsula with deep sea oxygen isotope records. *Earth Planetary Science Letters*, **141**, 227–236.

CHIOCCI, F.L. 1994. Very high-resolution seismics as a tool for sequence stratigraphy applied to outcrop scale-examples from eastern Tyrrhenian margin Holocene/ Pleistocene deposits. *American Association of Petroleum Geologists Bulletin*, **78**, 378–395.

CHIOCCI, F.L. 2000. Depositional response to Quaternary fourth-order sea-level fluctuations on the Latium margin (Tyrrhenian Sea, Italy). *In*: HUNT, D. & GAWTHORPE, R.L. (eds) *Sedimentary Responses to Forced Regressions*. Geological Society, London, Special Publications, **172**, 271–289.

CHIOCCI, F.L., ERCILLA, G. & TORRES, J. 1997. Stratal architecture of western Mediterranean margins as the result of the stacking of Quaternary lowstand deposits below 'glacio-eustatic fluctuation base-level'. *Sedimentary Geology*, **112**, 195–217.

ERCILLA, G. & ALONSO, B. 1996. Quaternary siliciclastic sequence stratigraphy of western Mediterranean passive and tectonically active margins: the role of global versus local controlling factors. *In*: DE BATIST, M. & JACOBS, P. (eds) *Geology of Siliciclastic Shelf Seas*. Geological Society, London, Special Publications, **117**, 125–137.

ERCILLA, G., ALONSO, B. & BARAZA, J. 1992. Sedimentary evolution of the northwestern Alboran Sea during the Quaternary. *Geo-Marine Letters*, **12**, 144–149.

ERCILLA, G., ALONSO, B. & BARAZA, J. 1994*a*. Post-Calabrian sequence stratigraphy of the northwestern Alboran Sea (southwestern Mediterranean). *Marine Geology*, **120**, 249–265.

ERCILLA, G., FARRÁN, M., ALONSO, B. & DÍAZ, J.I. 1994*b*. Pleistocene progradational growth pattern of the northern Catalonia continental shelf (northwestern Mediterranean). *Geo-Marine Letters*, **14**, 264–271.

FAUGÈRES, J.-C., GONTHIER, E. & STOW, D.A.V. 1984. Contourite drift molded by deep Mediterranean outflow. *Geology*, **12**, 296–300.

FIELD, M.E., CARLSON, P.R. & HALL, R.K. 1983. Seismic facies of shelfedge deposits, US continental margin. *In*: STANLEY, D.J. & MOORE, G.T. (eds) *The Shelfbreak: Critical Interface on Continental Margins*. Society of Economic Paleontologists and Mineralogists, Special Publications, **33**, 299–313.

HABGOOD, E.L., KENYON, N.H., MASSON, D.G., AKHMETZHANOV, A., WEAVER, P.P.E., GARDNER, J. & MULDER, T. 2003. Deep-water sediment wave fields, bottom current sand channels and gravity flow channel-lobe systems: Gulf of Cadiz, NE Atlantic. *Sedimentology*, **50**, 483–510.

HELLAND-HANSEN, W. & GJELBERG, J.G. 1994. Conceptual basis and variability in sequence stratigraphy: a different perspective. *Sedimentary Geology*, **92**, 31–52.

HERNÁNDEZ-MOLINA, F.J., SOMOZA, L. & LOBO, F.J. 2000. Seismic stratigraphy of the Gulf of Cádiz continental shelf: a model for Late Quaternary very high-resolution sequence stratigraphy and response to sea-level fall. *In*: HUNT, D. & GAWTHORPE, R.L.G. (eds) *Sedimentary Responses to Forced Regressions*. Geological Society, London, Special Publications, **172**, 329–361.

HERNÁNDEZ-MOLINA, F.J., LLAVE, E., SOMOZA, L., ET AL. 2003. Looking for clues to paleoceanographic imprints: a diagnosis of the Gulf of Cádiz contourite depositional systems. *Geology*, **31**, 19–22.

HISCOTT, R.N. 2001. Depositional sequences controlled by high rates of sediment supply, sea-level variations, and growth faulting: the Quaternary Baram Delta of northwestern Borneo. *Marine Geology*, **175**, 67–102.

HUNT, D. & TUCKER, M.E. 1992. Stranded parasequences and the forced regressive wedge systems tract: deposition during base-level fall. *Sedimentary Geology*, **81**, 1–9.

KINDINGER, J.L. 1988. Seismic stratigraphy of the Mississippi-Alabama shelf and upper continental slope. *Marine Geology*, **83**, 79–94.

KOLLA, V., BIONDI, P., LONG, B. & FILLON, R. 2000. Sequence stratigraphy and architecture of the Late Pleistocene Lagniappe delta complex, northeast Gulf of Mexico. *In*: HUNT, D. & GAWTHORPE, R.L. (eds) *Sedimentary Responses to Forced Regressions*. Geological Society, London, Special Publications, **172**, 291–327.

LOBO, F.J. 2000. *Estratigrafía de alta resolución y cambios del nivel del mar durante el Cuaternario del margen continental del Golfo de Cádiz (S de España) y del Roussillon (S de Francia): estudio comparativo*. Ph.D. Thesis, Univ. Cádiz, 618 pp.

LOBO, F.J., HERNÁNDEZ-MOLINA, F.J., SOMOZA, L., DÍAZ DEL RÍO, V. & DIAS, J.M.A. 2002. Stratigraphic evidence of an upper Pleistocene TST to HST complex on the Gulf of Cádiz continental shelf (south-west Iberian Peninsula). *Geo-Marine Letters*, **22**, 95–107.

LLAVE, E., HERNÁNDEZ-MOLINA, F.J., SOMOZA, L., DÍAZ DEL RÍO, V., STOW, D.A.W., MAESTRO, A. & ALVEIRINHO DIAS, J.M. 2001. Seismic stacking pattern of the Faro-Albufeira contourite system (Gulf of Cadiz): a Quaternary record of paleoceanographic and tectonic influences. *Marine Geophysical Researches*, **22**, 487–508.

MATTEUCCI, T.D. & HINE, A.C. 1987. Evolution of the Cape Fear terrace: A complex interaction between the Gulf Stream and a paleoshelf edge delta. *Marine Geology*, **77**, 185–205.

MCINTYRE, A., KIPP, N.G., BÉ, A.W.H., CROWLEY, T., KELLOGG, T., GARDNER, J.V., PRELL, W. & RUDDIMAN, W.F. 1976. Glacial North Atlantic 18,000 years ago: A CLIMAP reconstruction. *Geological Society of America*, Memoirs, **145**, 43–76.

MELLERE, D., PLINK-BJÖRKLUND, P. & STEEL, R. 2002. Anatomy of shelf deltas at the edge of a prograding Eocene shelf margin, Spitsbergen. *Sedimentology*, **49**, 1181–1206.

MITCHUM JR., R.M. & VAN WAGONER, J.C. 1991. High-frequency sequences and their stacking patterns: sequence-stratigraphic evidence of high-frequency eustatic cycles. *Sedimentary Geology*, **70**, 131–160.

MITCHUM, JR., R.M., VAIL, P.R. & THOMPSON III, S. 1977*a*. Seismic stratigraphy and global changes of sea level, Part 2: The depositional sequence as a basic unit for stratigraphic analysis. *In*: PAYTON, C.E. (ed.) *Seismic Stratigraphy-Applications to Hydrocarbon Explora-*

tion. American Association of Petroleum Geologists, Memoirs, **26**, 53–62.

MITCHUM JR., R.M., VAIL, P.R. & SANGREE, J.B. 1977*b*. Seismic stratigraphy and global changes of sea level, Part 6: Stratigraphic interpretation of seismic reflection patterns in depositional sequences. *In*: PAYTON, C.E. (ed.) *Seismic Stratigraphy-Applications to Hydrocarbon Exploration*. American Association of Petroleum Geologists, Memoirs, **26**, 117–133.

MORTON, R.A. & SUTER, J.R. 1996. Sequence stratigraphy and composition of Late Quaternary shelf-margin deltas, northern Gulf of Mexico. *American Association of Petroleum Geologists Bulletin*, **80**, 505–530.

MOUGENOT, D., BOILLOT, G. & REHAULT, J.-P. 1983. Prograding shelfbreak types on passive continental margins: some european examples. *In*: STANLEY, D.J. & MOORE, G.T. (eds) *The Shelfbreak: Critical Interface on Continental Margins*. Society of Economic Paleontologists and Mineralogists, Special Publications, **33**, 61–78.

NELSON, C.H., BARAZA, J. & MALDONADO, A. 1993. Mediterranean undercurrent sandy contourites, Gulf of Cadiz, Spain. *Sedimentary Geology*, **82**, 103–131.

NELSON, C.H., BARAZA, J., MALDONADO, A., RODERO, J., ESCUTIA, C. & BARBER JR, J.H. 1999. Influence of the Atlantic inflow and Mediterranean outflow currents on Late Quaternary sedimentary facies of the Gulf of Cadiz continental margin. *Marine Geology*, **155**, 99–129.

OCHOA, J. & BRAY, N.A. 1991. Water mass exchange in the Gulf of Cadiz. *Deep-Sea Research*, **38**, 5465–5503.

PIPER, D.J.W. & PERISSORATIS, C. 1991. Late Quaternary sedimentation on the north Aegean continental margin, Greece. *American Association of Petroleum Geologists Bulletin*, **75**, 46–61.

PLINK-BJÖRKLUND, P. & STEEL, R. 2002. Sea-level fall below the shelf edge, without basin-floor fans. *Geology*, **30**, 115–118.

PORĘBSKI, S.J. & STEEL, R.J. 2003. Shelf-margin deltas: their stratigraphic significance and relation to deep-water sands. *Earth-Science Reviews*, **62**, 283–326.

POSAMENTIER, H.W. & VAIL, P.R. 1988. Eustatic controls on clastic deposition II-Sequence and systems tracts models. *In*: WILGUS, C.K., HASTINGS, B.S., KENDALL, C.G.ST.C., POSAMENTIER, H.W., ROSS, C.A. & VAN WAGONER, J.C. (eds) *Sea Level Changes – An Integrated Approach*. Society of Economic Paleontologists and Mineralogists, Special Publications, **42**, 125–154.

RODERO, J., PALLARÉS, L. & MALDONADO, A. 1999. Late Quaternary seismic facies of the Gulf of Cadiz Spanish margin: depositional processes influenced by sea-level change and tectonic controls. *Marine Geology*, **155**, 131–156.

SHACKLETON, N.J. 1987. Oxygen isotopes, ice volume and sea level. *Quaternary Science Reviews*, **6**, 183–190.

SOMOZA, L., HERNÁNDEZ-MOLINA, F.J., DE ANDRÉS, J.R. & REY, J. 1997. Continental shelf architecture and sea-level cycles: Late Quaternary high-resolution stratigraphy of the Gulf of Cádiz, Spain. *Geo-Marine Letters*, **17**, 133–139.

STOW, D.A.V., FAUGÈRES, J.-C. & GONTHIER, E. 1986. Facies distribution and textural variation in Faro Drift contourites: velocity fluctuation and drift growth. *Marine Geology*, **72**, 71–100.

SUTER, J.R. & BERRYHILL JR., H.L. 1985. Late Quaternary shelf-margin deltas, northwest Gulf of Mexico. *American Association of Petroleum Geologists Bulletin*, **69**, 77–91.

SUTER, J.R., BERRYHILL JR., H.L. & PENLAND, S. 1987. Late Quaternary sea-level fluctuations and depositional sequences, southwest Louisiana continental shelf. *In*: NUMMEDAL, D., PILKEY, O.H. & HOWARD, J.P. (eds) *Sea Level Fluctuations and Coastal Evolution*. Society of Economic Paleontologists and Mineralogists, Special Publications, **41**, 199–219.

SYDOW, J. & ROBERTS, H.H. 1994. Stratigraphic framework of a late Pleistocene shelf-edge delta, northeast Gulf of Mexico. *American Association of Petroleum Geologists Bulletin*, **78**, 1276–1312.

TORRES, J., SAVOYE, B. & COCHONAT, P. 1995. The effects of late Quaternary sea-level changes on the Rhône slope sedimentation (northwestern Mediterranean), as indicated by seismic stratigraphy. *Journal of Sedimentary Research*, **65**, 368–387.

VAIL, P.R., MITCHUM JR., R.M. & THOMPSON III, S. 1977. Seismic stratigraphy and global changes of sea level, Part 4: Global cycles of relative changes of sea level. *In*: PAYTON, C.E. (ed.) *Seismic Stratigraphy-Applications to Hydrocarbon Exploration*. American Association of Petroleum Geologists, Memoirs, **26**, 83–97.

VAN GEEN, A., ADKINS, J.F., BOYLE, E.A., NELSON, C.H. & PALANQUES, A. 1997. A 120 yr record of widespread contamination from mining of the Iberian pyrite belt. *Geology*, **25**, 291–294.

VANNEY, J.-R. & MOUGENOT, D. 1981. La plate-forme continentale du Portugal et les provinces adjacentes: Analyse geomorphologique. *Memórias dos Serviços Geológicos de Portugal*, **28**, 86 pp.

VANNEY, J.-R. & STANLEY, D.J. 1983. Shelfbreak physiography: An overview. *In*: STANLEY, D.J. & MOORE, G.T. (eds) *The Shelfbreak: Critical Interface on Continental Margins*. Society of Economic Paleontologists and Mineralogists, Special Publications, **33**, 1–24.

YOO, D.G. & PARK, S.C. 1997. Late Quaternary lowstand wedges on the shelf margin and trough region of the Korea Strait. *Sedimentary Geology*, **109**, 121–133.

YOO, D.G., PARK, S.C., SHIN, W.C. & KIM, W.S. 1996. Near-surface seismic facies at the Korea Strait shelf margin and trough region. *Geo-Marine Letters*, **16**, 49–56.

Deposition and stratigraphic architecture of an outcropping ancient slope system: Tres Pasos Formation, Magallanes Basin, southern Chile

M.R. SHULTZ [1,2], A. FILDANI [1,2], T.D. COPE [1,3] & S.A. GRAHAM[1]

[1] *Department of Geological and Environmental Sciences, Stanford University, Stanford, CA 94305, USA*

[2] *Current address: ChevronTexaco ETC, 6001 Bollinger Canyon Road, San Ramon, CA 94583, USA (e-mail: mshu@chevrontexaco.com)*

[3] *Current address: Department of Geosciences, DePauw University, Greencastle, IN 46135, USA*

Abstract: The Tres Pasos Formation, Magallanes Basin, Chile, represents the deposit of a submarine slope depositional system. The formation is approximately 1500 m thick where exposed in the Ultima Esperanza district of southernmost Chile. It is characterized by a basal turbiditic sandstone unit up to 200 m thick that shows a north-to-south, proximal-to-distal facies evolution from turbidite channel-fill complexes to sheet-like sandstone units. This unit is interpreted as having been deposited at or near the base of slope. Overlying the basal sandstone unit is approximately 500 m of amalgamated mass transport complexes, fine-grained strata, and channelized and non-channelized turbidity current deposits, collectively comprising the middle part of the formation. Mass transport complexes exert a primary control on the character and grain size of turbidite sandstone bodies in the basal and middle part of the formation. In the southern part of the study area, a 300 m thick coarse-grained unit interpreted as a turbidite channel-fill complex partially replaces the middle part. The upper part of the formation is approximately 500 m thick and consists primarily of fine-grained strata. Failure scarps and thin turbidite channel-fill units are present in this upper part, interpreted as upper slope deposits.

As foci of hydrocarbon exploration shift to deep-water slope areas and associated depositional environments, outcrop analogue data provide increasingly important constraints on three-dimensional distribution of coarse-grained facies. The well-exposed Tres Pasos Formation of southern Chile provides an opportunity to document the architecture of a mixed-load slope depositional system from regional to bed-scale, providing new examples of coarse-grained turbiditic sedimentary bodies that add to the growing database of outcrop analogues for hydrocarbon reservoir intervals.

Stratigraphic architecture of slope depositional systems results from the interplay of tectonically-controlled basin configuration, climate- and tectonically-controlled sediment supply, and shelf geometry and highstand accommodation. High sedimentation rates in some slope systems lead to outbuilding of the shelf-break and oversteepening, which can result in mass failure of strata on many scales (Booth 1979; Van Weering *et al.* 1998). Three-dimensional remote sensing data show that such mass failure locally changes slope gradient, affects behaviour of turbidity currents and creates accommodation on the slope for deposition and preservation of coarse- and fine-grained strata (e.g. Nemec *et al.* 1988). Architectural relations between such slope failure features and coarse-grained depositional units can be documented explicitly in the Tres Pasos Formation.

Criteria for interpretation of ancient outcropping stratigraphic successions as deposits of slope depositional systems includes clinoform geometries (e.g. Browne & Slatt 2002), or the ability to document the shelf–slope–basin floor profile explicitly (e.g. Plink-Björklund *et al.* 2001). In the case of the Tres Pasos Formation, no shelf–slope break has been identified in outcrop and no subsurface data are available. Therefore, interpretation of this formation as an ancient slope depositional system must be based on alternative criteria such as stratigraphic architecture.

In ancient slope settings, turbiditic sandstone units are often present stratigraphically underlying and associated with thick accumulations of mass transport complexes (Galloway 1998), and this is the case with the Tres Pasos Formation. Such sandstone intervals are often interpreted as having been deposited at or near the base of the morphological slope (e.g. Pickering 1982; Heller & Dickinson 1985; Martinsen 1989). These sandstone units may record periods of increased sediment supply related to accelerated tectonic activity or deposition during lowstands of relative sea-level, during which time accommodation for coarse-grained sediment on the

From: HODGSON, D.M. & FLINT, S.S. (eds) 2005. *Submarine Slope Systems: Processes and Products*. Geological Society, London, Special Publications, **244**, 27–50. 0305–8719/$15.00

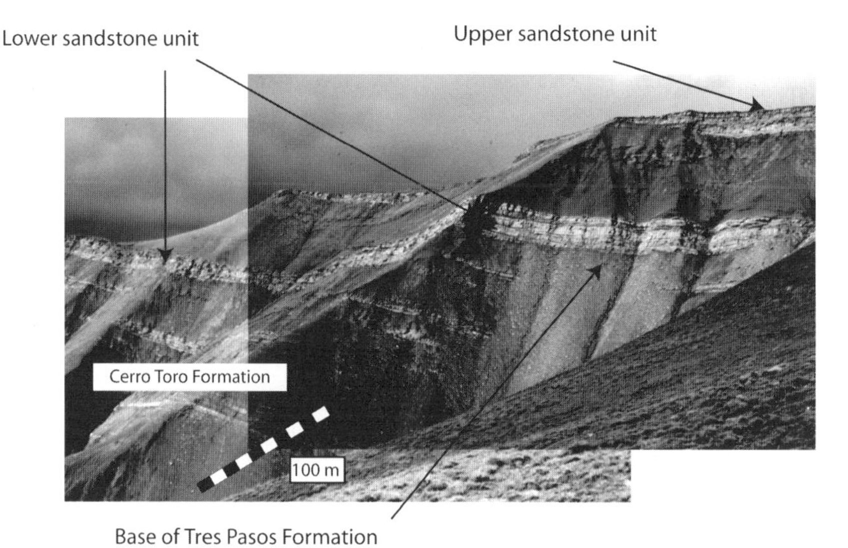

Fig. 11. Photomosaic of the west face of the Sierra Contreras showing two major coarse-grained turbidite units collectively comprising the basal Tres Pasos Formation sandstone (Refer to Fig. 1 for location). Both sandstone units overlie and interact with mass transport complexes, and are interpreted to represent fill of excavation features created through failure of semi-consolidated fine-grained slope sediments.

surface and thus represent initial channel infill, or if they provided the substrate over which a new channel was formed. In the present case, because the listric failure surface is preserved, we suggest that the slope failure captured pre-existing channels on the slope, and focused these flows into newly created accommodation. Alternatively, if the fine-grained strata underlying the upper sandstone unit represent levee deposits, then the failure could represent a levee failure, in which case the sandstone units exposed on Sierra Contreras might also be described as crevasse-splay or channel deposits. Because levee is a morphological term, and no morphological evidence for a levee was documented, levee facies *per se* are not interpreted and a generic interpretation as slide evacuation infill is preferred.

Stratigraphic architecture: lower sandstone unit. The stratigraphically lower sandstone unit exposed on the west face of the Sierra Contreras defines the base of the Tres Pasos Formation, and overlies an extensive mass transport complex with an irregular top topography (Fig. 15). The lower part of the sandstone consists of laterally variable beds of lithofacies 3 contained within the topography on the top of the underlying mass transport complex (Fig. 15). In the upper part of the sandstone unit, lateral continuity (tabularity of beds) increases suddenly and markedly, and sedimentation units maintain constant thickness for approximately 2 km along the west face of the Sierra Contreras, and for at least 1 km in the third dimension to the east, suggesting a sheet-like three-dimensional geometry. This change occurs stratigraphically above the topographically highest point exposed on the top surface of the underlying mass transport complex (Fig. 15).

Slide evacuation infill model for lower sandstone unit. Catastrophic failure of fine-grained hemipelagic and turbiditic facies in slope settings produces mass transport complexes such as those underlying the sandstone bodies at Sierra Contreras. Upper surfaces of recent and ancient mass transport complexes imaged by high-resolution seismic profiles, and TOBI from modern continental slopes (e.g. Van Weering *et al.* 1998) have irregular top surfaces, as did the top surfaces of those underlying both the upper and lower sandstone bodies at the Sierra Contreras immediately after emplacement. Where erosion along these surfaces is predominant, flows were energetic and scoured into the underlying mass transport complex. Silty mudstone drapes on scour surfaces (Fig. 13a) imply deposition by dilute tails of or lateral deposits to turbidity currents, possibly the same currents that were eroding the top of the mass transport complex elsewhere. Onlap (Fig. 13b) and extensive load casts (Fig. 13c) present at other localities along this surface indicate rapid deposition onto unconsolidated substrate, soon after mass transport complex emplacement. Conditions of concurrent erosion and deposition along this surface persisted as a more favourable slope profile was achieved by: (1) removal of material from the steep evacuation scarp and upper reaches of the mass transport complex, probably through additional small-scale

Fig. 13. Features exposed along the bases of slide evacuation fills in the basal Tres Pasos Formation sandstone unit exposed at the Sierra Contreras. (**a**) Scour surface draped by silty mudstone and sandstone at base of lower sandstone unit, indicating scour and draping by T_e deposits prior to sandstone deposition. (**b**) Basal surface of upper sandstone unit showing onlap of sandstone beds onto underlying mass transport complex. Person is standing on a sandstone raft block, beds lap out to the left behind person. (**c**) Large load cast (flame structure) exposed along the base of the lower sandstone unit, indicating rapid deposition onto the underlying unconsolidated mass transport complex.

failure along the margins of the main evacuation feature and by scouring turbidity currents; (2) by transfer and deposition of that eroded material downslope into local depressions in mass transport complex-top topography; and (3) by turbidite deposition from upslope, outside of failure scarp confinement. We interpret that the sandstone beds confined by the irregular top surface of the underlying mass transport complex collectively represent a fill phase, in which mass transport complex top topography was eliminated (Figs 15 & 16).

A thick, resistant, laterally continuous set of amalgamated coarse-grained beds of lithofacies 3 crop out over the entire length of the west face of the Sierra Contreras roughly in the middle of the lower sandstone body (Fig. 15). This continuity suggests that by the time that these beds were deposited, a relatively smooth depositional profile had been achieved within the relict failure scar. Although unconfined by the rugged mass transport complex topography, flow strength and confinement must have been significant in order to form laterally continuous, tabular, amalgamated beds. This suggests a broader confinement of the system by the entire evacuation feature, or an increase in the volume of individual sediment gravity flows. These tabular, coarse-grained beds may represent a spill and bypass phase of slide evacuation filling, after smoothing of slump-top topography through erosion and sedimentation (Fig. 16). The top of the lower sandstone body is sharp, suggesting that sedimentation ceased abruptly as flows were diverted to other localities, possibly resulting from up-system capture of sediment fairways by another failure feature nearby on the slope.

Multi-phase fill-spill models have been proposed for turbidite slope channel systems (Gardner & Borer 2000) and also for structural slope basins (e.g. Prather *et al.* 1998; Sinclair & Tomasso 2002). There are important differences between slope failure-generated accommodation and structurally created accommodation, most notably an important difference in scale of the container (minibasin) versus volumes of individual turbidity currents. In addition, the surface roughness of mass transport complexes may affect turbidity current behaviour and deposition. Turbidity currents that enter slide evacuation features with residual mass transport complex material within them must flow around irregular topography (Fig. 16), favouring development of laterally variable deposits, as opposed to sheet-like deposits observed in the basal cycles of salt withdrawal minibasin fills in the Gulf of Mexico (Sinclair & Tomasso 2002). However, the thick, tabular, amalgamated sandstone beds occurring in the centre of the stratigraphically lower sandstone unit at the Sierra Contreras indicates sediment bypass, and in this way may be similar to turbidite fills of structural basins in that bypass occurs after a spill point is reached (Figs 15 & 16). However, in the present case bypass (spill phase) occurs on a sand-rich plain, and not as channel levee complexes as is the case with salt withdrawal minibasins, and therefore results in a sheet-like geometry (Figs 15 & 16), rather than laterally variable channel/levee-type architecture.

Fig. 14. (**a**) Photomosaic and (**b**) interpretation of internal architecture of stratigraphically upper coarse-grained slide evacuation fill, basal sandstone unit of the Tres Pasos Formation, west face, Sierra Contreras. Note sandstone beds showing onlap or downlap relationship toward the south. (**c**) Close-up of a portion of (b) showing lateral facies change from thick-bedded, amalgamated sandstone (black arrow) to thin-bedded facies (toward the left-hand side of photo), suggestive of high energy, amalgamation, and channelization.

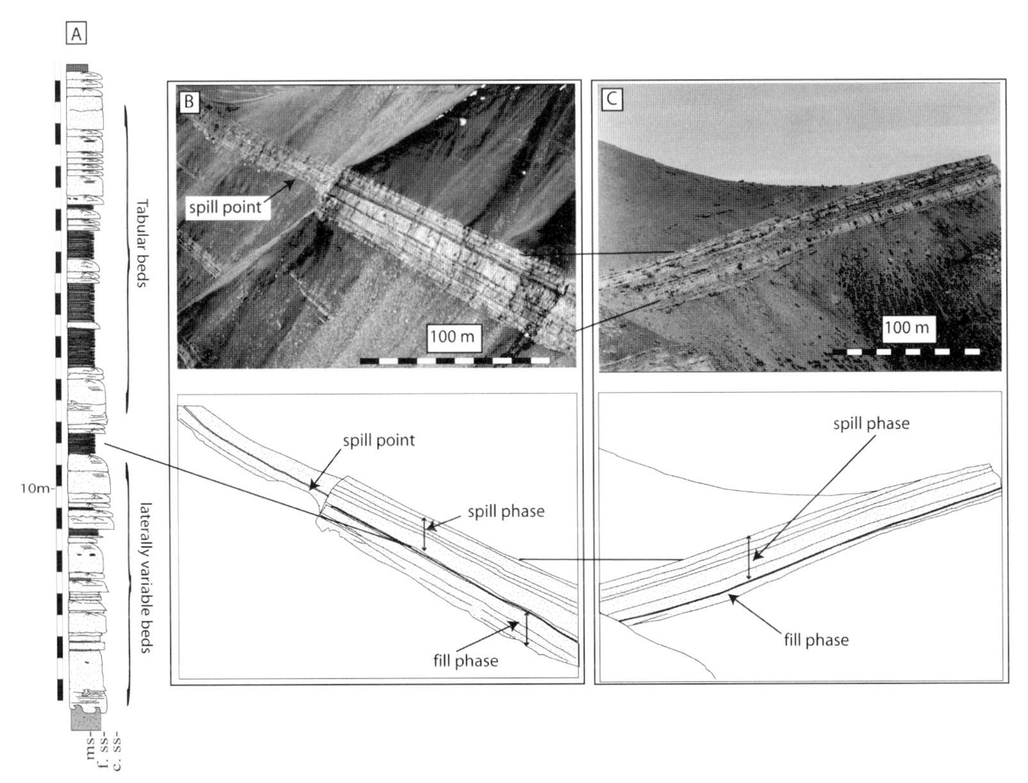

Fig. 15. Detailed measured section (**a**), photographs, and line-drawing interpretations of stratigraphically lower slide evacuation infill (**b**, **c**), west face, Sierra Contreras. The sandstone unit shows a two-phase evolution. Initially, mass transport complex-top topography influences turbidite deposition leading to laterally variable, channelized sandstone that fills and smoothes initially rough mass transport complex-top topography (fill phase, Fig. 14 b, c). This unit is overlain by tabular sandstone beds representing deposition after smoothing of mass transport complex top topography (spill phase).

El Chingue Bluff and Cerro Solitario: distal turbidite sheet sandstones

The Tres Pasos Formation basal sandstone exposed at El Chingue Bluff and Cerro Solitario (Figs 1 & 17) is approximately 70 m thick, and contrasts markedly with the more proximal exposures in the Sierra de los Baguales and the Sierra Contreras. It is characterized by tabular turbidite beds of lithofacies 2 with well developed T_{a-e} sequences (Fig. 17b). Although minor incision of up to about one metre is present in some localities, these beds show little scour or amalgamation (Fig. 17a). Bed thickness is generally less than one metre.

Sandstone bodies similar to these have commonly been interpreted as lobe deposits (Mutti & Normark 1991), and also as overbank deposits (Lien *et al.* 2003). Onlap of these beds onto tilted substrate is observed at El Chingue Bluff and suggests structural control of sandstone distribution (e.g. no lobate plan-view geometry) (Shultz 2004). Therefore, the more generic term sheet sandstone (*sensu* Galloway 1998) is preferred. Agreement of palaeocurrent indicators within these sandstones with general basin-scale palaeocurrent patterns makes an overbank origin of these sandstone beds less likely.

Mass transport complex-dominated middle part of the Tres Pasos Formation

The 600+ m thick middle part of the Tres Pasos Formation (Fig. 3) overlies the basal sandstone unit and is interpreted as middle or lower slope deposits. This portion of the formation consists primarily of mass transport complexes (lithofacies 4), thin-bedded sandstones and silty mudstone (lithofacies 1), and a wide variety of turbidite sandstone bodies (lithofacies 2 and 3). The coarse-grained units can be subdivided into erosional channel-fill units, mixed erosional/depositional channel-fill units (*sensu* Mutti & Normark 1991), and turbidite sheet sandstone units (*sensu* Galloway 1998).

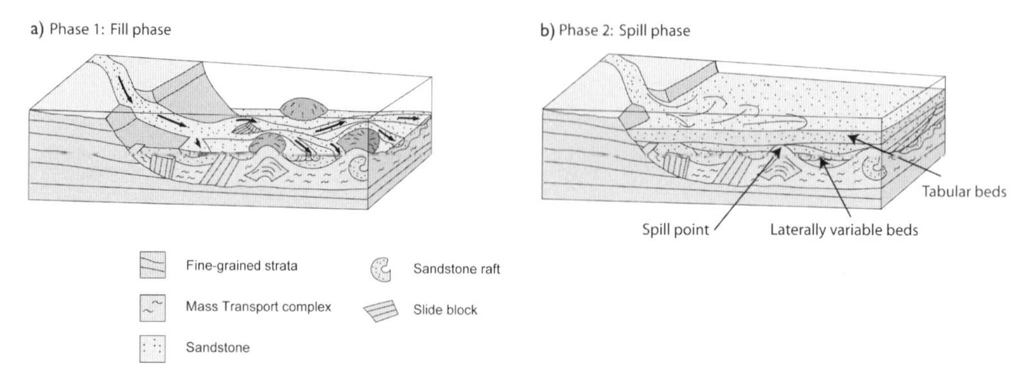

Fig. 16. Two phase fill history of slide evacuation feature such as that exposed in the Sierra Contreras (Fig. 15). (**a**) Initially, after failure of slope sediments, residual mass transport complex material is contained within a slide evacuation minibasin. If a deep-water channel is intersected, flows are diverted into the new accommodation. Flows entering the minibasin interact with irregular mass transport complex topography, leading to laterally variable, possibly channelized facies in the lower part of the fill sequence (fill phase). (**b**) As irregular mass transport complex top topography is reduced and a smooth depositional profile is achieved, flows spread laterally upon entering slide evacuation minibasin and form a laterally continuous sandstone sheet (spill phase).

Fig. 17. Photograph (**a**) and representative measured stratigraphic section (**b**) of basal Tres Pasos Formation sandstone unit exposed on Cerro Solitario. For legend of symbols, refer to Fig. 5. Note tabularity and unamalgamated nature of beds (lithofacies 2).

Erosional channel-fill units

Many coarse-grained, laterally variable sandstone units consisting of lithofacies 3 beds in the middle portion of the Tres Pasos Formation overlie and erode into mass transport complexes corresponding to lithofacies 4 (Fig. 18). Multiple internal scour surfaces are evident in one such sandstone body exposed at Cerro Mirador (Fig. 18), and intraclast conglomerate beds (lithofacies 3) lap out against these surfaces. Lateral facies changes from thick-bedded amalgamated sandstone (lithofacies 3) to thin-bedded sandstone (lithofacies 1) occur over distances of several to tens of metres (Fig. 18). A few large-scale scour features are filled with silty mudstone (Fig. 18), indicating bypass and subsequent abandonment of channel-form scours.

No lag or erosive surface is observed at the base of the mass transport complex that underlies the channel-fill unit documented in Figure 18, and therefore we do not consider the mass transport complex as part of the channel-fill itself. Instead, we suggest that stratal failure on the slope served to focus sediment transport, and a channel was developed atop the mass transport complex. Based on erosive bases, abundant internal scour, high-energy facies, and lateral discontinuity of these sandstone units (Fig. 18), we infer that they are contained within erosional features and therefore categorize such units as fills of erosional type channels (*sensu* Mutti & Normark 1991).

Mixed erosional/depositional channel fills

Other sandstone units in the middle part of the Tres Pasos Formation occur stratigraphically overlying concordant strata and contrast with erosional channel-fill sandstones described above in terms of lateral continuity, sedimentary facies, and underlying facies. One spectacularly exposed sandstone unit at Cerro Mirador (Figs 1, 3, 19 & 20) illustrates this type of deposit. The sandstone is approximately 15 m thick, and shows multiple superimposed incision surfaces stepping toward the south, in a down-palaeocurrent direction (Figs 1 & 19). At least five such surfaces are exposed, three of which can be seen in Figure 19. Sandstone beds grouped into lithofacies 3 overlie and lap out onto these surfaces, and are composed of coarse- to very coarse-grained, amalgamated, traction-structured sandstone beds (Fig. 20). Thinner beds occurring near the top of the channel-fill sequence thin laterally and drape incision surfaces (Fig. 19), indicating repeated periods of erosion and deposition in this location.

Multiple, regularly stepping scour surfaces (Fig. 19) and sedimentary facies indicative of high-energy and sediment bypass (lithofacies 3) (Fig. 20) suggest that this sandstone unit represents the deposit of a laterally migrating deep-water channel. Because evidence of both erosion and aggradation of strata categorize this sandstone unit (Fig. 19), we categorize it as the fill of a mixed erosional/depositional type channel, following Mutti & Normark (1991).

Sandstone sheets

In contrast to the channel form sandstone units described above (Figs 17 & 18), other sandstone units present in the middle portion of the Tres Pasos Formation indicate constructive slope processes characterized by sheet-turbidite deposition (Fig. 21). Individual beds correspond to lithofacies 2, and the composite units they form are tabular and maintain constant thickness for several kilometres. Although no statistical bed thickness analysis was performed, these sandstone bodies may comprise stacked thickening- and then thinning-upward successions (Fig. 21).

Tabularity, relatively fine grain-size (fine- to medium-grained sandstone), lack of erosion, and paucity of intraclasts indicate that the flows that deposited these beds were not highly erosive, and that sediment bypass was relatively less important than in channel complexes within the middle part of the Tres Pasos Formation (Figs 17 & 18). This may reflect deposition onto areas where slope processes such as growth faulting or sediment failure produced local low-gradient areas on the sea floor, or where channels confined by mass transport complexes debouched onto undeformed strata. Alternatively, they may represent channel-margin facies, lateral to unexposed channel-fill units out of the plane of exposure.

The Laguna Figueroa section: coarse-grained middle part of the Tres Pasos Formation in the southern part of the study area

South of Cerro Cazador (Fig. 1), a thick-bedded, coarse-grained to pebbly turbidite unit approximately 300 m thick partially replaces the mass transport complex-dominated middle part of the Tres Pasos Formation (Fig. 3). It crops out as a prominent hogback ridge for approximately 20 km, disappears into the subsurface in the vicinity of Puerto Natales, and appears to shale-out towards the north on Cerro Cazador (Figs 1 & 3). This section is well exposed in the vicinity of Laguna Figueroa (Figs 1 & 22), where it has been referred to informally as the middle Tres Pasos Formation and interpreted to represent a series of deep-water suprafan lobe deposits (Smith 1977). We refer to this unit as the Laguna Figueroa section in this paper. We discuss these deposits briefly, present a detailed measured stratigraphic section from this locality (Fig. 23) and offer an alternative interpretation for the Laguna Figueroa section as a deep-water channel-fill complex.

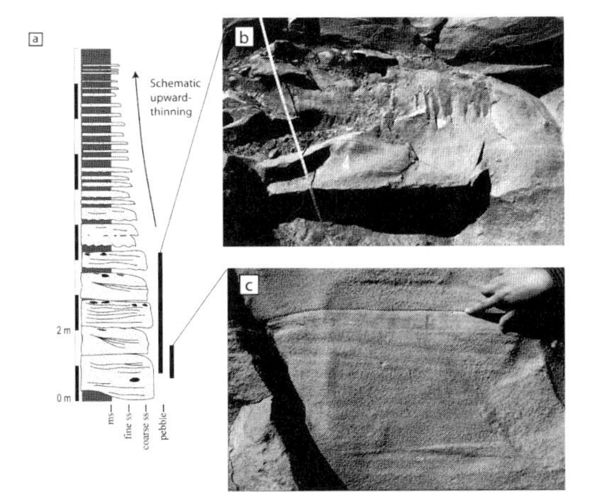

Fig. 20. Internal architecture of the fill of a mixed erosional/depositional type turbidity current channel exposed at Cerro Mirador (Cerro Mirador measured stratigraphic section, 500 m) (Fig. 19). (**a**) Detailed measured section from basal portion, and schematic upward-fining and thinning of turbidite channel fill. (**b**) Top of coarse-grained sandstone bed showing crude diffuse lamination interpreted as T_t traction deposits. (**c**) Amalgamated sandstone beds such as those in (b) comprise most of the channel-fill.

Fig. 21. Tabular sandstone beds overlying undeformed (concordant) fine-grained strata. (**a**) Cerro Mirador measured stratigraphic section, approximately 450 m. (**b**) Cerro Mirador measured stratigraphic section, approximately 550 m.

Fig. 22. Outcrop character of the Laguna Figueroa section, a coarse-grained unit that partially replaces the middle part of the Tres Pasos Formation in the southern part of the study area (Fig. 1). Note extremely sandstone-rich nature of the section.

Stratigraphic architecture

Approximately 75% of the Laguna Figueroa section consists of very coarse-grained or pebbly sandstone (Fig. 22), and comprises the relatively coarsest and thickest-bedded subset of lithofacies 3 sandstone beds exposed in the Tres Pasos Formation. Bed thickness may reach 10 m, and a spectrum of high-density turbidity current deposits are present (Fig. 23). In addition, this section contains a great abundance of sub- to well-rounded silty mudstone intraclasts up to several metres in diameter, occurring at the bases of beds (Figs 5 a, c & 23 a, d). A cyclical stacking pattern of lithofacies is observed in this section, consisting of lithofacies 2 beds overlain by beds of lithofacies 3 packaged within fine-grained deposits corresponding to lithofacies 1 and 4 (Fig. 24).

Laterally persistent erosion surfaces are present and define the bases of inferred sandstone cycles (Figs 24 & 25). Thick-bedded sandstone and intraclast conglomerate (lithofacies 3, Fig. 23d) occur at the bases of cycles and, in some cases, scour up to 10 m down into mass transport complexes (lithofacies 4), or thin-bedded sandstone and silty mudstone (lithofacies 1) (Fig. 25). Intraclasts almost always occur at the bases of beds, indicating their relatively high density, suggesting lithification and induration prior to erosion and entrainment in sediment gravity flows.

Re-interpretation of the Laguna Figueroa section

The Laguna Figueroa section is interpreted as a deep-water channel-fill complex based on: (1) deep scours indicating extensive erosion mantled by intraclast conglomerate units (lithofacies 3) interpreted as residual lag facies contained within palaeochannel thalwegs; (2) the abundance of traction-structuring in intraclast conglomerate and thick-bedded sandstone beds of lithofacies 3, indicating high energy individual flows and extensive sediment bypass; and (3) apparent thinning-upward character and increasing tabularity of beds vertically indicating decreasing confinement or reduced flow energy or volume. We consider these features inconsistent with suprafan lobe deposits (e.g. Smith 1977), and offer an alternative interpretation of this unit as a channel-fill complex.

Upper fine-grained part of the Tres Pasos Formation

The upper part of the Tres Pasos Formation exposed on Cerro Mirador and Cerro Cazador contrasts

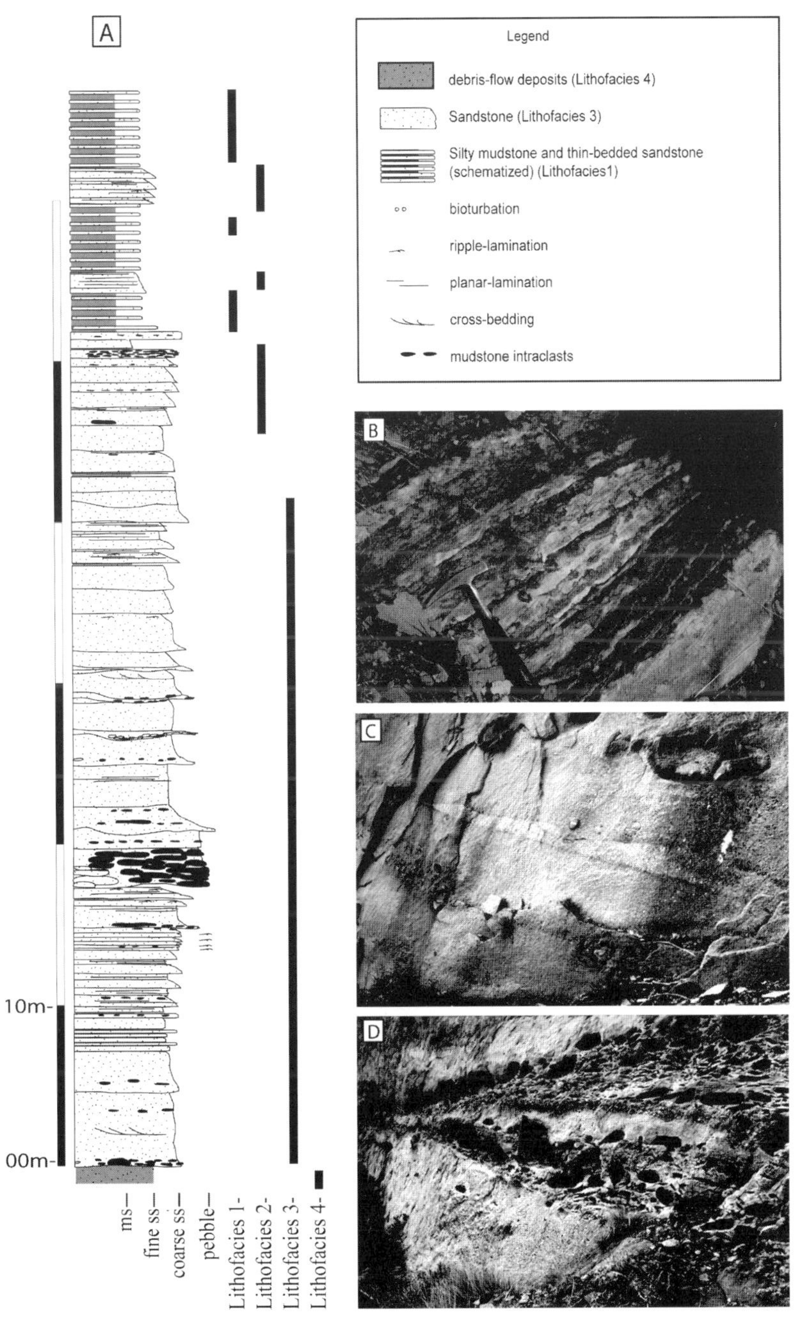

Fig. 23. (**a**) Representative detailed measured stratigraphic section from the sandstone-rich portion of the middle part of the Tres Pasos Formation exposed at Laguna Figueroa (Laguna Figueroa section) (see Fig. 1 for location) showing cyclical stacking pattern of lithofacies. The section is interpreted to consist of one or possibly two fining- and thinning-upward channel-fill cycles, the intraclast conglomerate interval near the base (18 m) possibly representing the base of another cycle superimposed on the sequence. In the upper part of the detailed measured stratigraphic section, lower energy conditions are interpreted based on lack of erosion, and tabularity of beds. (**a**) subset of lithofacies 3 (S_1 division, Lowe 1982). (**b**) Extensively bioturbated thin-bedded sandstone and silty mudstone lithofacies. (**c**) Thick-bedded sandstone bed of lithofacies 3 containing large dune train at the top of the bed (T_t division of Lowe 1982), indicative of sediment bypass. (**d**) Thick intraclast conglomerate.

Fig. 24. Photograph showing apparent cyclical nature of deposition of coarse-grained sandstone (lithofacies 3) at Laguna Figueroa, Tres Pasos Formation. Note apparent upward-thinning cycles overlying erosive surfaces interpreted as turbidite channel-fill sequences. Person (circled) for scale.

sharply with the underlying middle part of the formation in that it contains few to no mass transport complexes (Fig. 3). The section consists primarily of fine-grained turbiditic strata (lithofacies 1) with thin (less than 10 m), laterally discontinuous sandstone bodies (Fig. 23) interpreted as fills of depositional-type deep-water channels. Unlike other channel-fill units discussed so far in this paper in which lateral variability results from erosional processes, the architecture in this part of the formation is a result primarily of depositional processes.

Channel-fill architecture

Sandstone units exposed in the upper part of the Tres Pasos Formation consist primarily of lithofacies 2, but show lateral variability in bed thickness over distances of metres to tens of metres (Fig. 26). Bed thickness is typically less than one metre. In contrast to other sheet-like sandstone units consisting of lithofacies 2 beds, beds in these units show extensive planar-lamination and relatively little body grading, yet show a limited degree of internal erosion. Amalgamation of beds occurs only in axial zones, interpreted as palaeochannel axes or thalwegs.

Amalgamation is minor in interpreted channel axes, and sandstone bodies have heterolithic marginal areas where sandstone beds are interbedded with encasing fine-grained strata (Fig. 26). These units are interpreted as a complex of depositional type channel-fills, following terminology of Mutti & Normark (1991).

Upper slope setting

Features interpreted as relict failure evacuation features are present in the upper part of the Tres Pasos Formation (Fig. 26b), and lenticular sandstone units interpreted as channel-fill units are present immediately overlying these features (Fig. 26b). This relationship suggests that channel systems that deposited the sandstone units were localized within these evacuation features. The upper part of the Tres Pasos Formation is interpreted to represent an upper slope succession, based on the relative lack of mass transport complexes, evidence of failure scarps, and thin channel-fill sandstones. This upper slope may have been an area where fine-grained material was sequestered as overbank material, and provided a source area for the abundant mass transport complexes downslope, preserved as the middle part of the Tres Pasos Formation.

Tres Pasos Formation depositional model

The Tres Pasos Formation basal sandstone unit overlies at least one kilometre of fine-grained, bathyal strata corresponding to the upper part of the Cerro Toro Formation, and is overlain by hundreds of metres of amalgamated muddy and sandy mass transport complexes and submarine channel-fill sandstones (Fig. 3). Although alternative correlations of the stratigraphy cannot be excluded at present (see discussion in Shultz 2004), this facies organization favours correlation of the sandstone unit across the Ultima Esperanza region and suggests that sand-rich deposits at the base of the Tres Pasos Formation mark the initiation of a gravitationally unstable slope depositional system (Fig. 27). Depositional systems-scale vertical stratigraphic development characterized by fine-grained deposits overlain by sand-rich turbidite systems, and then by thick accumulations of mass transport complexes has been documented in other basins (Pickering 1982; Heller & Dickinson 1986; Martinsen 1989), suggesting that this facies organization may be typical of some slope depositional systems in elongate deep-water basins.

The lateral proximal–distal facies change recorded in the basal Tres Pasos Formation sandstone is not mimicked in a vertical sense, suggesting that the conditions that led to its development in early Tres Pasos time were not sustained. Thus, a progradational, Waltherian interpretation of the Tres Pasos Formation and the basal sandstone unit is not sufficient and an allocyclic mechanism may be required to modulate rates of coarse-grained sediment input and produce the basal Tres Pasos Formation sandstone unit. Possible drivers include single or multiple phases of relative sea-level fall

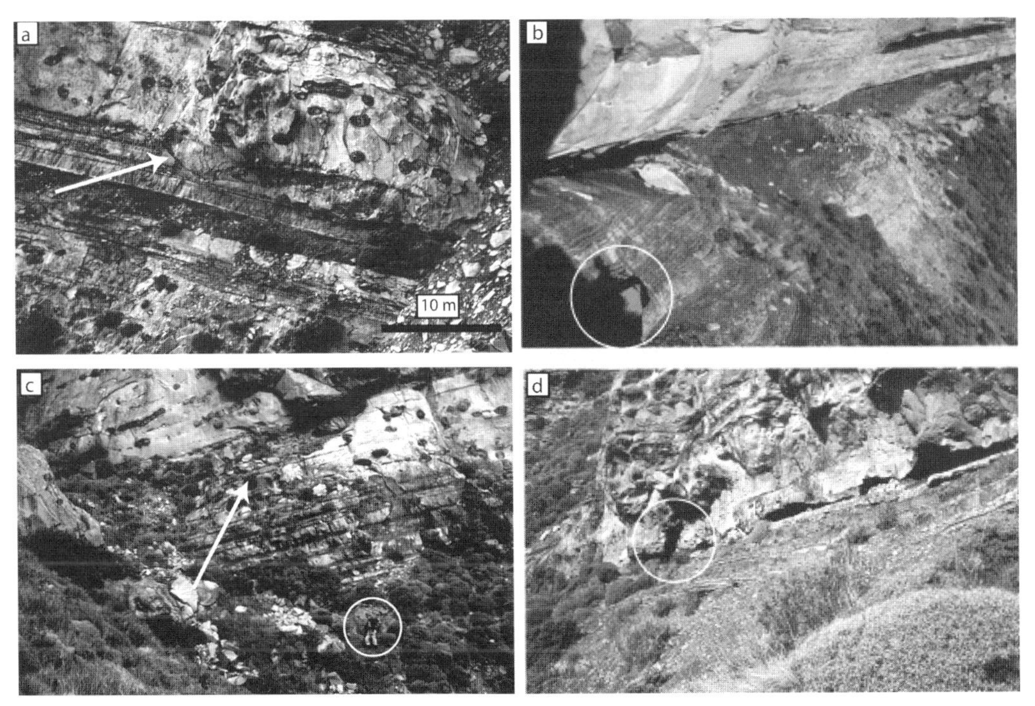

Fig. 25. Sharp, erosive bases of coarse-grained channel-fills, middle part of the Tres Pasos Formation at Laguna Figueroa. (**a**) Base of fill cycle showing several metres of incision into thin-bedded sandstone and silty mudstone (lithofacies 1). (**b**) Base of channel-fill is incised into a mass transport complex (lithofacies 4). (**c**) Channel or large scour filled with imbricated intraclast conglomerate. (**d**) Thick-bedded sandstone (lithofacies 3) sharply overlying lithofacies 1 thin-bedded sandstone and silty mudstone.

(the unit represents stacked lowstand fans), a pulse in coarse-grained sediment supply due to a tectonic driver, or a combination of these drivers. The detailed chronostratigraphic framework that will allow for detailed interpretation of the basal Tres Pasos Formation sandstone unit has not been developed.

The system that transported sediment off the shelf and into deeper waters to feed the basal Tres Pasos Formation sandstone is not available for inspection due to uplift and erosion. Channel-fill units such as those present in the middle part of the Tres Pasos Formation (Figs 17 & 18) may represent younger, preserved counterparts to such feeder channels. These channels may have coalesced in the elongate, tectonically confined Magallanes foredeep, forming a sand-rich apron showing a proximal–distal evolution on the lower slope (Fig. 27) (similar to submarine ramp of Heller & Dickinson 1985). Upper slope sequestration of fine-grained material as levee or distal overbank deposits (Fig. 26) may also have served to increase the sand:mud ratio of sediment gravity flows in a basinward direction.

After deposition of the basal Tres Pasos Formation sandstone, coarse-grained sediment input was reduced, and a mud-rich upper slope (source of mass transport complexes) and linked middle or lower slope (area of mass transport accumulation) prograded across the northern part of the field area (Phase 2, Fig. 27b). Turbidity current behaviour and resultant sandstone architecture in the middle and upper parts of the formation was controlled in part by interaction with slope topography (Figs 18–21). The extreme variety of sandstone body types exposed in this interval (fills of erosional-type channels and mixed erosional/depositional type channels, and sheet sandstones) suggests that linked channel– channel mouth splay complexes may have been present on the slope during deposition of the middle part of the Tres Pasos Formation, interacting with mass transport complexes.

A renewed phase of coarse-grained sedimentation was initiated with the deposition of the Laguna Figueroa section (Phase 3, Fig. 27c). Within these beds, well-rounded mudstone intraclasts as large as several metres in diameter are present at the bases of thick, high-density sediment gravity flow deposits. This indicates compaction and induration of mudstone prior to erosion and entrainment in turbidity currents, as well as relatively deep erosion up-system. However, the interval appears to shale

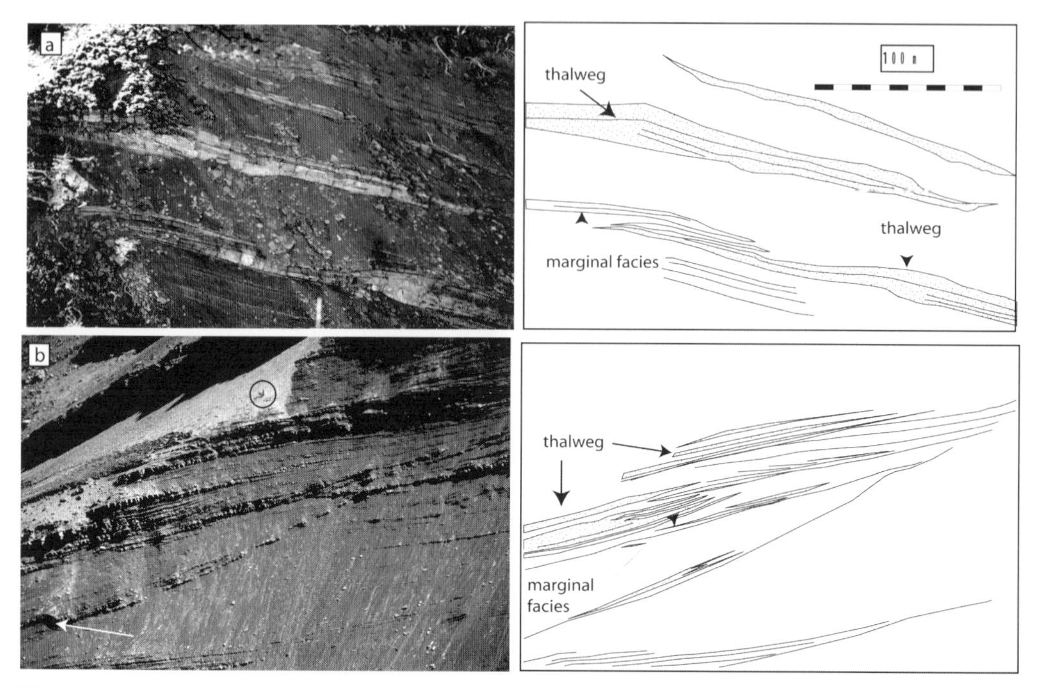

Fig. 26. Sandstone bodies exposed in upper part of the Tres Pasos Formation at Cerro Mirador with line drawing interpretations. These bodies are interpreted to represent fills of depositional type channels (*sensu* Mutti and Normark 1991). (**a**) Sandstone bodies exposed on west face of Cerro Mirador with slightly erosive bases, little internal scour and amalgamation. (**b**) Sandstone bodies exposed on the south face of Cerro Mirador, person (circled) for scale. Section is primarily fine-grained with thin, interbedded sandstone bodies. Note nested sandstone-filled incision surfaces tapering laterally away from interpreted channel axis. White arrow indicates an igneous dyke intruded along a relict failure scar. This failure feature may have focused the overlying channel.

out toward the north rather than lap out onto an erosive surface, and no feeder system has been identified for the Figueroa section. Palaeocurrent indicators show a southeasterly component (Fig. 1), suggesting that feeder channels or canyon systems depositionally updip from the Laguna Figueroa beds may have lain to the west, and are now uplifted and removed by erosion. Coarseness of sediment and shale-out relations towards the north suggest that the Laguna Figueroa section may represent the deposits of a depositional system distinct from, and not genetically linked to the outcrops towards the north in the Sierra de los Baguales and Sierra Contreras (Fig. 27, Phase 3). Extremely limited petrographic data (Smith 1977; Macellari 1989) indicate a significant proportion of volcanic lithic grains. Thus, tectonic activity may have been an important factor in the genesis of the very coarse-grained, thick-bedded Laguna Figueroa section. Ultimately, the mud-rich upper slope and linked mass-transport complex-dominated middle and lower slope prograded over the study area, covering the Laguna Figueroa section (Phase 4, Fig. 27).

Conclusions

The stratigraphic architecture of the Tres Pasos Formation indicates that the formation represents the deposit of a slope depositional system. The formation is characterized by a basal sand-rich unit deposited in a lower slope environment, overlying approximately one kilometre of fine-grained bathyal strata. This sand-rich unit is overlain by a thick accumulation of mass transport complexes and turbiditic sandstones deposited in a middle or lower slope environment. The middle portion of the formation is overlain by fine-grained strata and fills of depositional-type channels of the upper portion of the Tres Pasos Formation, comprising a remarkably well-exposed and complete example of a lower, middle, and upper slope system stratigraphy.

The authors thank the member companies of the Stanford Project on Deep-Water Depositional Systems (SPODDS), which funded this research. We thank D.R. Lowe, J.C. Ingle, Jr. and R. Dunbar at Stanford University for their help during the course of this research and critical reviews, and thank O. Martinsen and S. Flint for their insightful reviews. This work would not have been possible without

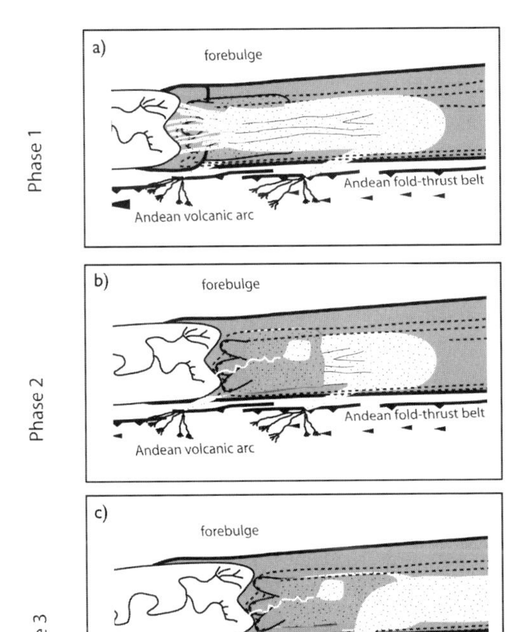

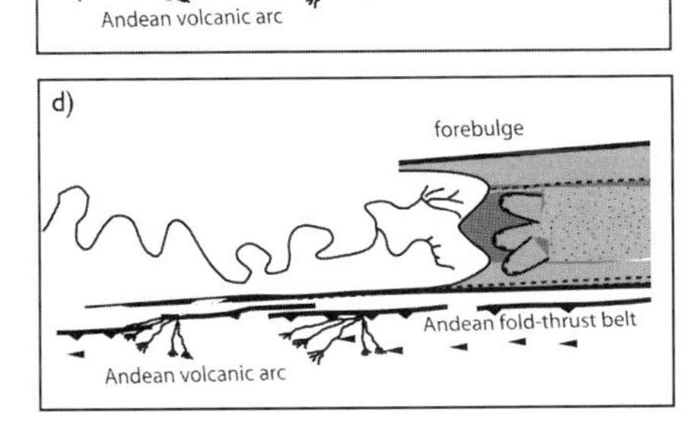

Fig. 27. Palaeogeographic reconstruction of Ultima Esperanza district, southern Chile, during Tres Pasos Formation deposition. (**a**) Delta-fed slope channels coalesced into Magallanes foredeep to form sand-rich apron showing proximal–distal facies evolution (Phase 1, refer to text for discussion). (**b**) Coarse clastic input diminished (see text for discussion), and mud-rich mass transport complex-dominated system with linked channel – channel-mouth splay complexes prograded over basal Tres Pasos Formation sandstone (Phase 2). (**c**) Laguna Figueroa beds were deposited as a canyon or structural basin fill (Phase 3). (**d**) Fluvial delta, mud-rich upper slope, and linked mass-transport complex-dominated middle and lower slope prograded over the study area (Phase 4).

the many Chileans who provided logistical and technical support including T. Hromic of the Instituto de la Patagonia in Punta Arenas, Chile, our able gaucho guides, and P. Rajcevic who provided access to key lands and generous hospitality. We also acknowledge the staff of SERNAGEOMIN, Santiago, Chile, and P. Hervé of the Universidad de Chile, Santiago for their continued support of SPODDS research in Patagonia.

References

BIDDLE, K.T., ULIANA, M.A., MITCHUM JR., R.M., FITZGERALD, M.G. & WRIGHT, R.C. 1986. The stratigraphic and structural evolution of the central and eastern Magallanes Basin, southern South America, *In*: ALLEN, P.A. & HOMEWOOD, P. (eds) *Foreland Basins*. International Association of Sedimentologists. Blackwell, Oxford, 41–63.

BOOTH, J.S. 1979. Recent history of mass-wasting on the upper continental slopes, northern Gulf of Mexico, as interpreted from the consolidation states of the sediment. *In*: DOYLE, L.J. & PILKEY, O.H.J. (eds) *Geology of Continental Slopes*. Society of Economic Paleontologists and Mineralogists Special Publication, **27**, 153–165.

BOUMA, A.H. 1962. *Sedimentology of some flysch deposits: a graphic approach to facies interpretation*. Elsevier, Amsterdam.

BROWNE, G.H. & SLATT, R.M. 2002. Outcrop and behind-outcrop characterization of a late Miocene slope fan system, Mt Messenger Formation, New Zealand. *American Association of Petroleum Geologists Bulletin*, **86**, 841–862.

CLARK, J.D. & PICKERING, K.T. 1996. Architectural elements and growth patterns of submarine channels; application to hydrocarbon exploration. *American Association of Petroleum Geologists Bulletin*, **80**, 194–221.

DALZIEL, I.W.D., DE WIT, M.J. & PALMER, K.F. 1974. Fossil marginal basin in the southern Andes. *Nature*, **250**, 291–294.

DE WIT, M.J. & STERN, C.R. 1981. Variations in the degree of crustal extension during formation of a back-arc basin. *Tectonophysics*, **72**, 229–260.

GALLOWAY, W.E. 1998. Siliciclastic slope and base-of-slope depositional systems: component facies, stratigraphic architecture, and classification. *American Association of Petroleum Geologists Bulletin*, **82**, 569–595.

GARDNER, M.H. & BORER, J.M. 2000. Submarine channel architecture along a slope to basin profile, Brushy Canyon Formation, West Texas: *In*: BOUMA, A.H. & STONE, C.G. (eds) *Fine-Grained Turbidite Systems*. Society for Sedimentary Geology, Special Publications **68**, 195–213.

HELLER, P.L. & DICKINSON, W.R. 1985. Submarine ramp facies model for delta-fed, sand-rich turbidite systems. *American Association of Petroleum Geologists Bulletin*, **69**, 960–976.

KATZ, H.R. 1963. Revision of Cretaceous stratigraphy in Patagonian cordillera of Ultima Esperanza, Magallanes Province, Chile. *American Association of Petroleum Geologists Bulletin*, **47**, 506–524.

LIEN, T., WALKER, R.G. & MARTINSEN, O.J. 2003. Turbidites in the Upper Carboniferous Ross Formation, western Ireland; reconstruction of a channel and spillover system. *Sedimentology*, **50**, 113–148.

LOWE, D.R. 1982. Sediment gravity flows: II. Depositional models with special reference to the deposits of high-density turbidity currents. *Journal of Sedimentary Petrology*, **52**, 279–297.

LOWE, D.R. 1988. Suspended-load fallout rate as an independent variable in the analysis of current structures. *Sedimentology*, **35**, 765–776.

Macellari, C.E., Barrio, C.A. & Manassero, M.J. 1989. Upper Cretaceous to Paleocene depositional sequences and sandstone petrography of southwestern Patagonia (Argentina and Chile). *Journal of South American Earth Sciences*, **2**, 223–239.

Martinsen, O.J. 1989. Styles of soft-sediment deformation on a Namurian (Carboniferous) delta slope, western Irish Namurian Basin, Ireland. *In*: Whateley, M.K.G. & Pickering, K.T. (eds) *Deltas: sites and traps for fossil fuels*. Geological Society, London, Special Publications, **41**, 167–177.

Mutti, E. & Normark, W.R. 1991. An integrated approach to the study of turbidite systems. *In*: Weimer, P. & Link, H. (eds) *Seismic facies and Sedimentary Processes of Submarine Fans and Turbidite Systems*. Springer-Verlag, New York, 75–106.

Natland, M.L., Gonzalez, P.E., Canon, A. & Ernst, M. 1974. *A system of stages for correlation of Magallanes Basin sediments*. American Association of Petroleum Geologists, Memoir, **139**, 126 p.

Nemec, W., Steel, R.J., Gjelberg, J., Collinson, J.D., Prestholm, E. & Oxnevad, I.E. 1988. Anatomy of collapsed and re-established delta front in Lower Cretaceous of Eastern Spitsbergen: gravitational sliding and sedimentation processes. *American Association of Petroleum Geologists Bulletin*, **72**, 454–476.

Pickering, K.T. 1982. A Precambrian upper basin-slope and prodelta in northeast Finnmark, North Norway — a possible ancient upper continental slope. *Journal of Sedimentary Petrology*, **52**, 171–186.

Plink-Björklund, P., Mellere, D. & Steel, R.J. 2001. Turbidite variability and architecture of sand-prone, deep-water slopes; Eocene clinoforms in the Central Basin, Spitsbergen. *Journal of Sedimentary Research*, **71**, 895–912.

Prather, B.E., Booth, J.R., Steffens, G.S. & Craig, P.A. 1998. Classification, lithologic calibration, and stratigraphic succession of seismic facies of intraslope basins, deep-water Gulf of Mexico. *American Association of Petroleum Geologists Bulletin*, **82**, 701–728.

Riccardi, A.C. & Rolleri, E.O. 1980, Cordillera Patagonica Austral. *In*: *Segundo simposio Geologico regional Argentino*, Cordoba, 1163–1306.

Shultz, M.R. 2004. *Stratigraphic architecture of two deep-water depositional systems: the Tres Pasos Formation, Chilean Patagonia, and the Stevens Sandstone, Elk Hills, California*. PhD thesis, Stanford University, 284 p.

Sinclair, H.D. & Tomasso, M. 2002. Depositional evolution of confined turbidite basins. *Journal of Sedimentary Research*, **72**, 451–456.

Smith, C.H.L. 1977. *Sedimentology of the Late Cretaceous (Santonian – Maestrichtian) Tres Pasos Formation, Ultima Esperanza District, southern Chile*. M.S. thesis, University of Wisconsin, 129 p.

Van Weering, T.C.E., Nielsen, T., Kenyon, N.H., Katja, A. & Kuijpers, A.H. 1998. Large submarine slides on the NE Faeroe continental margin. *In*: Stoker, M.S., Evans, D. & Cramp, A. (eds) *Geological Processes on Continental Margins: Sedimentation, Mass-Wasting, and Stability*. Geological Society, London, Special Publications, **129**, 5–17.

Wilson, T.J. 1991. Transition from back-arc to foreland basin development in the southernmost Andes: stratigraphic record from the Ultima Esperanza District, Chile. *Geological Society of America Bulletin*, **103**, 98–115.

Winn, R.D. & Dott, R.H.J. 1979. Deep-water fan-channel conglomerates of Late Cretaceous age, southern Chile. *Sedimentology*, **26**, 203–228.

Mass transport complexes and tectonic control on confined basin-floor submarine fans, Middle Eocene, south Spanish Pyrenees

KEVIN T. PICKERING[1] & JORDI CORREGIDOR[2]

[1] *Department of Earth Sciences, University College London, Gower Street, London WC1E 6BT, UK (e-mail: ucfbktp@ucl.ac.uk)*
[2] *Environmental Resources Management, Pau Claris 96, 3o, 1a 08010 Barcelona, Spain*

Abstract: The syn-tectonic deep-marine Ainsa fans (Eocene of the Ainsa basin, Spanish Pyrenees) were confined by lateral thrust ramps and influenced by intra-basinal growth anticlines. Mass transport complexes (MTCs) constitute a major component of the stratigraphy and represent an integral part of the evolution and depositional style of the deep-marine clastics. Using an integrated study of outcrop data from sedimentary logs and mapping, with core data from eight wells and micropalaeontological and palynomorph analyses, we demonstrate the lateral step-wise migration of sandy channelized submarine fans, as a foreland-propagating clastic wedge on a time-scale of hundreds of thousands of years. The deep-marine expression of the inferred tectonic pulses began with the large-scale basin-slope collapse as sediment slides and debris flows that formed much of the seafloor topography for each fan and contributed to their lateral confinement. The uppermost slope and any shelf-edge, including the narrow shelf, then collapsed, redepositing unconsolidated sands and gravels into deep water. This is overlain by an interval of mainly channelized and amalgamated sandy deposits, passing up into several tens of metres of less confined, non-amalgamated, medium- and thin-bedded, finer grained sands and marls. These deposits represent the phase of most active fan growth, initially by erosional channel development, sediment bypass and backfill (in several cycles), giving way to non-channelized, finer grained sandy deposition, interpreted as a response to the flushing out of the coarser clastics from the coastal and near coastal fluvial systems. During this latter stage in active fan growth and when sediment accumulation rates probably remained high, the degraded submarine slope was regraded and healed by finer grained depositional events. The high amount of woody material and the high non-marine palynomorph signal in these sandy deposits suggest direct river input as both turbidity currents and hyperpycnal flows for the silty marls. In the upper few metres, a thinning-and-fining-upward sequence shows a return to background marl deposition, representing fan abandonment. Many sequences are overlain by intraformational sediment slides that attest to the increasing seafloor gradients associated with the regrading and healing stage in slope development. These organized, predictable vertical sedimentary sequences provide a testable generic model for submarine fan development where fan growth is strongly influenced by tectonic processes.

In thrust-front settings, researchers have argued that relative sea-level change affects slope instability (Mutti 1985), tectonics determines long-term sediment flux and temporary storage of sediment in terms of accommodation and sediment availability, and climate determines the transport efficiency and sediment calibre from marginal alluvial systems (Heller & Paola 1992; Paola *et al.* 1992). Eustatic sea-level changes will also control accommodation, and hence the timing of sediment storage and delivery, in different profile positions from the shelf to the deep water. In the Eocene Ainsa basin, Spanish Pyrenees, the focus of this study (Figs 1 & 2), type I, II and III deep-water depositional units have been ascribed to relative sea-level fluctuations (Mutti 1985). However, there is now, an emerging consensus that tectonic processes were the principal driver in the Ainsa basin fill (Fontana *et al.* 1989; Bentham *et al.* 1992; Dreyer *et al.* 1999; Pickering & Corregidor 2000; Fernandez *et al.* 2004).

This paper has two principal inter-related aims: to describe and interpret the range of mass transport complexes (MTCs) in the Middle Eocene Ainsa basin, Spanish Pyrenees, and to assess the stratigraphic position of these MTCs within the context of a tectonic control as the main driver on the timing, location and architecture of deep-water sandbodies. The idea of discontinuous, pulsed, deformation in the Pyrenean orogen on a time frame of several million years, both in deposits that are slightly younger than those described in this study (Burbank *et al.* 1992; Meigs *et al.* 1996), and also in contemporaneous non-marine and shallow-marine strata (Holl & Anastasio 1993), is not new. Presently, there are no detailed studies relating the internal architecture of deep-marine clastic systems to such tectonic pulses. Furthermore, there are also no detailed examples that document fan migration rates and the way in which individual linear basin-floor fans stack in relation to the mobile fold-and-thrust belt, despite

From: HODGSON, D.M. & FLINT, S.S. (eds) 2005. *Submarine Slope Systems: Processes and Products*. Geological Society, London, Special Publications, **244**, 51–74. 0305-8719/$15.00

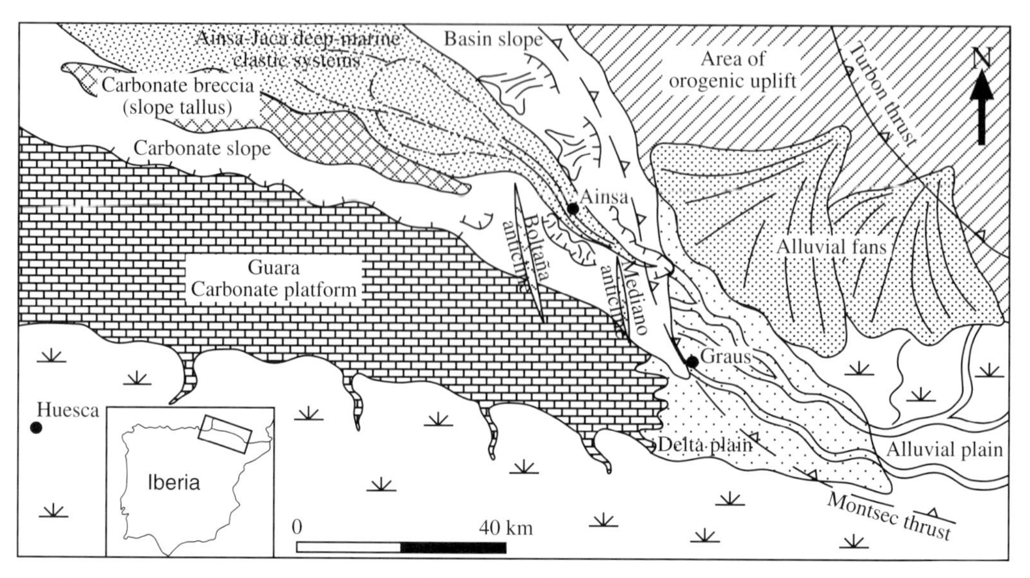

Fig. 1. Palaeogeographic reconstructions of the Ainsa basin and surrounding areas during deposition the early Lutetian. After Dreyer *et al.* (1999). Slope marls and basinal turbidite systems accumulated along the axis of the Ainsa basin, and a major carbonate platform existed in the southwestern portion of the South Pyrenean foreland basin. The Mediano anticline is present as an intra-slope lineament, and the Boltaña anticline probably represented a subtle submarine high. The main source area was located in uplifted terrains at the northern margin of the Tremp–Graus basin.

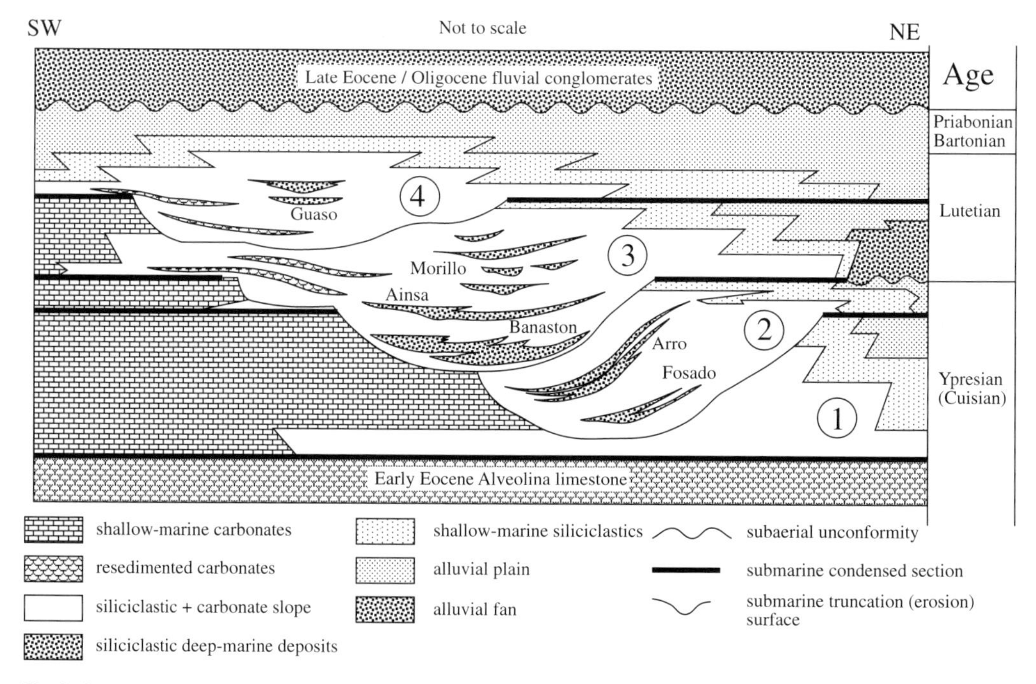

Fig. 2. General stratigraphy of the Ainsa basin (not to scale, but cumulative stratigraphic thickness of deep-marine deposits *c.* 4 km, and width of panel in order of 8–10 km). Numbers 1–4 indicate the four unconformity-bounded units. Modified after Fernandez *et al.* (2004), but compare with unconformity-bounded units shown in fig. 5 of Mutti *et al.* (1985).

intensive recent research on modern submarine trenches and foreland basins.

Data acquisition

The Ainsa Project is an integrated outcrop–subsurface study of deep-marine clastic systems. Eight wells were drilled at 400–500 m spacing, typically to subsurface depths of *c.* 250 m each, through *c.* 1.5–2 million years of stratigraphy, with about 96 % core recovery. Micropalaeontological and palynological analyses were carried out to constrain the age, and provide a sequence stratigraphic framework. A standard suite of wireline logs was run in each hole (calliper, gamma, spectral gamma, sonic, neutron, density). Seismic reflection lines were made, but the density contrasts militated against good seismic resolution and, therefore, a programme of synthetic seismic was undertaken. Outcrop work included detailed geological mapping, to provide the first detailed map of these systems (Fig. 3), and over 1500 m of outcrop sedimentary logs were measured. As we observe many striking similarities both in architecture and vertical distribution of facies associations between the extremely well-studied Ainsa fans and other depositional elements within the Ainsa basin, we include, where appropriate (such as the sedimentary characteristics of MTCs and vertical sequences within the sandbodies) data from other sandbodies (for mapped distribution of other sandbodies, see Mutti *et al.* 1985).

South Pyrenean foreland basin

Collision of the Iberian and European plates created a compact two-sided orogen (Muñoz 1992), with paired fold-and-thrust belts and foreland basins north and south of the Axial Zone, an imbricate stack of crystalline thrust sheets. In the central Pyrenees, maximum shortening occurred between 55–28 Ma (Meigs & Burbank 1997). Verges *et al.* (1998) show that maximum rates of tectonic subsidence in the foreland basin coincided with the maximum rates of shortening and thrust front advance at *c.* 41.5 Ma (late Lutetian), which was broadly contemporaneous with the accumulation of the deep-marine Ainsa basin sediments. In slightly younger stratigraphic sequences east of the Ainsa Basin (*c.* 42–35 Ma), structural and magneto-stratigraphic work show phases of thrusting, duplex growth, and related deposition on a time scale of *c.* 1.5–3 million years (Burbank *et al.* 1992). The Middle Eocene South Pyrenean foreland basin evolved with mainly non-marine/marginal marine environments in the eastern sectors, whereas further west, in the Ainsa basin, there was an overall change from fluvio-deltaic to deep-marine systems (Fig. 1).

Ainsa basin

Stratigraphy of the Ainsa basin

The Ainsa basin comprises up to 4 km of deep-marine deposits, as four unconformity-bounded depositional units in which each succeeding unit is both structurally less deformed and shows a south-westward shift in depositional axis (fig. 6 in Fernandez *et al.* 2004, see also fig. 5 in Mutti *et al.* 1985). These four major unconformity-bound depositional units, with their foreland-stepping clastic wedges, suggest a first-order tectonic control on deposition of the deep-marine systems. The deep-water clastic part of the Ainsa basin represents around 10–12 million years duration during the Early to Middle Eocene (Ypresian/Cuisian and entire Lutetian stages). The deep-marine deposits are overlain by *c.* 1 km of fluvio-deltaic and related systems mainly fed from the SE (Mutti 1985; Mutti *et al.* 1985; Bentham *et al.* 1992; Dreyer *et al.* 1999).

The Ainsa basin contains about fifteen deep-water sandbodies, typically tens of metres thick but packaged into six coarse clastic depositional complexes, each in the order of 100–200 m thick which, from the oldest, are: (1) Arro-Charo (including Fosada); (2) Gerbe; (3) Banaston; (4) Ainsa (Fig. 4); (5) Morillo; and (6) Guaso (Mutti *et al.* 1985). These depositional complexes typically contain 2–3 individual sandbodies from 30–100 m thick that are separated by mainly thin- and very thin-bedded sandstones with subordinate marls. The depositional complexes are separated vertically from other complexes by several hundred metres of mainly marl deposits with relatively minor amounts of thin- to very thin-bedded sandstones. Although some sandbodies show a vertical (aggradational) stacking pattern, they show an overall WSW foreland-stepping pattern. Furthermore, within individual sandbodies, the submarine channels show a similarly consistent foreland-propagating stacking pattern.

Tectonic setting of the Ainsa basin

Within the mountain front of the evolving Pyrenean orogen, propagation of the thrust front caused the deep-water Ainsa basin fill to be segmented into four depositional units that are separated by widespread angular unconformities and that are stepped towards the foreland (Fernandez *et al.* 2004). The Ainsa basin was bounded to the east by the embryonic (growing) Mediano anticline, and to the west by another seafloor high, that later formed the Boltaña anticline (Fig. 1). The earliest parts of the deep-marine fill in the Ainsa basin are the most highly deformed. The degree of tectonic deformation decreases upwards

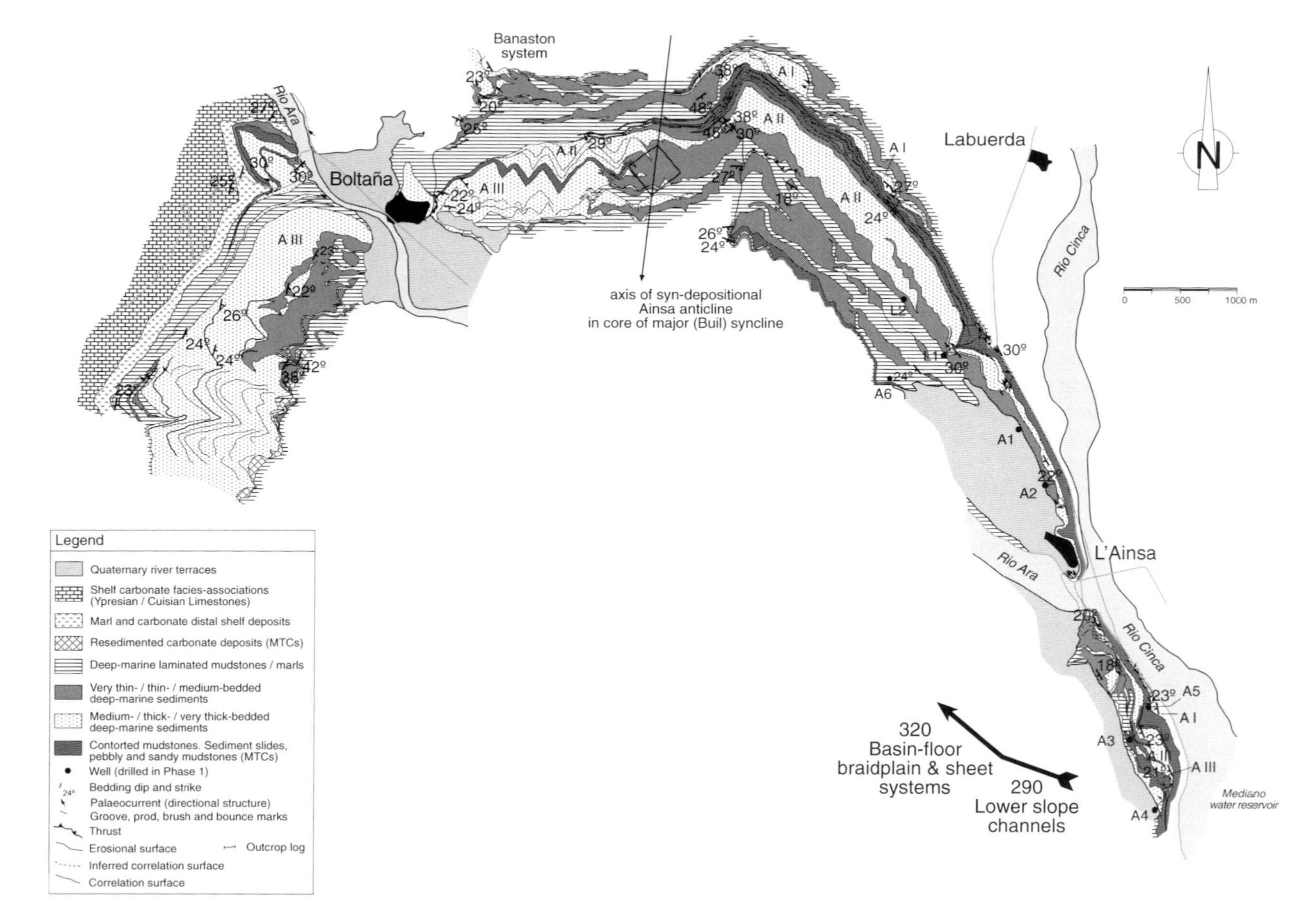

Fig. 3. Geological map of the three Ainsa fans (I, II, III), and enveloping sediments exposed around the limbs of a major southward-plunging syncline with syn-depositional anticline in core (modified after Pickering & Corregidor 2000). Note basinward (westward) thinning and pinch-out of (type Ia) MTCs into bedded heterolithics and laminated mudstones between Ainsa I and II fans at inferred base-of-slope west of Labuerda. These intervals of type Ia MTCs show continuity along the NNW–SSE oriented outcrops (almost parallel with the inferred eastern margin of the basin floor and base-of-slope. Without detailed mapping, these large outcrops give the erroneous impression that the sandbodies are everywhere encased by MTCs. Note the eastern margin of one of the Banaston channels north of Boltaña.

until the deep-marine Guaso system and overlying Sobrarbe deltaics are only gently folded in the Buil syncline. Indeed, progressive (syn-depositional) tectonics resulted in parts of the earliest deep-marine sandbody — the Arro sandbody — being overturned with a top-to-the-west sense of shear. The sense of overturning is consistent with the thrust direction for the local Peña Montañesa (Cotiella) nappe with WSW translation (Travé *et al.* 1998). This progressive decrease in tectonic deformation through time within the Ainsa basin demonstrates an important syn-sedimentary tectonic influence on deposition within the deep-marine basin.

The present western margin of the deep-marine Ainsa basin is bounded by the Boltaña anticline, exposing mainly Eocene and older carbonate sequences. Mutti (1985) and Mutti *et al.* (1985) have shown that the Boltaña anticline was, in part, a growth structure during accumulation of the deep-marine basin fill, and that this structure provides the basis for recognizing an inner (Ainsa) and outer (Jaca) basin. Palaeocurrent data (such as reflected and deflected flows) do not support the notion that there was any significant cross-basin high that physically compartmentalized the Ainsa and Jaca basins in the vicinity of the Boltaña anticline, and, therefore, the concept or description of two basins is adopted purely for convenience. The embryonic Boltaña anticline would have been sub-parallel or oblique to the original basin axis. Later uplift and tightening of the Boltaña anticline has resulted in the erosion of the physical continuity of deep-marine deposits, with the more proximal Ainsa basin containing most of the channelized deposits, and the down-dip Jaca basin being characterized by less-confined, more sheet-like, lobe and related deposits. The deep-marine fill of the Ainsa basin thins and pinches out at its western lateral margin against the Boltaña anticline (Mutti *et al.* 1985; Bentham *et al.* 1992, their fig. 9).

A detailed palaeomagnetic study of the Mediano anticline, on the eastern side of the Ainsa basin, combined with the identification of significant unconformities, suggests fold initiation at *c.* 52 Ma, with significant development by *c.* 42 Ma (Holl & Anastasio 1993). This study also recognized the episodic emplacement of the Cotiella-Montsec thrust sheet, with intervals of slow fold growth (tilting at 2.2°–4.2° per million years) punctuated by intervals lasting about 1.5 million years when fold growth was 3–5 times faster and produced angular unconformities. The deep-marine systems of the Ainsa basin accumulated during this development of the Mediano anticline (mainly Lutetian, 48.6–40.4 Ma, using the revised geological time-scale; Gradstein *et al.* 2004). As there is no palaeocurrent or petrographic evidence to suggest that the growing Mediano anticline was a recognizable sediment source during the fill of the deep-marine basin, we infer that it remained a submarine topographic high.

Age and water depth of Ainsa basin deposits

Using the planktonic foraminifera zonation of Berggren *et al.* (1995) and the new geological time-scale of Gradstein *et al.* (2004), the age of the deep-marine parts of the Ainsa and Jaca basins spans the early to Middle Eocene (Cuisian/Ypresian and Lutetian Stage) and, therefore, records about 10–12 million years of deep-marine sediment accumulation. The overlying fluvio-deltaic Escanilla system is Bartonian in age (figs 11 and 36 in Remacha *et al.* 2003). A detailed magneto-stratigraphic study of deep-marine sediments that were fed mainly via the Ainsa basin into the down-dip Jaca basin (Oms *et al.* 2003), suggests that deposition there spans chrons C20r to C18n.2n (Lutetian–Bartonian), a time that overlaps with, but is also slightly younger than some of our age dating based on biostratigraphy.

Age dating of the planktonic foraminifera indicates deposition of the Ainsa fans within the mid Lutetian Stage around the boundary of planktonic foraminifera zones P11–P12 (calcareous nannofossil zones NP14 and NP15). Our age dating appears to be in some disagreement with that of Remacha *et al.* (2003), who assign the Ainsa system in their TSU 5 (tectono-stratigraphic unit 5) to a younger age range of P12–P13, something that must call into question any correlations between sandbodies in the Ainsa and Jaca basins.

The narrowness of our age dating, therefore, favours a relatively short duration for development of the three Ainsa fans together, i.e. in the order of 1–2 million years, around 45–47 Ma. In the absence of any alternative and ultra-high-resolution chronostratigraphic framework, it seems reasonable to infer that each fan and the associated enveloping fine-grained inter-fan sediments represents less than 1 million years duration. Furthermore, it is likely that the sandy fans accumulated much more rapidly than the laminated and fine-grained inter-fan sediments. As the Ainsa fans comprise several submarine channels (with only one channel active at any time), with the Ainsa II fan containing 5–6 discrete 10–35 m-deep (pre-compaction) channels (Clark 1995; Clark & Pickering 1996), channel erosion and infill probably lasted in the order of 10^4–10^5 years. By comparison, in extreme cases, as during Pleistocene glacial intervals on the Amazon Fan, channel development lasted as little as 1–3 ka (Mikkelsen *et al.* 1997).

The autochthonous component of agglutinated foraminifera indicate mid to upper bathyal water depths (*c.* 500 m), but with some lower bathyal species (*c.* 500–1000 m). These foraminifera consist predominantly of epifaunal morphotypes, suggesting either anaerobic interstitial waters, and/or low availability of oxygen for the infauna to colonize the sediment surface. The laminated nature of the marls and fine-grained very thin- and thin-bedded turbidites favour low oxygen levels. The epifaunal morphotypes are characterized mainly by calcareous spirals of the *Nuttallides* type. This *Nuttallides* biofacies expanded its bathymetric range from abyssal depths to mid bathyal in the Eocene (Tjalsma & Lohmann 1983). Allowing for realistic submarine gradients, the best estimate of water depth suggests that the deep-marine Ainsa basin clastic systems, including the Ainsa fans, accumulated essentially in upper to mid bathyal depths of about 400–600 m. Although water depths may have varied significantly during deposition of the Ainsa system, this issue requires a more detailed quantitative micropalaeontological study throughout the entire Ainsa basin.

An additional pilot study was undertaken to identify diagnostic benthic foraminifera from eight samples in the youngest of the turbiditic sandbodies in the Ainsa basin, the Guaso system. The samples show that agglutinated benthic foraminifera comprise most of the *in-situ* fauna, with a minimal amount of reworking. Some of the foraminifera, (i.e. *Globobulimina* spp.) occur in the oxygen minimal zone, just off the shelf/upper bathyal zone whereas the rest are found in upper to mid bathyal depths (i.e. *Anomalinoides* and the *Nuttallides* species). Most of the species can be used to give only a broad age. The planktonic foraminifera occur mainly in the middle Eocene, appearing rounded, compacted and multispiral. The occurrence of the planktonic foraminifera *Hantkenina alabamensis* provides a zonal indicator, with its first occurrence in the mid to low latitudes, at P12 (the middle part of the Middle Eocene). The foraminifera from the youngest sandbodies, the Guaso system, therefore suggest fully marine conditions, with upper bathyal water depths (*c*. 500 m). It appears, therefore, that the entire stratigraphy of the Ainsa basin clastics represents deep-marine systems.

Palynofloral and microfaunal data from the Ainsa complex suggest a tropical to subtropical climate with moderately high rainfall patterns. Hinterland flora was dominated by coniferous vegetation on upland areas and/or well-drained lowlands. The relative paucity of pteridophyte and associated spores suggests only limited fringing swamps/mangrove belts, consistent with a relatively narrow coastal plain (unpublished Robertson Research International report commissioned for UCL Ainsa Project).

Palaeocurrents within the Ainsa basin

The Ainsa clastic systems have been interpreted as the proximal parts of topographically- and structurally-confined, coarse-grained sand-rich, lower-slope and axial basin-floor submarine fans (Pickering & Corregidor 2000). This is supported by palaeogeographic reconstructions (Dreyer *et al.* 1999, fig. 1) and palaeocurrents that show a generally consistent palaeoflow, in all three Ainsa sandbodies, towards approximately 320°. Similar palaeocurrent trends are reported from the other deep-marine sandbodies in the Ainsa basin, e.g. Mutti *et al.* (1985, fig. 7) and the oldest (Arro) sandbody (Millington & Clark 1995*a*, *b*).

MTCs and their stratigraphic significance

Mass transport complexes include chaotic deposits, typically with visco-plastically deformed rafts of disrupted bedding, cobble-pebble conglomerates, pebbly mudstones, mud-flake breccias, and pebbly sandstones. These deposits represent a range of processes, including slides, slumps, turbidity currents and debris flows. We use this general term to embrace a wide range of deposits, because it is less process-specific (cf. controversy of high versus low concentration, or hyper-concentrated, turbidity currents, sandy debris flows, hyperconcentrated flows, etc.) and does not imply that it is always possible to recognize individual flow events.

Some deposits within this range of facies could be interpreted as the deposits of high-energy turbidity currents, debris flows and sediment slides; however, the Ainsa basin also contains many coarse clastics with ambiguous attributes *vis à vis* a conventional process interpretation, or that appear as hybrids of sediment gravity flows that might be called turbidity currents or debris flows. The complexity of many of these deposits suggests flows with transitional properties between turbidity currents and debris flows (Lowe *et al.* 2003), linked flow processes (e.g. Haughton *et al.* 2003), flow transformations and/or multiphase flows (e.g. Sohn *et al.* 2002).

MTCs may create accommodation in various ways. First, their initiation may evacuate large recesses on the upper and mid slope that then act as 'containers' for channels or channel complexes (e.g. Hackbarth & Shew 1994). Second, they may create obstacles or ridges, in channels, on the slope or base of slope, against which turbidites may be deflected. Third, they may have irregular upper surfaces that create local ponded accommodation within the depressions (e.g. Pickering & Corregidor 2000). Where turbidity currents flow over these regions, sand may be deposited within this local accommodation and/or bypassed through adjacent areas. Thus the geometry of the initial failure and that of the deposit potentially have a significant impact on sand distribution and sandbody geometry at several scales, particularly on basin slopes, in mass-flow-dominated base-of-slope muddy aprons, in canyons, and in

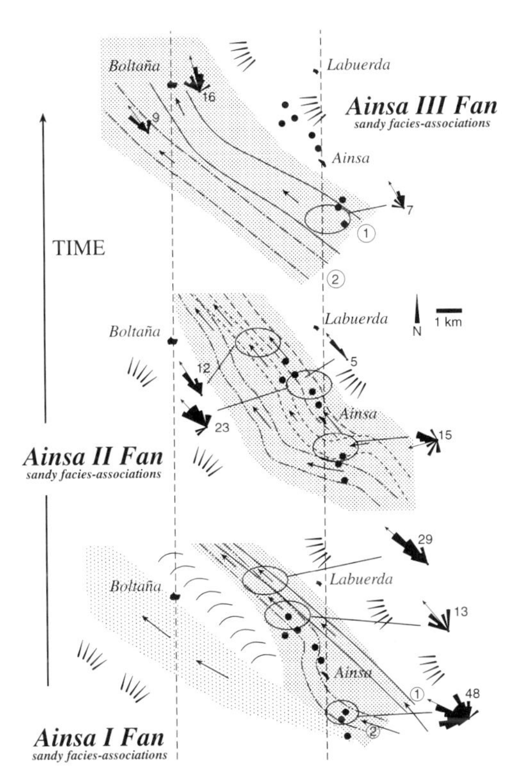

Fig. 4. Palaeogeography of Ainsa I, II and III fans showing lateral (towards the foreland) stacking, Ainsa basin, based on detailed mapping (Pickering & Corregidor 2000). The loci of coarse clastics (not restored for folding), directional palaeocurrents, and location of wells shown and three towns/villages shown as reference frame. See Fig. 3 for outcrop position of Ainsa fans. Vertical dashed lines constructed as guidelines to emphasize WSW step-wise migration of successive fans. Note growth anticline during Ainsa I fan time, but with channelized sands to east of this structure, and only very thin packet of less-confined sandy turbidites accumulating to west.

levéed channels. In the subsurface and at outcrop the supra-MTC sandbodies may easily be misidentified (e.g. as channels at the scale of the mass failure).

Mutti (1985) first drew attention to the stratigraphic significance of the large-scale collapse of the upper basin slope and shelf-edge early in the evolution of the Ainsa sandbodies (here referred to as fans), yet placed the base of the depositional systems below the first significant sands. In this paper, we document the mass transport complexes, as the earliest events of depositional cycles within the Ainsa basin. We recognize three broad categories of MTCs, designated types I–III with subdivisions of type Ia, Ib and Ic (Table 1). Their internal sedimentary characteristics and geometry appear to be environmentally diagnostic.

Type I MTCs

Type Ia MTCs typically range from metres to tens of metres thick, and comprise either entirely intraformational marly and heterolithic sediments (Fig. 5), or extrabasinal carbonate platform collapse deposits in a marl matrix. In general, they occur between the thick sandbodies within the Ainsa basin, and formed depositional topography upon which the fans, or thin packets of sandy turbidites, accumulated (Fig. 5). Cronin *et al.* (1998) correlated the north–south base of the Ainsa II system as the onset of thick sands (their fig. 4), but detailed correlation and mapping shows that this 'base' is strongly diachronous, by up to several tens of metres, mainly due to significant depositional mounding by type Ia and II MTCs (Fig. 5). Also, in the depositional model of Cronin *et al.* (1998) they show only chaotic deposits (here defined as MTCs) between the sandbodies, whereas our mapping has demonstrated that type Ia MTCs are laterally equivalent over tens of metres to bedded heterolithic and very thin-bedded and fine-grained sediments (cf. Pickering & Corregidor 2000, fig. 3; Fig. 3 here). The orientation of sedimentary folds in the type 1a MTCs suggests a predominant down slope translation from the east. No folds were measured from the entirely carbonate MTCs (type Ic), but their composition suggests sourcing from a carbonate platform west of and/or in the vicinity of the Boltaña anticline.

Most type Ia MTCs comprise fine-grained marls and very thin-bedded sandy turbidites, together with abundant redeposited nummulites, rarely as millimetre to centimetre thick layers of concentrated nummulites. It is these layers that Cronin *et al.* (1998) appear to have misinterpreted as shallow-marine limestones (p. 431, '. . . in the case of the limestones suggest water depths above storm wave base, whereas ichnofacies and foraminiferal assemblages from the channel bodies indicate deeper water.'). There are also thin (decimetre- to metre-scale) intraformational deformed horizons of local origin. These contain folded, attenuated, and partially disaggregated, sands in a sandy to marly matrix. They occur preferentially in off-axis channel sites; because they represent highly localized redeposition events, they are designated type Ib MTCs.

Microfaults are a common feature in many of the type Ia MTCs, a microstructure that is only well seen in the cut cores. These locally pervasive faults show millimetre-scale displacements and typically have a spacing of a few millimetres. In core, where the fine detail is best preserved, then normal faults predominate over reverse faults. Microfaults in sandstones and heterolithic sediments, are relatively uncommon, compared with type Ia MTCs. Similar microfault arrays are

Table 1. *Classification of mass transport complexes (MTCs) in the Ainsa basin, and interpreted sediment transport process/es*

Type I	Ia	Range in – tens of m thick of entirely intraformational marly and heterolithic sediments. Generally occur between thick sandbodies, and created seafloor topography upon which fans, or thin packets of sandy turbidites, accumulated. Visco-plastic deformation, varying degrees of disruption	Sediment slide (mid/upper basin slope)
	Ib	Thin (dm- to m-scale) intra-formational deformed horizons of clearly local origin, with folded, attenuated, and partially disaggregated, sands in a sandy to marly matrix. Occur especially off-axis channel sites	Sediment slide (local, e.g. channel margin)
	Ic	16-m-thick marl-matrix-supported deposit with clasts to cobble/boulder size of carbonate platform material, with varying degrees of visco-plastic deformation. No terrigenous material even in matrix.	Sediment slide/debris flow (carbonate platform collapse + upper/mid slope)
Type II		Typically range m – tens of m thick, cummulative erosion at the base of tens of m. Contains extra-formational material, e.g. very well-rounded pebbles, shallow-marine shells and abundant reworked nummulites. Occur as lateral equivalent of sandbodies, particularly in older part of fans. Thin packets (typically dm – few m) of heterolithics above irregular surface infilling residual topography.	Multiphase granular flow (shelf + fluvio-delatic input)
Type III		Thinnest type, typically dm – m thick. Typically, contain extra-formational clasts of very well rounded pebbles, and angular to rounded intra-formational silt-mud clasts. Tend to contain greatest proportion of sand-grade sediment. Occur within sandbodies (fans), and appear to define erosive base of sandy submarine channels and other less-confined but significant erosional events.	Flow transformation (erosive turbidity current bulking up and freezing)

documented from associated submarine faults where their origin has been ascribed to the passage of seismic after-shock waves through the sediments (e.g. Pickering 1983).

Locally within the Ainsa basin, type Ia MTCs stacked to create significant seafloor topography with, for example, cumulative relief of about 35 m created in the region of the Forcaz stream, also called Forcat, or the Barranco del Estañuelo (Fig. 6). Depositional relief, created by the cohesive MTCs, caused the sandy turbidity currents to flow around such obstacles, resulting in onlap of sandy turbidites against this topography.

Within the Morillo system, in the stream section near Sieste is a *c.* 16 m-thick MTC with a pure carbonate (marl) matrix (verified by thin-section analysis), and outsize visco-plastically deformed rafts of intraformational sandstones and subrounded to poorly rounded limestone clasts. The latter are derived from the Boltaña anticline and the type is referred to as a type Ic MTC. A medium-grained sand is present in the upper *c.* 2 m of this MTC. There is no clear contact between these two distinctive parts of this deposit, but we infer that an amalgamation surface must be present.

Type II MTCs

Type II MTCs (Figs 7–9) typically range from a few metres to tens of metres thick, and may show cumulative basal erosion of up to tens of metres (Fig. 10). This type contains extra-formational material, e.g. very well-rounded pebbles (limestone, chert, vein quartz, sandstone and igneous rocks including granite), shallow-marine shells and abundant reworked nummulites. Also, type II MTCs contain incipient slide units as disrupted essentially *in-situ*, fine-grained facies-associations. They occur as the lateral equivalent of the sandbodies, particularly in the older part of fans. Thin packets (typically decimetres to a few metres) of heterolithic sediments occur along the upper, irregular, surface of these MTCs, infilling the residual topography.

Type II MTCs are the most varied in appearance and, therefore, show a range of internal complexity. Typically, they can be divided into two parts. The lower part may have an erosional base with flutes and grooves and is overlain by up to 50 cm of clast-supported pebble-grade conglomerate. Inverse grading may occur in the lowest few centimetres. In general, this part of a bed shows poorly developed or no

Fig. 5. Left: Type Ia MTC. Interfan wet-sediment deformation, Forcaz Stream. The base of the Ainsa II fan in this section is immediately above this prominent type Ia MTC. **Right**: Type Ib MTC with erosive base, cutting down to left, and overlain by sandy turbidites, Ainsa II fan channel off-axis, Forcaz stream section.

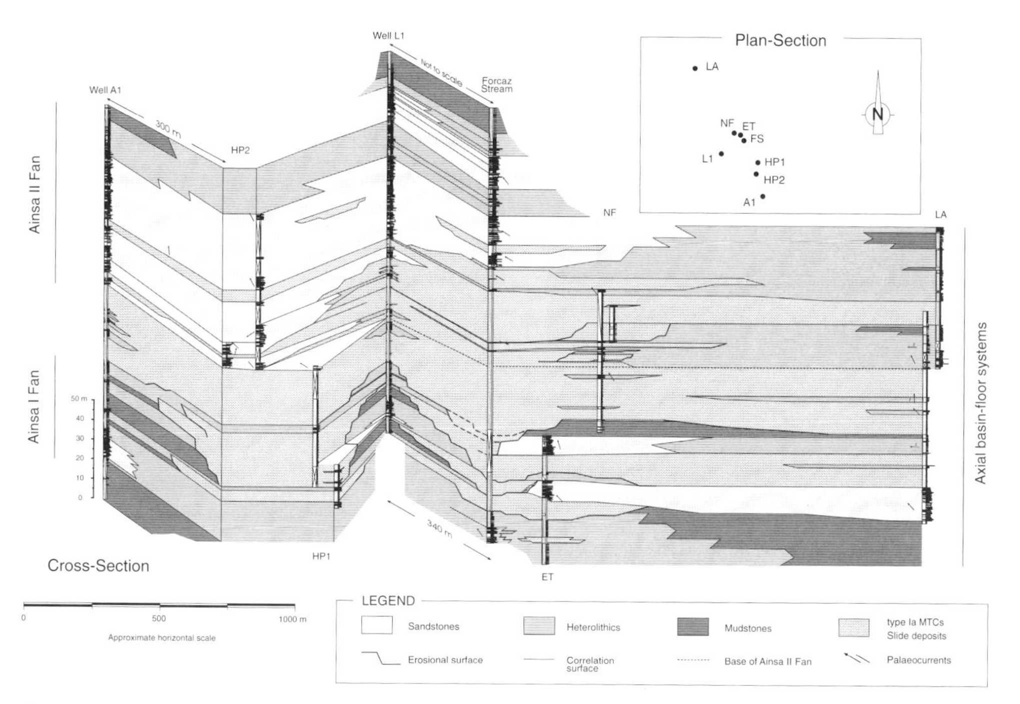

Fig. 6. 2D panel (inset planform map with location of logs) showing the importance of type Ia MTCs both between and within the Ainsa fans. Note the cumulative relief of *c.* 35 m created by the stacking of successive type Ia MTCs in the centre of this panel (in region of the Forcaz Stream, also called Barranco del Estañuelo, or Forcat stream) and Well L1. The overlying and laterally equivalent sandy turbidites onlap against this seafloor topography. Individual type Ia MTCs are typically metres thick.

Fig. 7. Left: Type II MTC immediately right of vehicle, in the Banaston system near Boltaña. Bedding youngs to the right. Note the large raft of partially disaggregated intraformational sandstone turbidite beds. **Right**: Close up in same MTC to show well-rounded limestone cobbles and pebbles that include many with molluscan borings formed in the littoral zone prior to redeposition.

Fig. 8. (A) Example of very thick type II MTCs in the basal part of the Morillo fan system, Sieste river section. Note thick package of sandy turbidites above. Human scale left of centre (arrowed). **(B)** Amalgamated type II MTCs (basal zones defined by pebble layers), Morillo system, Sieste river section.

normal grading, or lamination, and pebble imbrication may be present. The upper part of a bed is characterized by a chaotic, marl-matrix-supported pebble conglomerate, and may comprise an intraformational clast-rich breccia of variably deformed thin-bedded rafts of heterolithic sediments and marls. In core, there is no visible break between the upper and lower parts of a bed (Fig. 9). The upper, chaotic, part varies from decimetres to several metres thick.

Type III MTCs

Type III MTCs are the thinnest type, typically decimetres to metres thick (Fig. 11). Characteristically, they contain extra-formational clasts of very well rounded pebbles and angular to rounded intraformational silt–mud clasts. They tend to contain the greatest proportion of sand-grade sediment. They occur within the sandbodies (fans), and appear to be major erosional events, particularly but not exclusively associated with the erosive base of sandy submarine channels (Fig. 11) and other less-confined but significant erosional events.

Similarly to type II MTCs, type III MTCs, may contain a basal clast-supported gravel layer from a few clasts to about 50 cm in thickness, below a matrix-supported (typically much thicker) layer that contains dispersed pebbles.

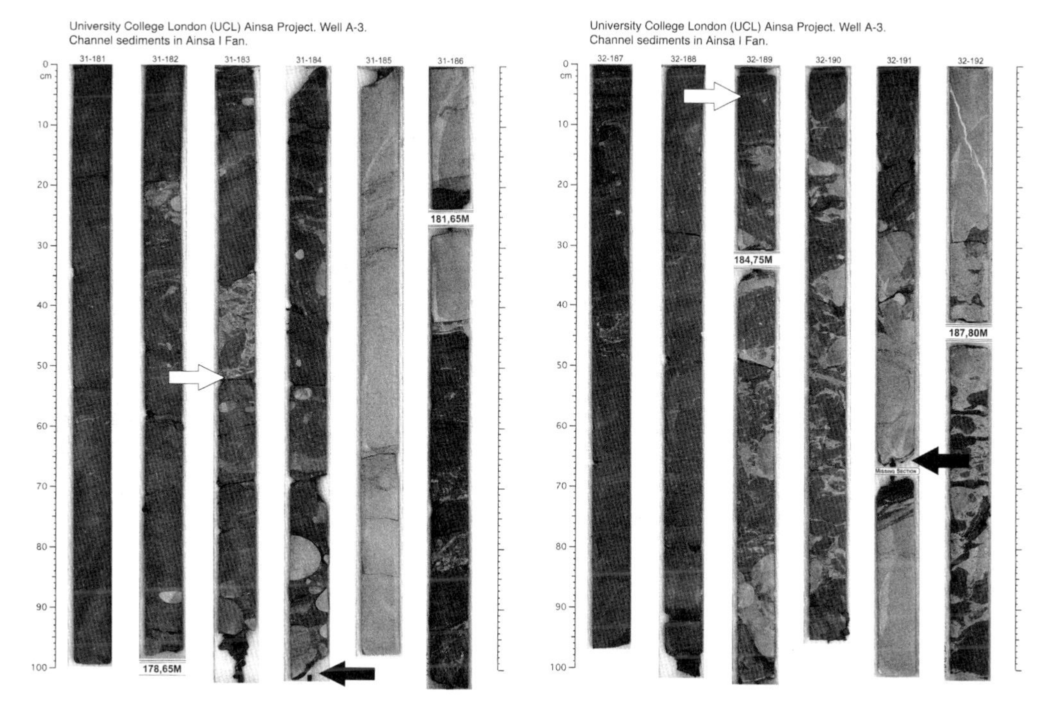

Fig. 9. Two examples of type II MTCs with basal clast-supported gravel below matrix-supported part from Ainsa I Fan channel sediments (Well A3, Fig. 3). Base of each MTC approximately 70 cm below top marked 32–191 and 100 cm for 31–184. The bedding youngs from right to left, with the white arrows denoting the base and the black arrows the top of the MTCs, respectively. Note that there is no discontinuity between clast-supported and matrix-supported intervals, suggesting a single depositional event. Such deposits are interpreted to represent multiphase granular flow with an initial (lower) high-energy turbulent and erosive part immediately followed by a (bulked up) flow behaving like a cohesive debris flow.

Sediment transport processes and depositional environments of MTCs

Type I MTCs. The disorganized internal structure of type I MTCs, characterized by abundant visco-plastic deformation of the incorporated, originally bedded sediments, showing all degrees of disaggregation from 'clasts' to almost completely liquefied beds, suggests that they represent the products of sediment slides and slumps, with possible subordinate debris-flow processes. A very similar range of chaotic deposits, even including layers of redeposited carbonate clast in mud matrix, have been described from an Ashgill–Llandovery foreland basin, the Point Leamington Formation, Notre Dame Bay, north central Newfoundland (Pickering 1987), suggesting that such facies associations may be typical of the proximal parts (*vis à vis* sediment delivery points) of many deep-marine foreland basins.

The occurrence of layers rich in redeposited carbonate clasts mixed in a marl matrix, and lacking any coarse (terrigenous) clastics, suggests that the growing (submarine) Boltaña anticline was a source of rare but large-scale MTCs that were shed into the Ainsa basin from its confining western slope. The scale of such deposits and the active-margin setting of the Ainsa basin favour a seismic trigger. The type Ic MTC in the Morillo system (Sieste), essentially a carbonate-mass flow, has many petrographic and textural similarities with the Roncal megabed documented from the Jaca basin (Labaume *et al.* 1983, 1985, 1987; Puigdefabregas pers. comm. 2003). The Roncal megabed, up to 200 m thick (Labaume *et al.* 1987), has three distinct intervals: (1) a lower carbonate megabreccia including large limestone slabs; (2) an intermediate mud-dominated chaotic interval; and (3) an upper carbonate megaturbidite (Puigdefabregas pers. comm. 2003). The origin of this, and similar beds in the Jaca basin, is explained as deposition from a single large-volume sediment gravity flow, with a lower debris flow deposit overlain by a linked (decoupled) turbidite deposited from in-flow surges during quasi-steady phases in a large turbulent flow (Puigdefabregas pers. comm. 2003).

Thus, type I MTCs are interpreted mainly as sediment slide and slump deposits, with subordinate debris-flow processes. Type Ia involves the mass wastage mainly of the mid and upper basin slopes

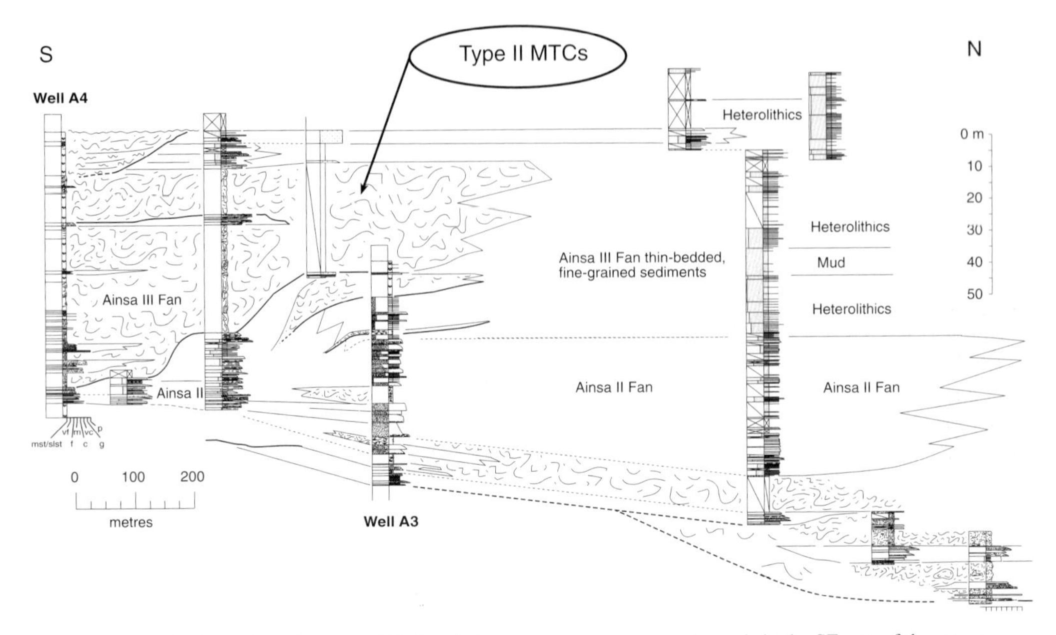

Fig. 10. Type II MTCs within Ainsa II and III fans (interpreted as lower-slope channels in the SE part of the outcrop area) 1 km south of Ainsa. Note the erosive bases with cumulative cut-down up to 10 s m. See Fig. 3 for placement of Well A4 and A3.

(shelf edge) along the lateral margins. Type Ib represents more localized slope instability within depositional environments in the deep-marine Ainsa basin, particularly along channel margins. Type Ic is the product of the collapse of the carbonate platform fringing the southwestern side of the Ainsa basin in the region of the present Boltaña anticline.

Type II MTCs. Type II MTCs are interpreted as representing the early phases of fan development when the upper slope, and outer shelf to littoral zone collapsed, and was redeposited in deeper water. Redeposition processes included sediment slides, debris flows, and complex (multiphase) granular flows (see below). These MTCs also created seafloor topography of several metres, and acted to deflect turbidity currents around the cohesive depositional mounds on the seafloor. Since the base of the immediately overlying sandstone packets appears essentially non-erosive, these MTCs were probably amongst the most cohesive types, creating seafloor topography of at least several metres. Their upper surfaces created accommodation for the accumulation of sandy turbidites during the early phases of fan evolution (below).

The composite nature of many type II MTCs, with basal gravel division, suggests multiphase granular flows as described by Parsons *et al.* (2001) and Sohn *et al.* (2002). By contrast, mud-rich sandstone beds in the Lower Cretaceous Britannia Formation, UK North Sea, have been interpreted as the deposits of sediment flows transitional between debris flows and turbidity currents, termed slurry flows (Lowe *et al.* 2003). They postulate that much of the mud in these flows was transported as sand- and silt-sized grains that were approximately hydraulically equivalent to suspended quartz and feldspar. They note that there is no thin-bedded facies that might represent waning flows analogous to low-density turbidity currents. The development of laminar, cohesion-dominated shear layers during sedimentation prevented most bed erosion, and the depositional system lacked channel, levee and overbank facies that commonly make up turbidity current-dominated systems. Britannia slurry flows, although turbulent and capable of size-fractionating even fine-grained sediments, left sand bodies with geometries and facies more like those deposited by poorly differentiated laminar debris flows. In many cases within the Ainsa basin, however, channel development is clearly above most of the MTCs, with channel margins showing sand-on-sand contacts (e.g. Clark 1995), and showing well-developed finer grained and thin-bedded overbank-levee environments (e.g. Ainsa Project Wells A2 and A4 as levee-overbank to the Ainsa I Fan channel axes as drilled in Wells A3 and A1; Pickering & Corregidor 2004). However, it is possible that some of the sandbodies represent highly confined sand ribbons with similar aspect ratios to submarine channels. The outcrop and sub-

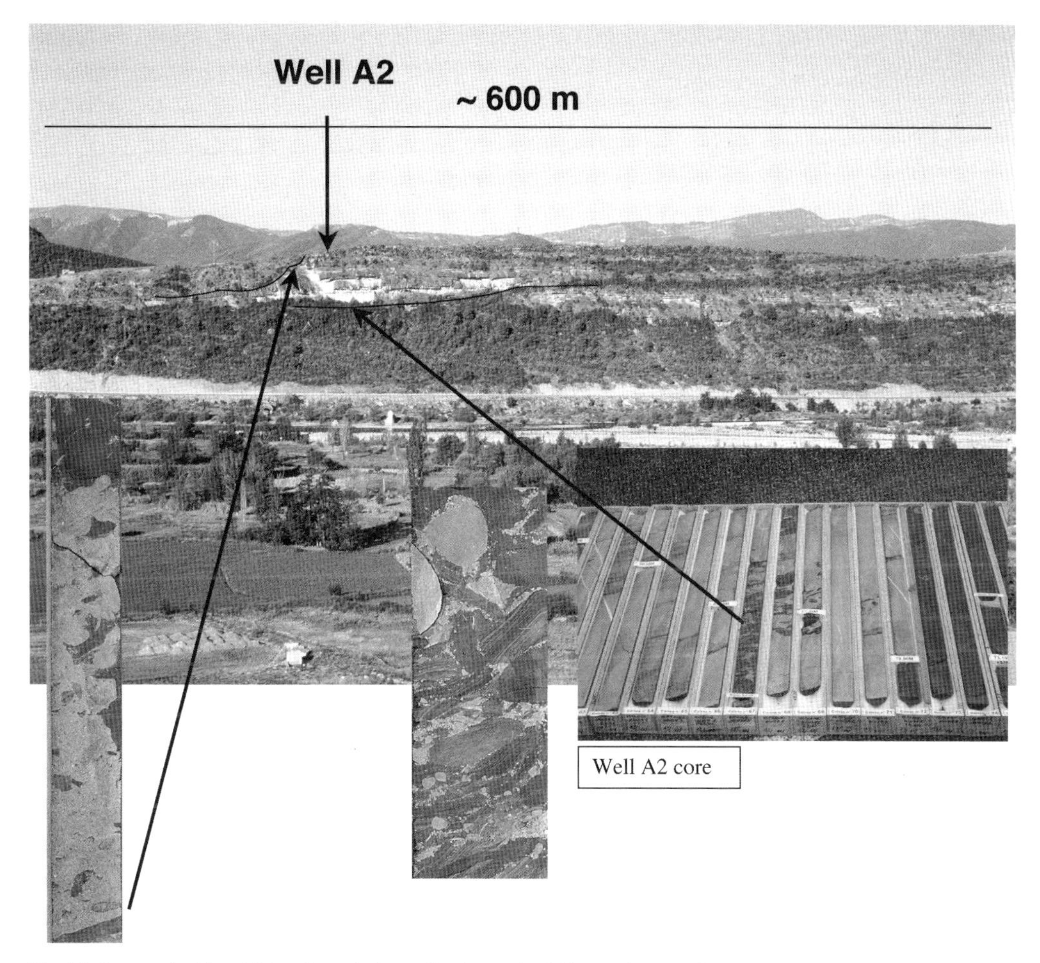

Fig. 11. Outcrop in Ainsa II fan channels immediately north of Ainsa, along road to Labuerda, showing major erosional surfaces associated with the stepwise WSW migration of channels. Projection of Well A2 (*c.* 80 m behind outcrop) onto cliff face shown. Example at left only shows basal (pebbly sandstone) part of type III MTC. Palaeoflow, towards 320° and into the cliff face is very oblique to this outcrop, at about 20°. These intrafan erosional surfaces are overlain by type III MTCs, with two examples shown here. Core youngs from right to left in continuous 1-m-lengths (*c.* 7 cm wide). Note basal Ainsa II sands (start of light-coloured section), above type Ia MTC, with type III MTC about 4 m above base of start of sands. Inset core image shows detail from this type III MTC. The steep-sided, compound erosional surface on left represents a channel margin created by successive very erosive (mainly bypassing) flows and subsequent infill by decimetre thick gravels, pebbly mudstones, pebbly sandstones, sands and marls.

surface data do not permit a resolution of this problem.

Haughton *et al.* (2003) document sharp-based, structureless and dewatered sandstone beds directly overlain by mud-clast breccias that are commonly rich in terrestrial plant fragments and capped by thin laminated sandstones, pseudonodular siltstones and mudstones. The contacts between the clast-rich breccias and the underlying sandstones are typically highly irregular with evidence for liquefaction and upward sand injection. The breccias contain fragments (up to metre scale) of exotic lithologies surrounded by a matrix that is extremely heterogeneous and strewn with multiphase and variably sheared sand injections and scattered coarse and very coarse sand grains (often coarser than in the immediately underlying sand bed). They interpret the breccias as deposition from debris flows that rode on a water-rich sand bed just deposited by a co-genetic concentrated gravity current. Consequently, Haughton *et al.* (2003) coined the term 'linked debrites' to distinguish these from debrites emplaced in the absence of a precursor sand bed. The sedimentary characteristics, including internal structures and grain-size distributions of most (but not all) of the Ainsa basin MTCs appear very different from the linked debrites

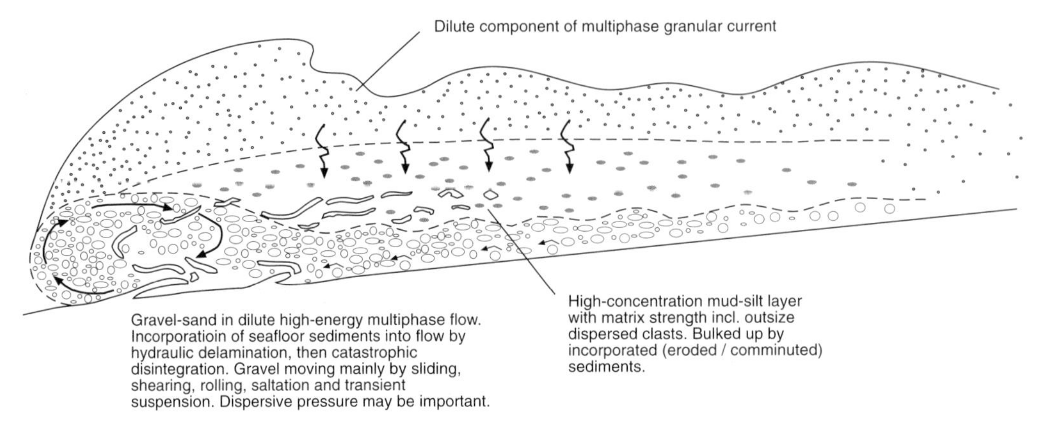

Fig. 12. Multiphase granular flow process to explain type II MTCs. See Fig. 13 for outcrop view of frozen erosional mechanism by which the highly energetic flows may bulk up to suppress turbulence and lead to a rapid freezing of the flow above the traction carpet.

described by Haughton *et al.* (2003) and, therefore, an alternative explanation is required.

Work on the Neogene Marnoso Arenacea Formation, Italian Apennines, suggests that individual beds may be the product of deposition in a single flow event, resulting in a deposit that comprises both turbidite and debrite sandstone (Talling *et al.* 2004). These beds have been called 'cogenetic debrite-turbidite' beds. They are believed to be particularly common in relatively distal fan fringe environments. We suspect that these foreland basin deposits might represent a more distal expression, in much finer grained sediments, of what we refer to as multiphase granular flows.

Type III MTCs. Type III MTCs are interpreted as the likely product of flow transformations or, as invoked for type II MTCs, some type III MTCs may have resulted from multiphase flows created by abrupt momentum changes, from strongly erosive, high-energy, sandy turbidity currents carrying very well-rounded pebbles (that excavated the channels) and picked up intra-formational fine-grained silty and muddy sediments along the flow path, thereby becoming over laden with respect to their flow competence and capacity, leading to rapid deposition. In many respects, both type II and type III MTCs can be considered as created by flow transformations. In the case of type II MTCs, however, we suspect that these multiphase granular flows may have travelled for some distance as complex flows, whereas the process for type III MTCs appears to have been both very rapid (angular intra-formational mud clasts) and over short distances (poor lateral continuity).

Multiphase granular flows (MGFs). The internal succession of structures in type II and some type III MTCs are consistent with temporal changes in flow type associated with the passage of a 'multiphase granular flow', i.e. a flow with varying spatial and temporal rheological properties both vertically and laterally within the flow (Figs 12 & 13). The erosional base to the lower part may contain well-developed flute and groove casts, and show cut-downs up to tens of metres over lateral distances of hundreds of metres, indicating an initial erosional event caused by a highly energetic and turbulent flow. In such cases, erosion was immediately followed by deposition from a clast-rich flow, possibly with inverse grading and imbrication of pebbles, suggesting high rates of shear strain, clast interactions, presumably associated with dispersive pressure, and rapid deposition of the gravel without rolling or prolonged friction-dominated movement on the bed (cf. Walker 1975; Lowe 1982). The high shear strains and clast collisions in the gravelly flow were probably supplied from an overriding high-energy turbulent flow (cf. Sohn *et al.* 2002). These deposits are interpreted as the product of two-layer or bipartite (multiphase granular flows), comprising a high-concentration gravelly dispersion or a traction carpet at its base, and an overlying lower-concentrated and turbulent suspension (cf. subaerial [hyper]concentrated flows described by Smith (1986), Pierson & Costa (1987), Costa (1988) and Sohn (1999), and subaqueous high-density turbidity currents of Lowe (1982), and Postma *et al.* (1988), or concentrated density flows of Mulder & Alexander (2001)). Deposition of the lower unit appears to have been rapid and immediately overlain by processes equivalent to a co-genetic cohesive debris flow (cf. slurry flows of Lowe *et al.* 2003 and 'linked debrites' of Haughton *et al.* 2003). However, there is no erosional or loaded break between the lower and upper depositional units and, therefore, we favour an explanation that involves deposition from a single multiphase granular flow.

In comparable deposits described by Sohn *et al.* (2002), most multiphase 'debris-flow' beds show prominent normal grading composed of clast-supported pebbles and cobbles in their lower part and loosely clast-supported or matrix-supported pebbles in their upper part. The lower part commonly shows up-current-dipping imbrication of gravel and well-developed inverse grading near the base, all features observed in some type II MTCs. The lower bed contact is generally erosional, with flute or groove casts. The upper part of the bed shows disorganized fabric and characteristically contains abundant intraformational clasts, ranging from fine pebble-size mudstone chips to several metre-long sandstone blocks.

In experimental studies of debris flows, Parsons *et al.* (2001) observed that shear rates were significantly higher (6–15 s^{-1}) than expected, given the modest slopes examined (10.7°–15.2°). They attributed these large values as due primarily to the concentration of shear into narrow bands between a central non-deforming plug and the sidewall. The slurries exhibited predominantly fluid-mud behaviour with finite yield strength and shear-thinning rheologies in the debris-flow body, while frictional behaviour was often observed at the front, or snout. The addition of sand or small amounts of clay tended to make the body of the flows behave in a more Bingham-like fashion (i.e. closer to a linear viscous flow for shear stresses exceeding the yield stress). The addition of sand also tended to accentuate the frictional behaviour at the snout. Where body friction numbers were in the order of 100, Parsons *et al.* (2001) observed a transition to frictional grain-flow behaviour that occurred first at the front, and they explained this as the snout–grain-flow transition being a result of concentration of the coarsest material at the flow front, reduced shear near the snout, and loss of matrix from the snout to the bed. We believe that many of the type II MTCs in the Ainsa system are well explained by such complex flow behaviour in a granular fluid that locally exhibits a range of flow rheologies. We interpret the clastsupported pebble conglomerates at the base of some type II MTCs as a likely result of similar frictional grain-flow behaviour under the snout of flows in which very high shear stresses existed.

The lack of any sharp break between the lower clast-supported gravel layer and overlying matrix-supported part of type II MTCs favours a complex, multiphase flow in which the gravel was concentrated in the head (turbulent mixing with high shear stresses), and the body was dominated by high concentrations of suspended load mixed with dispersed sand and gravel-grade material (greater cohesion, matrix strength, rapid freezing below a critical yield strength). In this respect, we suspect that such bipartite 'beds' represent the deposits of flows with fluid dynamical attributes of both turbidity currents and debris flows: a deposit from a multiphase granular flow.

Fig. 13. Erosional mechanism frozen in the process of hydraulic jacking up and delamination of the seafloor, leading to such highly energetic flows very rapidly bulking up to suppress turbulence and cause the rapid freezing of the flow above the traction carpet. Location in the Banaston system immediately north of Boltaña. Sole marks show flow was from right to left (towards 320°).

One of the critical issues associated with our hypothesis for multiphase granular flow is the mechanism by which the highly energetic, erosive and turbulent flow (*sensu* turbidity current) effectively bulks up in a catastrophic manner. Studies of the NW African continental margin have shown, as one might predict from the Bernoulli principle in fluid dynamics, that turbidity currents undergo substantial acceleration and significantly enhanced erosive capability as they pass through seafloor constrictions (Gee *et al.* 2001). Given the tectonic position of the Ainsa basin and from our research, it is likely that the seafloor was characterized by substantial changes in gradient over only several hundred metres along the basin axis, and that the seafloor was rough. Sediment gravity flows, therefore, would have been typified by significant flow unsteadiness at a range of scales, something that could well explain the observations made in many of our type II, and type III MTCs. Until more experimental work has been undertaken on high-energy, high-concentration sediment gravity (granular) flows, our understanding of the spatial and temporal internal structure of multiphase flows and their deposits remains speculative.

Summary of MTC deposits

Type I MTCs commonly occur between the sandbodies, and represent basin slope and shelf mass wastage events (slides and slumps, with minor debris flow processes), mainly when coarse clastics were stored on the inner shelf and in subaerial environments. Type I MTCs also occur at the top of some of the sequences, and are interpreted as failure events linked to the regarding and healing of the basin slope during the final active phase of fan growth when direct river input was by finer grained turbidity currents and hyperpycnal flows (see below). Type II MTCs typify the lower part of sandbodies, and/or occur laterally to the sandbodies. They represent the deposits from multiphase granular flows that accumulated in the deep basin as the upper slope and shelf collapsed, as relative base level fell. Their stratigraphic context is consistent with the onset and early stages of fan sedimentation. Type III MTCs define significant erosional surfaces within the sandbodies, particularly but not exclusively the channel base and channel margins. As such, they are candidate high-order sequence boundaries within the fans.

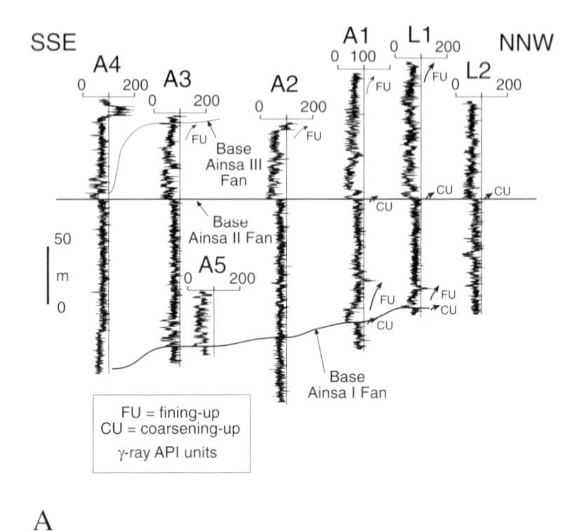

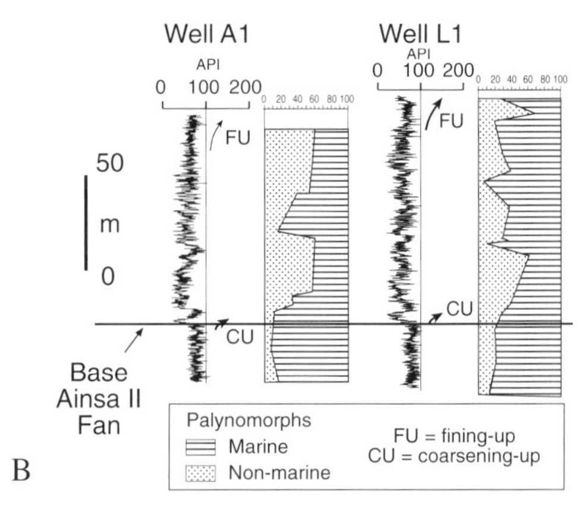

Fig. 14. (**A**) Total gamma-ray logs for 7 drill sites (API units). See Fig. 3 for well placement. Note the coarsening-up (CU) at base of parts of the Ainsa II fan at fan initiation, and fining-up (FU) of Ainsa I and II fans, as active fine-grained fan deposition with the uppermost few metres as gradual abandonment. Intrafan sequences not shown. (**B**) Comparison of gamma-ray logs for Wells A1 and L1 to show that the dramatic increase in land-derived (relative to marine) palynomorphs occurs with a significant time lag after the onset of fan sedimentation, interpreted as commensurate with direct fluvial input to the deep-marine basin after the shelf had collapsed. See Fig. 16 for sequence stratigraphic explanation.

Tectono-stratigraphic control on fans

The Ainsa clastic systems have been interpreted as the proximal parts of topographically- and structurally-confined, coarse-grained sand-rich, lower-slope and axial basin-floor submarine fans (Pickering & Corregidor 2000). Typically, the thickness of individual sandbodies varies from 10–70 m and shows an overall thinning-and-fining-upward succession. The fining-upward is a characteristic motif that is well seen on the gamma-ray logs from the Ainsa I and II fans (Fig. 14A). In other sandbodies within the Ainsa basin, we identify similar vertical sequences to those seen in the Ainsa fans, e.g. in the underlying Banaston and overlying Morillo and Guaso systems. These sequences are interpreted as a response to tectonic processes during an orogenic event (Fig. 15).

The characteristic sedimentary motif in most of the sandbodies throughout the Ainsa basin, as typified by the Ainsa fans, shows a fourfold division, which we interpret as a genetically linked set of processes representing the sequential sedimentary response to phases of thrust-related uplift-erosion in the adjacent central Pyrenees (Fig. 15).

Fan template (Stage 1), and early fan (Stage 2)

The first events (Stage 1) in any sequence caused large-scale collapse of the submarine fine-grained basin slopes to deposit type Ia MTCs at the base of slope and on the basin floor. These MTCs, lacking extrabasinal material such as fluvial pebbles or sand, formed much of the depositional surface or template for subsequent fan accumulation. Later (Stage 2), the upper slope, and any narrow shelf and coastal zone sands and gravels were cannibalized and redeposited in deep water, mainly as type II MTCs and sandy turbidity current deposits, during the early stage of fan development. The abundance of gravel lags, pebbly sandstones and pebbly mudstones, and common scours up to metres to tens of metres deep, suggest that it was during this early stage of fan accumulation in the proximal Ainsa basin that sub-

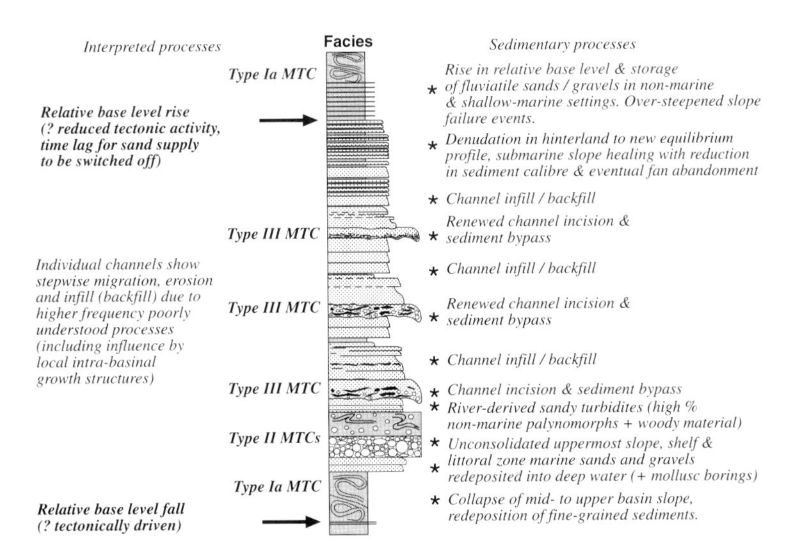

Fig. 15. Idealized clastic sequence in the deep-marine Ainsa basin. Although this sedimentary motif represents a complete sedimentary sequence in a single sandbody (fan), non-deposition and erosion, together with basinal location (axial, lateral, etc.) means that some sequences are base- or top-absent, and show variations on this depositional pattern. The sequence stratigraphic position of each major MTC type is indicated. Thickness of type Ia MTCs below sandbodies typically tens of metres.

stantial sediment bypass occurred, leading to deposition of the thick and extensive lobe deposits downdip in the Jaca basin.

The type Ia and type II MTCs created mounded topography because the flows were cohesive, and the turbidity current deposits infilled the complex seafloor topography. These sands are relatively well sorted and cleaner, with abundant mollusc borings in many of the very well and well rounded pebbles and cobbles, showing that they resided for at least some time in the littoral zone; they also contain reworked shallow-marine faunas. Later, coarse fluvial sediments poured into the basin, probably directly fed from river mouths/shelf-edge deltas.

In high-resolution seismic sections, researchers have begun to recognize high amplitude reflection packages (HARPs) of relatively less confined sediments (commonly sand-rich, and in some cases chaotic) that underlie, or are pre-cursors to, submarine channels with erosive bases to tens of metres over many hundreds of metres laterally (Pirmez *et al.* 1997; Beaubouef *et al.* 1998; Friedman & Beaubouef 1999; Beaubouef & Friedmann 2000). We observe similar deposits in the Ainsa fans below the channelized sands, which we designate as 'early fan (Stage 2)' sandy packages. These less-confined sandy deposits were first described by Mutti et al. (1985) from near Labuerda, in the Ainsa II sandbody, with their lobe-like geometry. Also, because the early stage of fan development was associated with abundant MTCs, initially as intraformational sediment slides (type Ia MTCs), at a scale of hundreds of metres to several kilometres, the base of the fans must be defined by large-scale truncation surfaces, something that would be seen clearly at the seismic scale.

Sandy fan growth (Stage 3)

Typically, the main sandbody (up to many tens of metres thick) shows several cycles of erosional channel development and infill, associated with the development of relatively straight, erosive channels (0.5–1 km wide and 10–40 m deep), constrained by tectonic and depositional topography to narrow down-slope and axial basin transport paths (Fig. 4). In the Ainsa I and II fan, the channels, like the fans, show overall WSW migration away from the fold-and-thrust belt (Clark & Pickering 1996). The development of several erosional channels within individual fans suggests repeated channel incision, sediment bypass and infill (backfill). Type III MTCs commonly occur along the base of these erosional surfaces (Fig. 11). The sandy infill of channels contains abundant woody material, show an abrupt increase in land-derived palynomorphs (Fig. 14B), and may be compositionally less mature, reflecting fluvio-deltaic rather than shallow-marine sources. Nummulites are abundant in all the deposits.

Integrated outcrop and core studies, combined with micropalaeontological work to define bio-events, suggest that the larger channels were associated with finer grained levee-overbank sediments

(Pickering & Corregidor 2004). As the axis of coarse clastic deposition within the Ainsa basin was only several kilometres wide at any time, and because the larger channels were typically in the order of 0.5 km wide and 20–40 m deep, the levee-overbank complexes were effectively interfingering with the thin-bedded and fine-grained basin slope deposits.

Fine grained fan and abandonment (Stage 4)

The fourth division in our sequence is defined by up to tens of metres of medium- to very thin-bedded, coarse- to fine-grained sands that appear relatively tabular over hundreds of metres down-flow and gently lens over tens of metres across flow. They are capped by a thinning-and-fining-upward sequence, up to few metres thick, that immediately precedes marl deposition (Figs 14A & 15). Collectively, these deposits are interpreted to record a significant reduction in the coarse clastic supply to the deep marine environment. This decrease in sediment calibre probably reflects the flushing out of the coarser grain sizes from the coastal and near-coastal fluvial systems and, critically, not the actual shutting down of the fan system. The fact that the non-marine palynomorph signal remains high (or even higher) in the thin-bedded succession (that is up to several tens of metres thick), when compared to the base of the fan, and as it immediately overlies the sandy deposits (Fig. 14A), supports the inference that much of the heterolithic part of the sequence does not represent fan abandonment, but rather a response to a change in the sediment supply to the active fan. However, the uppermost metres of this sequence tend to show an abrupt thinning-and-fining up, that is interpreted as fan abandonment, with a return to background marl accumulation, sometime during, or with some unspecified time-lag after the termination of tectonic events that released or conditioned the release of the coarse clastic supply via transport and redeposition into deep water.

At outcrop in a quarry 1 km south of Ainsa, Cronin *et al.* (1998, p. 431) observed that the top of the Ainsa I sandbody is deeply eroded by a 'debris flow deposit' (type II MTC in our terminology) and that, therefore, this sandbody was '. . . not marked by a progressive shut-down of the channel as recorded by a progressive decrease in grain size, . . .'. However, both at outcrop (by correlation) and in the drill sites, the Ainsa I fan shows tens of metres of undisturbed and non-amalgamated, mainly medium- and thin-bedded, fine-grained sediments capped by a thinning-and-fining upward sequence (expressed in the gamma-ray logs, Fig. 14), although the Ainsa I fan in the quarry 1 km south of Ainsa is truncated by a type II MTC. On the basis of observations made in the Ainsa quarry, Cronin *et al.* (1998) questioned the evidence for fan abandonment, and also underestimated the presence of bedded inter-sandbody thin- and very thin-bedded sediments, here interpreted as active fine-grained fan, interfan and levee-overbank, e.g. the well exposed laminated marls between Boltaña and San Vicente (a village 2 km WNW of Labuerda) that are laterally equivalent to MTCs on the eastern limb of the Ainsa (Buil) syncline (Fig. 3).

Active compression from the NNE margin of the basin caused the periodic collapse of the slope as intraformational, intra-basinal type I MTCs, both between and within the sandbodies. MTCs, particularly type II and III MTCs, also occurred throughout fan growth, with type II MTCs containing extrabasinal material such as very well rounded pebbles, sand and wood fragments. Although some of these MTCs probably reflect random (catastrophic) oversteepening processes as the fans became incorporated into the dynamic basin slope, our research suggests that, in most cases, the stratigraphic position of the different types of MTC is diagnostic of a particular stage in the evolution of the sandbodies or fans and their enveloping sediments.

Seafloor growth structures in the Ainsa basin

The three Ainsa fans show a progressive WSW shift in the axis of sedimentation, towards the foreland and away from the active fold-and-thrust belt, specifically the actively growing submarine Mediano anticline (Figs 1–4). This suggests an important intra-basinal control on sand accumulation within the deep basin. Also, mapping shows that the sand supply was switched on and off to the deep basin (with shale or marl deposition predominating at times when there was virtually no sand supply) and, therefore, the observed distribution and architecture of the sandbodies cannot be explained by the lateral switching of sand deposition as compensation cycles (Mutti & Sonnino 1981).

We have mapped a north–south oriented kilometre-scale anticline that was a seafloor high at least several to a few tens of metres high during deep-water deposition, and that influenced the location of the Ainsa fans, here referred to as the Ainsa anticline (Figs 3 & 4). Coarse clastics of the Ainsa I fan accumulated east of this high, with onlap of two stacked channels against it and the northeastern basin-slope. The relatively narrow gap created by this feature was associated with erosion and sediment bypass, as turbidity currents accelerated through the constriction. The Ainsa II fan covered the high, due either to the rate of sedimentation outstripping the anticline growth and, or, its passive burial. The NE part of the Ainsa III fan onlaps the western flank of this anticline (Figs 3 & 4). By analogy with seismic interpretations of modern fold-and-thrust belts, we postulate that it developed above a blind thrust-tip that began to destroy the basin floor by cannibalization of earlier fans to incorporate them into the slope/basin-floor system. The Ainsa fans around Boltaña show little evidence for the deflection or reflection of sediment gravity flows against the Boltaña anticline, suggesting that it developed significant relief much later (cf. Mutti *et al.* 1985).

Tectonic pulses linked to WSW-directed thrust-tip propagation, uplift and erosion also explain the WSW channel migration. The Ainsa II fan occupied the topographically lowest part of the foreland basin, and shifted WSW as the basin uplifted in the ENE, associated with the rising thrust pile at the laterally-confining lower basin slope. Succeeding channel fills would naturally tend to develop outboard, towards the foreland, as linear or ribbon-like (tectonically-driven) compensation cycles. Both active fold-and-thrust belt tectonics, and depositional mounding as channelized sands along the base-of-slope, would have caused the lateral-offset stacking of channels. A thick type II MTC separates the Ainsa II and III fans (Fig. 3), probably directly linked to the event that forced the WSW migration of the latter fan.

Our study shows that intrabasinal topographic highs acted to confine the fans laterally. Whether these ridges were cross-basinal highs, or simply constrictions on the seafloor as at the northern margin of the Ainsa basin, they were associated with considerable coarse sediment bypass into the more distal Jaca basin. A few hundred metres below the Ainsa fans, at the level of the Banaston system, an erosional channel cut through this northern (growing) intrabasinal ridge, and older sandy lobe deposits, to be filled mainly by gravels/sands (see Fig. 3 for eastern margin of one of Banaston channels). This observation provides evidence that there was an intrabasinal ridge with the same orientation (approximately north–south) in existence at an earlier time in the basin history. Indeed, the Arro sandbody also shows substantial depositional thickness changes over this earlier anticline (Bayliss, pers. comm. 2004), and that, therefore, the Ainsa anticline and its northerly extension (the Añisclo anticline of Remacha *et al.* 2003 and Fernandez *et al.* 2004), was an important seafloor ridge throughout much of the deposition history of the Ainsa basin.

Discussion

Slope channels versus fans or fan-delta

Most researchers refer to the Ainsa systems as channels, a channelized slope system or slope complex (e.g. Cronin *et al.* 1998). We designate them as fans because they comprise more than erosional channels, with all fan elements recognized both proximally within the Ainsa basin, and distally from the Ainsa to Jaca basins. There are varying degrees of confinement (erosional, depositional and tectonic), and the system can be linked to inferred feeder canyons and distal sandy lobes, i.e. they represent part of longitudinally confined fans. We interpret the Ainsa system as basin-floor fans, because they are axial in the foreland basin/thrust-top basin. Although the Ainsa basin floor sloped NNW, it is misleading to refer to these systems as slope channels, since the basin clearly had substantially steeper basin slopes on both lateral margins and more proximally. A basin-floor interpretation is supported by:

1. the absence of substantial erosion at the base of the sandbodies (which are dominated by depositional processes of infilling complex seafloor topography created by MTCs);
2. their lateral confinement and offset stacking by syndepositional basin-margin structures;
3. the recognition that intraformational sediment slides and slumps were mainly sourced from the eastern basin margin and pinch-out between the Ainsa fans; and
4. the paucity of remobilization processes, particularly of the sands. However, the basin floor had a gradient towards the more distal parts of the depositional systems within the Jaca basin, towards the NW.

There is also no palaeocurrent evidence to suggest that the Ainsa basin was an intra-slope basin with a down-dip bounding rim where the present Boltaña anticline now separates the Ainsa and Jaca basins (e.g. flow reflections). In agreement with Cronin *et al.* (1998), we find no evidence for substantial erosion at the base of the Ainsa fans, something that would be expected from slope channels. Any deep erosion (metres to tens of metres) occurs within the fans. We also mapped the westward thinning and pinch-out of stacked sediment slides (type Ia MTCs) from the eastern margin of the Ainsa basin, an observation that supports our interpretation of a basin floor with toe-of-slope MTCs along the eastern outcrops within the basin (Fig. 3).

The bulk mean grain size of the depositional systems in the Ainsa basin, the abundance of MTCs, and the relatively straight channels, are all typical features of the toe-of-slope and basin-floor components of deep-water fan deltas, in particular the 'subaqueous segmented segments of a meandering-river delta' described by Prior & Bornhold (1988): even the water depths of *c.* 600 m. However, the length of the linked Ainsa-Jaca deep-marine clastic systems extending more than 150 km, with proximal submarine canyons (e.g. Charo canyon), leveed channels (e.g. Ainsa I fan; Pickering & Corregidor 2004), channel-lobe transitions, and depositional lobes that pass distally into basin floor fan fringe, favour a submarine fan or hybrid fan-delta/submarine-fan interpretation for these systems.

In many respects, the Ainsa basin deep-marine systems provide good analogues for slope-basin depositional systems, because the seafloor gradients appear to have been relatively high, even on the basin floor. Also, the Ainsa basin was the proximal part of a linear (foreland, then piggyback) basin system in which channelized sandbodies predominate, and in which there is an intimate association of MTCs, many of which contain pebble- and boulder-grade material, together with coarse-grained sandy turbidites. Such facies associations are generally associated with basin slopes *sensu stricto*, whereas in this case we interpret these deposits to have accumulated on the floor and base-of-slope of a relatively small deep-marine basin. Our arguments are neither inconsistent, nor semantic; a basin floor must be defined with respect to a particular basin (as in this case), and not on the basis of a particular seafloor gradient. Thus, despite being essentially a basin-floor setting, the Ainsa basin also provides a useful analogue for many aspects of the sedimentology and stratigraphy of slope basins. In particular, the deep-marine Ainsa basin sediments provide an ideal natural laboratory for the further testing of ideas about proximal, coarse clastic systems, whether for understanding redeposition processes (e.g. interpretations of the MTCs), or system-based (rates of fan growth and stacking patterns, tectonics versus eustasy, sequence stratigraphic interpretations).

Eustatic versus tectonic control on sediment supply

We favour a tectonic rather than a eustatic driver as the principal driver on sediment supply to the four major, unconformity-bounded depositional units with upward-decreasing internal tectonic deformation (Mutti *et al*; 1985; Fernandez *et al.* 2004) because of:

1. the syn-depositional growth of the Mediano anticline and its associated migration of facies belts (Holl & Anastasio 1993);
2. the syn-depositional growth of the Boltaña anticline (Mutti *et al.* 1985);
3. the stepwise physical migration of the Ainsa fans towards the foreland and the migration away from the deformation front of individual channels;
4. the lack of any clearly defined cyclicity in the frequency and thickness of the individual sandbodies and the intervening finer grained sediments;
5. the apparent absence of candidate highstand condensed intervals at outcrop, in the wells and on the wireline logs (e.g. high or 'hot' gamma shales etc.); and
6. the likely time scales involved (in the order of at least several hundred thousand years for each fan, and about 1.5–2 million years for each of the six groups of sandbodies or complexes, such as the three Ainsa fans). Superficially similar vertical sequences to our vertical sequences have been proposed for the West Africa deep-marine slope systems by Mayall & Stewart (2000). However, the latter sequences are substantially thicker than in the Ainsa basin (up to hundreds of metres), and the internal sedimentary nature of the MTCs is unresolved.

We cannot unequivocally rule out the role of eustasy in exacerbating or attenuating the sediment flux during fan evolution. The basin was active tectonically; it was contemporaneous with the main phase of Pyrenean orogenesis, a crustal process that was discontinuous and episodic at a time scale of 1.5–3 million years (Burbank *et al.* 1992, Meigs *et al.* 1996). By contrast, during icehouse periods such as the Neogene, a clear glacio-eustatic control, both at a Milankovitch precession and eccentricity beat, has been documented as the principal driver on the accumulation of deep-marine sandbodies in tectonically very active forearc regions (Pickering *et al.* 1999).

Figure 16 illustrates our interpretation of the evolution of individual sandbodies within a sequence stratigraphic framework of changing relative base level and sediment supply (particularly sediment calibre), in this case inferred to be tectonically driven. The vertical sedimentary sequence that we propose for deep-marine sandbodies provides a testable generic model for submarine fan evolution and deposition within other active modern and ancient plate margins. If fifth (0.01–0.1 million year) and higher frequency eustatic sea-level changes are eventually identified within the deep-marine sediments of the Ainsa basin, we suspect that this will be at the decimetre to metre scale (where we also recognize sediment packages).

There has also been a recent emphasis on recognizing direct sediment input to the shelf, slope, and deep basin from flood-stage rivers as bedload and/or hyperpycnal flow (Mutti *et al.* 1996). Such forcing by weather and climate is consistent with our concept of a first-order tectonic control on sandbody growth, because tectonic processes may have provided the fundamental driver via uplift-erosion processes in the linked growing Pyrenean mountain belt that determined the sediment flux to the major tributary rivers and fan-deltas supplying the deep basin. Tectonic uplift in the source area would have created steeper gradients from mountain to basin (equilibrium profile) and favoured a longer run-out length of flood-stage riverine sediment gravity

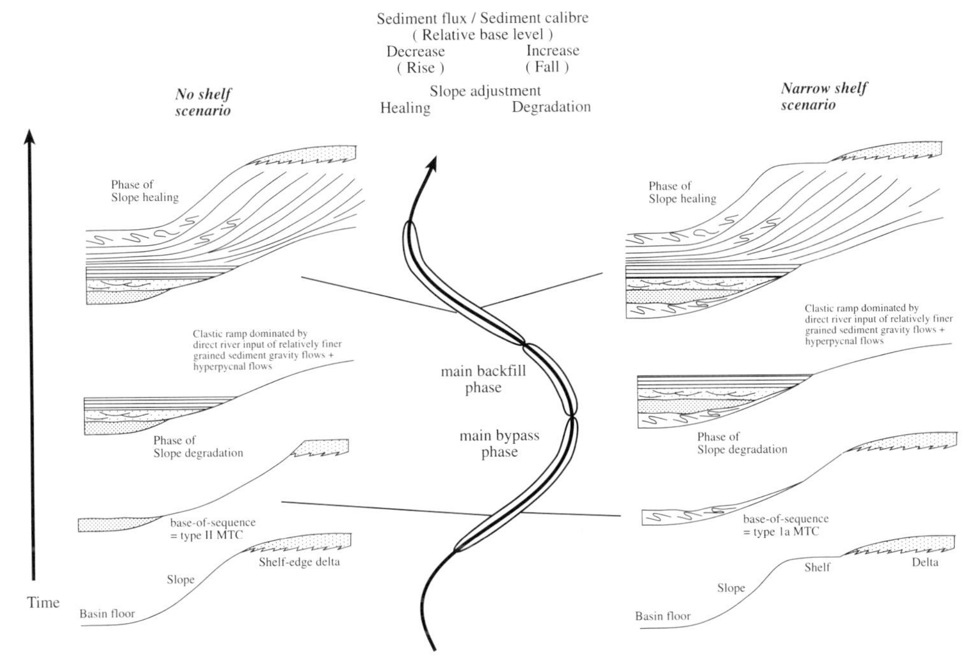

Fig. 16. Sequence stratigraphic interpretation of clastic sequences in the deep-marine Ainsa basin for a scenario with a shelf-edge delta (effectively no shelf), and with a shelf. The evolution of these sequences is shown within the context of changing sediment supply (flux) and sediment calibre (bulk grain size), and inferred changes in base level (tectonically or eustatically driven). Tectonic controls on sequence development and a narrow shelf, are favoured (see arguments in text). Type Ia MTCs occur throughout the basin but are most common both immediately below, and at tens of metres above the clastic sequences. Slope and delta-front failure events are shown as most likely during both the initial collapse of the upper slope (as base level falls), and during the time interval of most rapid slope healing associated with processes that increase the slope gradients (as base level rises).

flows, i.e. a basinal expression of tectonic events until regrading of the equilibrium profile favours the temporary storage of fluvial sediments on the shelf. Although there is increasing evidence to suggest a Middle Eocene (Lutetian) deterioration in global climate (Abreu & Baum 1997), any glacio-eustatic signal is likely to have been extremely small to insignificant, such that the tectonic (seismic) signal was more important, at least at the scale of the development of the sandy fans and their major channels.

We acknowledge the generous financial support from British Petroleum (then Amoco), Chevron, ConocoPhillips, Exxon-Mobil, Statoil and Total-Fina-Elf, all under the auspices of the Norwegian Petroleum Directorate (NPD FORCE project), who supported the Ainsa Project. This manuscript has gone through many revisions and has been improved considerably because of the thoughtful and constructive criticisms by Trevor Elliott, Stephen Flint, David Hodgson, Mike Underwood, Julian Clark, Peter Sixsmith and Gilbert Kelling. Their advice and comments are greatly appreciated.

References

ABREU, S. & BAUM, G. 1997. Glacio-eustasy: a global link for sequence boundaries during the Cenozoic. *In*: BEAUCHAMP, B. (ed.) CSPG-SEPM Joint Convention 1997. *Sedimentary Events and Hydrocarbon Systems*. Program with abstracts, Canadian Society of Petroleum Geologists, Calgary, Canada, pp. 17.

BEAUBOUEF, R.T. & FRIEDMANN, S.J. 2000. High resolution seismic/sequence stratigraphic framework for the evolution of Pleistocene intra slope basins, western Gulf of Mexico: depositional models and reservoir analogs. GCS-SEPM Foundation 20th Annual Bob F. Perkins Research Conference, 40–60.

BEAUBOUEF, R.T., FRIEDMANN, S.J. & ALWYN, B. 1998. High resolution seismic/sequence stratigraphy of intra-slope basins, Western Gulf of Mexico. American Association of Petroleum Geologists International Meeting, Rio de Janeiro, Abstracts with program.

BENTHAM, P.A., BURBANK, D.W. & PUIGDEFABREGAS, C. 1992. Temporal and spatial controls on the alluvial architecture of an axial drainage system: late Eocene Escanilla Formation, southern Pyrenean foreland basin, Spain. *Basin Research*, **4**, 335–352.

BERGGREN, W.A., KENT, D.V., SWISHER, C.C., III & AUBRY, M.-P. 1995. A revised Cenozoic geochronology and chronostratigraphy. *In*: BERGGREN, W.A., KENT, D.V.,

AUBREY, M.-P. & HARDENBOL, J. (eds) *Geochronology, Time Scales and Global Stratigraphic Correlation*. SEPM (Society for Sedimentary Geology) Special Publication, **54**, 129–212.

BURBANK, D.W., VERGES, J., MUNOZ, J.A. & BENTHAM, P. 1992. Coeval hindward- and forward-imbricating thrusting in the south-central Pyrenees, Spain: timing and rates of shortening and deposition. *Geological Society of America Bulletin*, **104**, 3–17.

CLARK, J.D. 1995. Detailed section across the Ainsa II Channel complex, south central Pyrenees, Spain. *In*: PICKERING, K.T., HISCOTT, R.N., KENYON, N.H., RICCI LUCCHI, F. & SMITH, R.D.A. (eds) *Atlas of Deep Water Environments: Architectural Style in Turbidite Systems*. Chapman & Hall, London, 139–144.

CLARK, J.D. & PICKERING, K.T. 1996. Architectural elements and growth patterns of submarine channels: application to hydrocarbon exploration. *American Association of Petroleum Geologists Bulletin*, **80**, 194–221.

COSTA, J.E. 1988. Rheologic, geomorphic, and sedimentologic differentiation of water floods, hyperconcentrated flows, and debris flows. *In*: BAKER, V.R., KOCHEL, R.C. & PATTON, P.C. (eds) *Flood Geomorphology*. John Wiley & Sons, Inc., Chichester, 113–122.

CRONIN, B.T., OWEN, D., HARTLEY, A.J. & KNELLER, B. 1998. Slumps, debris flows and sandy deep-water channel systems: implications for the application of sequence stratigraphy to deep water clastic sediments. *Journal of the Geological Society, London*, **155**, 429–432.

DREYER, T., CORREGIDOR, J., ARBUES, P. & PUIGDEFABREGAS, C. 1999. Architecture of the tectonically influenced Sobrarbe deltaic complex in the Ainsa Basin, northern Spain. *Sedimentary Geology*, **127**, 127–169.

FERNANDEZ, O., MUÑOZ, J.A., ARBUES, P., FALIVENE, O. & MARZO, M. 2004. Three-dimensional reconstruction of geological surfaces: an example of growth strata and turbidite systems from the Ainsa basin (Pyrenees, Spain). *American Association of Petroleum Geologists Bulletin*, **88**, 1049–1068.

FRIEDMANN, S.J. & BEAUBOUEF, R.T. & 1999. Relationships between depositional process, stratigraphy, and salt tectonics in a closed, intraslope basin: E. Breaks area, Gulf of Mexico. American Association of Petroleum Geologists, Annual Meeting, San Antonio, Abstracts with program.

FONTANA, D., ZUFFA, G.G. & GARZANTI, E. 1989. The interaction of eustacy and tectonism from provenance studies of the Eocene Hecho Group Turbidite Complex (South-Central Pyrenees). *Basin Research*, **2**, 223–237.

GEE, M.J.R., MASSON, D.G., WATTS, A.B. & MITCHELL, N.C. 2001. Passage of debris flows and turbidity currents through a topographic constriction: seafloor erosion and deflection of flow pathways. *Sedimentology*, **48**, 1389–1409.

GRADSTEIN, F.M., OGG, J.G., SMITH, A.G., *et al.* 2004. *A Geologic Time Scale 2004*. Cambridge University Press.

HACKBARTH, C.J. & SHEW, R.D. 1994. Morphology and stratigraphy of a Mid-Pleistocene turbidite leveed channel from seismic, core, and log data. *In*: BOUMA, A., WEIMER, P. & PERKINS, B. (eds) *Submarine fan and turbidite systems*, GCS-SEPM Foundation, Houston, 127–133.

HAUGHTON, P.D.W., BARKER, S.P. & MCCAFFREY, W.D. 2003. 'Linked' debrites in sand-rich turbidite systems — origin and significance. *Sedimentology*, **50**, 459–482.

HELLER, P.L. & PAOLA, C. 1992. The large-scale dynamics of grain-size variation in alluvial basins, 2: application to syntectonic conglomerate. *Basin Research*, **4**, 91–102.

HOLL, J.E. & ANASTASIO, D.J. 1993. Paleomagnetically derived folding rates, Southern Pyrenees, Spain. *Geology*, **13**, 271–274.

LABAUME, P., MUTTI, E., SEGURET, M. & ROSELL, J. 1983. Mégaturbidites carbonates du basin turbiditique de l'Eocene inférieur et moyen sud-pyrénéen. *Bulletin of the Geological Society, France*, **25**, 927–941.

LABAUME, P., SÉGURET, M. & SEYVE, C. 1985. Evolution of a turbiditic foreland basin and analogy with an accretionary prism: example of the Eocene South-Pyrenean basin. *Tectonics*, **4**, 661–685.

LABAUME, P., MUTTI, E. & SÉGURET, M. 1987. Megaturbidites: a depositional model from the Eocene of the SW-Pyrenean foreland basin, Spain. *Geo-Marine Letters*, **7**, 91–101.

LOWE, D.R. 1982. Sediment gravity flows. II. Depositional models with special reference to the deposits of high-density turbidity currents. *Journal of Sedimentary Petrology*, **52**, 279–297.

LOWE, D.R., GUY, M. & PALFREY, A. 2003. Facies of slurry-flow deposits, Britannia Formation (Lower Cretaceous), North Sea: implications for flow evolution and deposit geometry. *Sedimentology*, **50**, 45–80.

MAYALL, M. & STEWART, I. 2000. The architecture of turbidite slope channels. *In*: WEIMER, P., COLEMAN, J., ROSEN, N.C., NELSON, H., BOUMA, A.H., STYZEN, M.U. & LAWRENCE, D.T. (eds) *Deep-Water Reservoirs of the World*. Gulf Coast Society of Economic Paleontologists and Mineralogists Foundation 20th Annual Bob F. Perkins Research Conference, Houston, Texas, 578–586.

MEIGS, A.J., VERGÉS, J. & BURBANK, W. 1996. Ten-million-year history of a thrust sheet. *Geological Society of America Bulletin*, **12**, 1608–1625.

MEIGS, A.J. & BURBANK, D.W. 1997. Growth of the South Pyrenean orogenic wedge. *Tectonics*, **16**, 239–258.

MIKKELSEN, N., MASLIN, M., GIRAUDEAU, J. & SHOWERS, W. 1997. Biostratigraphy and sedimentation rates of the Amazon Fan. *In*: FLOOD, R.D., PIPER, D.J.W., KLAUS, A. & PETERSON, L.C. (eds) *Proceedings of the Ocean Drilling Program, Scientific Results*, **155**, 577–594.

MILLINGTON, J.J. & CLARK, J.D. 1995*a*. The Charo/Arro canyon-mouth sheet system, south-central Pyrenees, Spain: a structurally influenced zone of sediment dispersal. *Journal of Sedimentary Research*, **65**, 443–454.

MILLINGTON, J. & CLARK, J.D. 1995*b*. Submarine canyon and associated base-of-slope sheet system: the Eocene Charo-Arro system, south-central Pyrenees, Spain. *In*: PICKERING, K.T., HISCOTT, R.N., KENYON, N.H., RICCI LUCCHI, F. & SMITH, R.D.A. (eds), *Atlas* *of Deep Water Environments: Architectural style in turbidite systems*. Chapman & Hall, London 150–158.

MULDER, T. & ALEXANDER, J. 2001. The physical character of subaqueous sedimentary density flows and their deposits. *Sedimentology*, **48**, 269–299.

MUÑOZ, J.A. 1992. Evolution of a continental collision belt: ECORS-Pyrenean crustal balanced section. *In*: MCCLAY, K.R. (ed.) *Thrust Tectonics*. Chapman & Hall, New York, 235–246.

MUTTI, E. 1985. Turbidite systems and their relations to depositional sequences. *In*: ZUFFA G.G. (ed.) *Provenance of arenites*, 65–93. NATO Advanced Scientific Institute. D. Reidel, Dordrecht, Holland.

MUTTI, E. & SONNINO, M. 1981. Compensation cycles: a diagnostic feature of turbidite sandstone lobes. *In*: Abstracts Volume, 12S 123. *2nd European Regional Meeting, Bologna, Italy. International Association of Sedimentologists*.

MUTTI, E., REMACHA, E., SGAVETTI, M., ROSELL, J., VALLONI, R. & ZAMORANO, M. 1985. Stratigraphy and facies characteristics of the Eocene Hecho Group turbidite systems, south-central Pyrenees. *In*: MILA, M.D. & ROSELL, J. (eds) *Excursion Guidebook of the 6th European Regional Meeting of International Association of Sedimentologists*, Llerida, 521–576.

MUTTI, E., DAVOLI, G., TINTERRI, R. & ZAVALA, C. 1996. The importance of ancient fluvio-deltaic systems dominated by catastrophic flooding in tectonically active basins. *Memorie di Scienze Geologiche*, **48**, 233–291.

OMS, O., DINARÈS-TURELL, J. & REMACHA, E. 2003. Magnetic stratigraphy from deep clastic turbidites: an example from the Eocene Hecho Group (Southern Pyrenees). *Studia Geophysica et Geodaetica*, **47**, 275–288.

PAOLA, C., HELLER, P.L. & ANGEVINE, C.L. 1992. The large-scale dynamics of grain-size variation in alluvial basins, 1. Theory. *Basin Research*, **4**, 73–90.

PARSONS, J.D., WHIPPLE, K.X. & SIMONI, A. 2001. Experimental study of the grain-flow, fluid-mud transition in debris flows. *Journal of Geology*, **109**, 427–447.

PICKERING, K.T. 1983. Small-scale syn-sedimentary faults in the Upper Jurassic 'Boulder Beds'. *Scottish Journal of Geology*, **19**, 169–181.

PICKERING, K.T. 1987. Wet-sediment deformation in the Upper Ordovician Point Leamington Formation: an active thrust-imbricate system during sedimentation, Notre Dame Bay, north-central Newfoundland. *In*: JONES, M.E. & PRESTON, R.M.F. (eds) *Deformation of Sediments and Sedimentary Rocks*. The Geological Society, London, Special Publications, **29** Blackwell Scientific Publications, Oxford, 213–239.

PICKERING, K.T. & CORREGIDOR, J. 2000. 3D Reservoir scale study of Eocene confined submarine fans, South Central Spanish Pyrenees. *In*: WEIMER, P., *et al*. (eds) *Deep Water Reservoirs of the World*. Gulf Coast Section, Society of Economic Palaeontologists and Mineralogists, Foundation 20th Annual Bob F. Perkins Research Conference, Houston, Texas, 776–781.

PICKERING, K.T. & CORREGIDOR, J. 2004. Tectonic control, rates of lateral migration and growth patterns of confined basin-floor submarine fans (seismosequences), and importance of mass transport complexes (MTCs), mid-Eocene, south-central Pyrenees. Core Display H5 (with posters). Petroleum Geology of NW Europe: Proceedings of the 6th Conference, London. CD-Rom. The Geological Society, London.

PICKERING, K.T., SOUTER, C., OBA, T., TAIRA, A., SCHAAF, M. & PLATZMAN, E. 1999. Glacio-eustatic control on deep-marine clastic forearc sedimentation, Pliocene – mid-Pleistocene (*c*. 1180–600 ka) Kazusa Group, SE Japan. *Journal of the Geological Society, London*, **156**, 125–136.

PIERSON, T.C. & COSTA, J.E. 1987. A rheologic classification of subaerial sediment-water flows. *In*: COSTA, J.E. & WIECZOREK, G.F. (eds) *Debris Flows/Avalanches: Processes, Recognition, and Mitigation*. Geological Society of America Reviews Engineering Geology, **7**, 1–12.

PIRMEZ, C., HISCOTT, R.N. & KRONEN, J.D. JR. 1997. Sandy turbidite successions at the base of channel-levee systems of the Amazon Fan revealed by FMS logs and cores: unravelling the facies architecture of large submarine fans. *In*: FLOOD, R.D., PIPER, D.J.W., KLAUS, A. & PETERSON, L.C. (eds) Proceedings of the Ocean Drilling Program, Scientific Results, **155**, 7–33.

POSTMA, G., NEMEC, W. & KLEINSPEHN, K. 1988. Large floating clasts in turbidites: a mechanism for their emplacement. *Sedimentary Geology*, **58**, 47–61.

PRIOR, D.B. & BORNHOLD, B.D. 1988. Submarine morphology and processes of fjord fan deltas and related high-gradient systems: modern examples from British Columbia. *In*: NEMEC, W. & STEEL, R.J. (eds) *Fan Deltas: Sedimentology and Tectonic Settings*. Blackie & Sons Ltd, London, 125–143.

REMACHA, E., OMS, O., GUAL, G., ET AL. 2003. *Sand-rich turbidite systems of the Hecho Group from slope to basin plain. Facies, stacking patterns, controlling factors and diagnostic features*. Geological Field Trip 12, South-Central Pyrenees. AAPG International Conference and Exhibition, Barcelona, Spain, September 21–24.

SMITH, G.A. 1986. Coarse-grained nonmarine volcaniclastic sediment: terminology and depositional process. *Geological Society of America Bulletin*, **97**, 1–10.

SOHN, Y.K. 1999. Rapid development of gravelly high-density turbidity currents in marine Gilbert-type fan deltas, Loreto Basin, Baja California Sur, Mexico-Discussion. *Sedimentology*, **46**, 757–761.

SOHN, Y.K., CHOE, M.Y. & JO, H.R. 2002. Transition from debris flow to hyperconcentrated flow in a submarine channel (the Cretaceous Cerro Toro Formation, southern Chile). *Terra Nova*, **14**, 405–415.

TALLING, P.J., AMY, L.A., WYNN, R.B., PEAKALL, J. & ROBINSON, M. 2004. Beds comprising debrite sandwiched within co-genetic turbidite: origin and widespread occurrence in distal depositional environments. *Sedimentology*, **51**, 163–194.

TJALSMA, R.C. & LOHMANN, G.P. 1983. Palaeocene – Eocene bathyal and abyssal benthic foraminifera from the Atlantic Ocean. *Micropaleontology*, Special Publication, **4**, 1–90.

TRAVÉ, A., LABAUME, P., CALVET, F., ET AL. 1998. Fluid migration during Eocene thrust emplacement in the south Pyrenean foreland basin (Spain): an integrated structural, mineralogical and geochemical approach.

In: MASCLE, A., PUIGDEFABREGAS, C., LUTERBACHER, H.P., FERNANDEZ, M. (eds) *Cenozoic Foreland Basins of Western Europe*. Geological Society, London, Special Publication, **134**, 163–188.

VERGES, J., MARZO, M., SANTAEULARIA, T., SERRA-KIEL, J., BURBANK, D.W., MUNOZ, J.A. & GIMENEZ-MONTSANT, J. 1998. Quantified vertical motions and tectonic evolution of the SE Pyrenean foreland basin. *In*: MASCLE, A., PUIGDEFABREGAS, C., LUTERBACHER, H.P. & FERNANDEZ, M. (eds) *Cenozoic Foreland Basins of Western Europe*. Geological Society, London, Special Publication, **134**, 107–134.

WALKER, R.G. 1975. Generalized facies models for resedimented conglomerates of turbidite association. *Geological Society of America Bulletin*, **86**, 737–748.

High-resolution borehole image analysis in a slope fan setting: examples from the late Miocene Mt Messenger Formation, New Zealand

M. JOHANSSON

Schlumberger, 25 Misr Helwan Road, Zeiny Tower, Maadi, Cairo, Egypt, P.O.Box 790/11728 Maadi (e-mail: mjohansson@slb.com)

Abstract: High-resolution resistivity image surveys and core were acquired from two wells 150 m apart within the late Miocene Mt Messenger Formation. The wells were located at Pukearuhe Beach, Taranaki, New Zealand and were situated along strike of the palaeoslope. The formation is interpreted as a slope fan setting and the interval logged was dominated by a major channel that incised into older channel-levee and overbank fan facies. The scour surface and the distinctive channel-fill enabled the two wells, Pukearuhe Central and Pukearuhe North, to be correlated with the local outcrop. The sedimentary deposits within the studied section were divided into three facies associations: channel-fill, channel levee and overbank deposits. The channel deposits exhibited similar facies in both wells. The dip data from the image logs indicate that the original channel was in-filled by sedimentation dipping towards the NW, the same orientation as the regional palaeoslope. In contrast, analysis of the levee and overbank deposits indicated little correlatability between the two wells, with beds dipping, locally up to 10°, in directions ranging from up-slope (SE) to oblique (NE) to the palaeoslope. The variation in dip directions in the levee and overbank deposits is attributed to scouring and infilling of irregular topography at and beyond the channel margin. As a reservoir prospect the thicker channel sands would be a preferential play to the laterally discontinuous thin beds.

The Taranaki Basin is the most explored and currently the only commercial hydrocarbon province of New Zealand. One of the major reservoir sandstones in this basin is found in Miocene deep-water sediments deposited in slope and basin floor fan settings. Oil was discovered in the late Miocene Mt Messenger Formation in the Kaimiro Field in 1991, and continued exploration led to further discoveries in several other fields in the same basin e.g. Ngatoro and Windsor Fields. Thin-bedded sandstones are the main reservoir facies of the Mt Messenger Formation, and a better understanding of their depositional environment is critical to continued exploration success. The late Miocene Mt Messenger Formation crops out 40–60 km NE of Taranaki Peninsula, New Zealand (Fig. 1). Numerous field studies have been carried out in this area (King *et al.* 1993, 1994; King & Thrasher 1996; Browne & Slatt 2002). This study integrates and interprets additional subsurface data using two high-resolution resistivity images acquired from two research wells, 150 m apart, drilled 100 m behind coastal outcrops.

Geological setting

Episodes of rifting and convergence occurred through the Cretaceous–Tertiary time span in the Taranaki Basin (King & Thrasher 1996). During the early Miocene, basement rocks of the Murihiku Supergroup were thrust from the east along the Taranaki Fault, forming the Patea-Tongaporutu High to the east of the basin. This high is considered to have been a local clastic source, and was progressively onlapped and overtopped by Miocene shallow marine sediments (Mokau Formation), deep-water volcaniclastic sediments (Mohakatino Formation), and deep-water clastic sediments (Mt Messenger Formation and Urenui Formation) (Fig. 2).

Depositional setting

The late Miocene Mt Messenger Formation in the Taranaki Basin consists of well-sorted, very fine- to fine-grained, thin-bedded sandstones and siltstones deposited in deep-water basin floor fan and slope fan settings (Browne & Slatt 2002). The overall sedimentary succession is progradational, with slope and continental shelf successions prograding NW during the late Miocene. The sandstones of the upper slope fan portion of the formation are predominantly planar-laminated, occasionally ripple-laminated and rarely massive. The siltstone facies of the slope fan interval are predominantly massive, occasionally laminated and locally contorted. These sediments form vertically stacked cycles ranging from centimetre to metre scale and have been interpreted as channel-fill successions interbedded with channel levee/overbank deposits (Browne & Slatt 2002). Channels observed in outcrop are typically 5 m deep, locally up to 20 m in depth, and up to 135 m in width,

From: HODGSON, D.M. & FLINT, S.S. (eds) 2005. *Submarine Slope Systems: Processes and Products*. Geological Society, London, Special Publications, **244**, 75–88. 0305–8719/$15.00

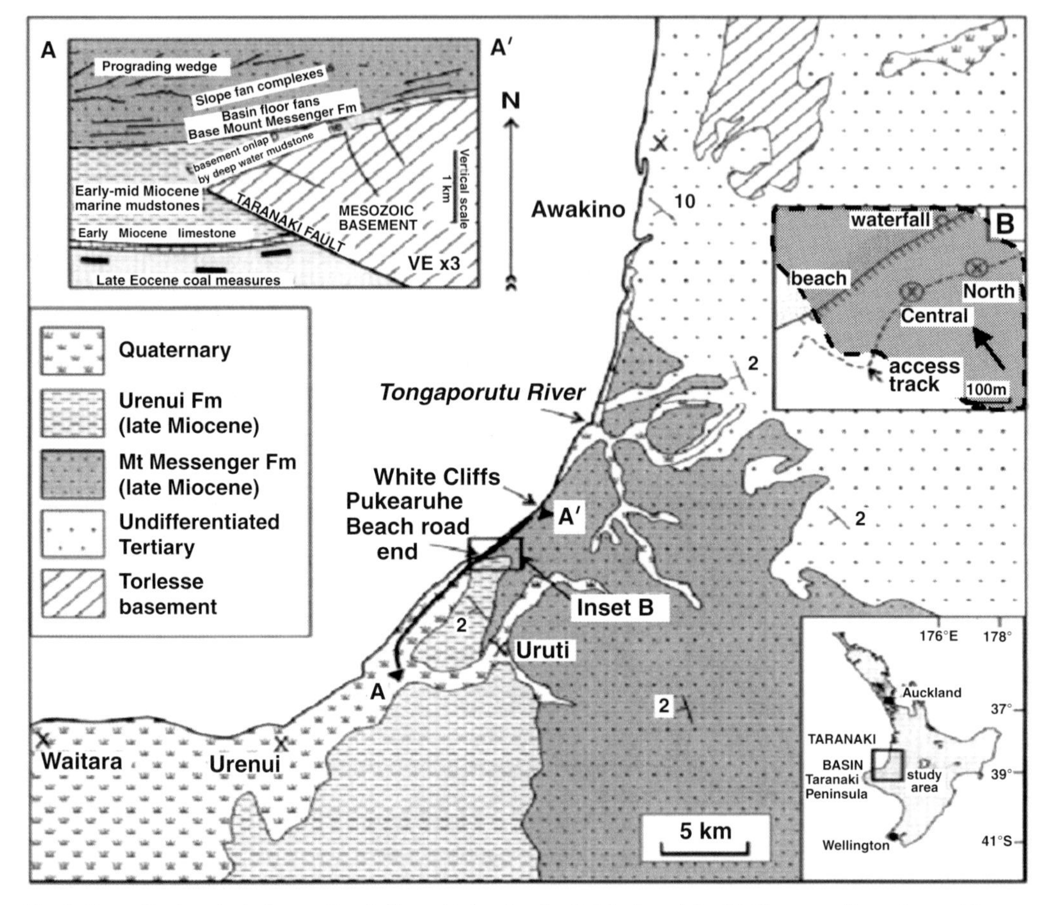

Fig. 1. Generalized geological map of north Taranaki showing the distribution of the Mt Messenger Formation and the location of the coastal outcrop section at Pukearuhe Beach. Inset map AA′ is a structural cross-section from NE to the SW through the coastal section showing the onlap of middle and late Miocene sedimentary rocks onto greywacke basement rocks to the east. This cross section is based on seismic reflection line PR83-14, which is indicated by the solid line AA′ on the map. Inset map B shows the location of the two boreholes (Central and North) at Pukearuhe Beach, and the orientation of the incised channel (red). Location of Figure 12b is on the beach (Modified from Browne & Slatt 2002).

resulting in an aspect ratio (width:depth) that averages 23:1 (Browne & Slatt 2002). Petrographically, the sandstones are dominated by litharenites and feldspathic litharenites. Metamorphic grains dominate the rock fragments.

Borehole image analysis

Two boreholes, Pukearuhe Central and Pukearuhe North, were drilled 100 m behind the coastal outcrop section at Pukearuhe Beach, 40 km NE of the Taranaki Peninsula (Fig. 1). In addition to the standard open hole logs (e.g. gamma ray, neutron and density), a high-resolution microresistivity image and some conventional core were acquired. The core is only used in this study to calibrate to the electrofacies derived from the images, as a full core description can be found in Browne & Slatt (2002). This microelectrical borehole imaging tool generates an electrical image of the borehole from 192 microresistivity measurements. Special circuitry ensures that the currents emitted by the electrodes are proportional to the formation resistivities immediately in front of them, to produce interpretable high-resolution borehole image (Hansen & Fett 1998). The maximum depth of investigation is about 75 cm, similar to that of a shallow lateral resistivity device. The spacing of the bottom electrodes on four pads and four flaps and the high-frequency data transmitted by the digital telemetry system result in a vertical and azimuthal image resolution of 1 cm (for further discussion see Luthi 2000). Borehole coverage is 80% in an 8 inch diameter borehole. Pad 1 of the tool

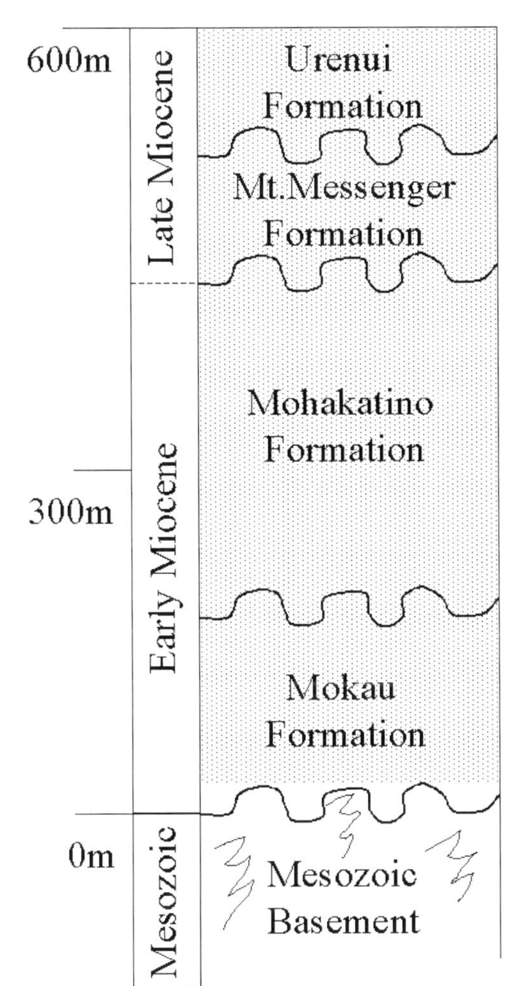

Fig. 2. Stratigraphy of the Taranaki Basin, adapted from King *et al.* (1993). The Miocene sequence overlies deformed Mesozoic basement with each formation separated by an unconformity.

is delineated by a green curve. The image is displayed as an oriented unwrapped borehole with the left and right margin representing north (0° and 360° respectively). During processing, two images are produced, called the static and the dynamic images. The static image takes the highest and lowest resistivity over the total depth of acquisition and divides them into a 42-colour histogram, with the dark browns being more conductive and the more yellow to white colours being more resistive. In this outcrop study, where the pore fluids are cemented or air-filled (i.e. no oil or gas), the lighter, more resistive colours represent sandstones and the darker, more conductive colours represent mudstones. The dynamic image uses the same 42-colour histogram over a 0.6 m sliding window. This enhances local contrasts and therefore the stratigraphic and sedimentological features not previously exposed in the static image. The dynamic image is used in most of the figures displayed in this paper.

Vertical variations

Pukearuhe Central and Pukearuhe North wells, situated 150 m apart, provide a SW–NE cross-section, parallel to the strike of the palaeoslope which dips towards the NW. Three lithologies were identified from image logs together with a combination of gamma-ray, neutron and density logs and these were sandstone, siltstone and mudstone. As a consequence of the feldspar rich sediments (i.e. feldspathic litharenite), the gamma-ray readings were not representative of the coarser clastic material and, therefore, the high-resolution images were critical in distinguishing between sandstones and siltstones. The siltstones were differentiated from sandstones using the high resolution stacked resistivity curve derived from the image. This curve was used as a clay content indicator, based on the assumption that clay is more conductive and is more likely to be proportionally larger in siltstones rather than sandstones. This inference was confirmed with calibration and observation of the core. Therefore sandstones tend to be more resistive on the image as a result. It is acknowledged that this method does not strictly adhere to traditional grain size measurements.

The depth of interest for the vertical comparison of the Mt Messenger Formation is between 20.27 m and 64.00 m in Pukearuhe Central well and 27.00 and 64.00 m in Pukearuhe North well, measured from the surface (the boreholes are vertical). In Pukearuhe Central, the microimaging log extends to a greater depth of 115 m, where a sandy fan lobe facies was encountered. This section is included in the facies analysis. A distinctive channel marked by an erosional base can be correlated between the two wells near the top of the section and the outcrop exposure.

Pukearuhe Central well

A 43.73 m thick section (20.27–64.00 m MD) was analysed in Pukearuhe Central well, 150 m SW of Pukearuhe North well (Fig. 1). In general, Pukearuhe Central is characterized by packages of sandstone around 2–4 m thick separated by 4–5 m thick mudstone units intercalated with thin siltstones. Lithology in the section was 26% sandstone, 52% siltstone and 22% mudstone as defined by log image studies. The mean bed thickness was 30 cm for sandstone, 30 cm for siltstone and 15 cm for mudstones.

Bed thickness remains fairly constant throughout the section, although subtle differences can be discerned with slightly thicker sandstone beds towards the base, and thicker siltstone beds towards the top. Markov analysis was applied to the section. This analysis is a statistical testing method that determines whether successive mutually exclusive facies are independent or show a tendency to be organized vertically (Tucker 1986). Markov cycles in Pukearuhe Central well indicate a probability of 69.7% that sandstone will be overlain by siltstone and a 30.3% chance that sandstone will be overlain by mudstone. Siltstone had a 56.1% probability of being overlain by mudstone and a 30.3% chance by sandstone. The mean thickness of an elementary cycle was calculated at 1.9 m, and these stack to form the larger clastic units. It is interpreted that These depositional cycles are interpreted as representing fining-upward successions.

Pukearuhe North well

In Pukearuhe North, a 37.00 m section (27.00–64.00 m MD) was examined. Overall, the section exhibits a lower thinly interbedded sandstone and siltstone unit (56.00–64.00 m), a thick mudstone section (51.00–56.00 m), and an upper interbedded sandstone and siltstone unit (27.00–51.00 m). The section comprises 26% sandstone, 48% siltstone and 26% mudstone defined from images. The mean bed thickness for sandstone and siltstone beds is 15 cm for each, and 30 cm for mudstone. Overall, the sandstone bed thickness remains fairly constant throughout the lower section. Towards the top (27.00–40.00 m), small (around 2 m thick) thinning-up cycles are evident. Siltstone beds appear to have a fairly constant bed thickness, interspersed with apparently random thick siltstone beds. Markov analysis indicates a 92.9% probability that sandstone will be overlain by a siltstone, and a 7.1% chance that it will be overlain by mudstone, and a 74.4% probability that a siltstone will be overlain by sandstone, rather than a mudstone. The mean thickness of an elementary cycle mean was calculated as 2.4 m thick comprising sandstones overlain by siltstone. The mudstones in Pukearuhe North, although proportionally similar to Pukearuhe Central, form a thick massive unit towards the base of the section, in contrast to Pukearuhe North where the mudstones cap the individual turbidite units. This variation is thought to account for the different Markov cycles.

Fig. 3. Massive sandstones in core (71.9–73.9 m), Pukearuhe Central. Scale = 2 cm per colour unit (courtesy of Greg Browne).

Facies analysis

Sandstone and siltstone comprised 70% of the two well sections. Distinctive sedimentary features characteristic of tractional flows were observed in the sandstones identified from high-resolution microresistivity images and core. The sandstone beds were very well sorted, exhibiting grain sizes ranging from very-fine- to fine-grained sandstones. A number of

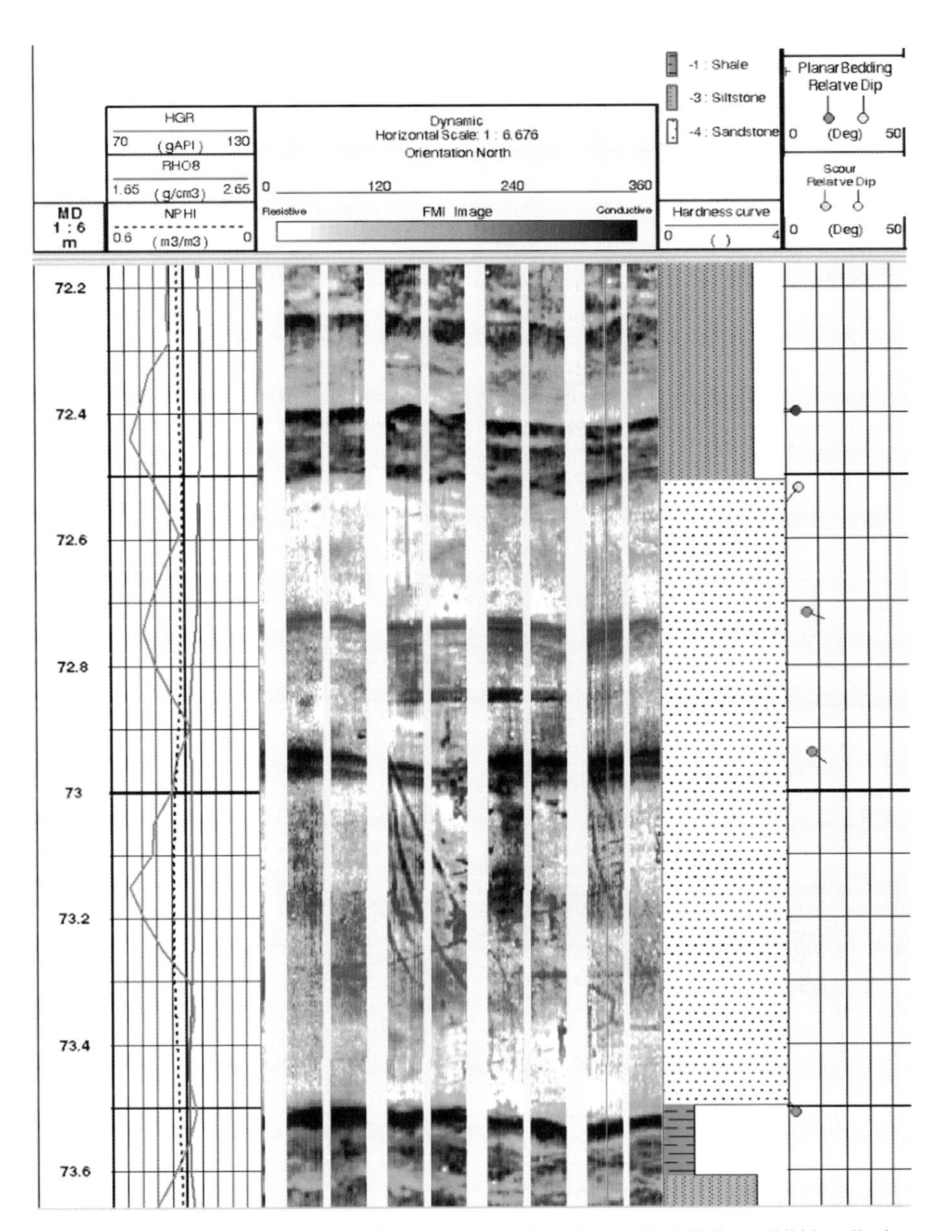

Fig. 4. Massive sandstones as seen in a dynamically processed resistivity image (72.5–73.5 m) exhibiting silty interval at 72.95 m, Pukearuhe Central. Note planar bedding is dipping to the SW, although the erosive scour at 73.5 m dips to the NW. A number of dips were picked interactively from the workstation as scour dips (yellow), ripple/cross-bedding (dark blue), planar bedding (green), highly bioturbated (light blue) and faults (pink).

dips were picked interactively from the workstation as scour dips (yellow), ripple/cross-bedding (dark blue), planar bedding (green), highly bioturbated (light blue) and faults (pink). A low-angle structural dip oriented to the west (268°/dip 07°) was determined from the planar bedding in the mudstones below the channel, and the image log dataset was corrected in order to obtain the depositional sedimentary dips. Palaeocurrent orientation was derived from the scour and cross-bedding surfaces.

Massive sandstones and siltstones. Massive sandstones and siltstones were common in the lower section of Pukearuhe Central (56.0–112.0 m) (Fig. 3). A good example of this facies can be observed between 72.5 and 73.5 m (Fig. 4). The unit is 1.0 m

Fig. 5. Planar laminated sandstones in core (59.8–61.8 m), Pukearuhe Central. Scale = 2 cm per colour unit (courtesy of Greg Browne).

thick, with a sharp, planar basal surface and a partially scoured, or low-angle (5°), upper surface. A thin, more conductive (i.e. muddier) interval divides the unit at 72.95 m and represents a thin, fining-up horizon. Some incipient laminations are observed on the images in the sandstones dipping around 8° to the SE.

This facies represents rapid deposition from high-energy turbulent flows and into traction carpet deposits at the base of a turbidity current. Gradual aggradation of the sediment is inferred from the incipient planar lamination evident within the predominantly massive sandstones. The SE dipping laminations are opposed to the palaeoslope, suggesting onlapping and/or back-stepping bedforms (e.g. Pickering *et al.* 2001) rather than cross-bedding (local palaeoslope dips towards the NW).

Planar laminated sandstones/siltstones. Planar laminated sandstones and siltstones are also observed in the lower section of Pukearuhe Central (56.0–112.0 m) (Fig. 5). A good example of this facies is between 89.40 and 90.25 m (Fig. 6). The laminations are often delineated by a more conductive characteristic on the image, suggesting either fining-up or heavy mineral concentrations along the planar surfaces. The dips, after structural dip removal, are subhorizontal dipping generally towards the north; this orientation is probably influenced by the palaeoslope direction (NW), suggesting low-angle cross-bedding.

This facies is interpreted to have been deposited through tractional flows at the base of high-velocity turbidity currents. The thick stacking of an individual facies suggests substantial durations of the flow regime.

Rippled sandstones/siltstones. Rippled sandstones are also common in the lower section of Pukearuhe Central (56.0–112.0 m). A good example can be observed between 90.5 and 91.7 m (Figs 7 & 8). The ripples are often capped by a thin mudstone facies, which thus form stacked fining-up beds. The bedding planes measured within the mudstones, dip 4–5° and indicate no preferred orientation, probably due to the effect of the irregular ripple surfaces on the mudstone deposition. The laminations within the ripples are below the resolution of the image tool.

This facies is interpreted as a tractional flow deposit. The ripples terminate abruptly and are overlain by mudstones, suggesting that the ripples were starved as the flow waned.

Inclined-bedded sandstones/siltstones. This facies comprises stacked fining-up sandstones and siltstones exhibiting inclined (10–20°) bedding planes. A good example of this facies is between 37.2 and 38.2 m at Pukearuhe Central and between 40.0 and 41.2 m in Pukearuhe North (Fig. 9a, b). This facies is particularly common towards the top of the wells, where it is observed in-filling a major channel scour. The dips are consistently towards the NW, exhibiting a decreasing dip magnitude upward in the section. These bed surfaces are oriented parallel to the palaeocurrent direction.

It is interpreted that the inclined beds were deposited as barforms which, based on their dip direction, were migrating down the channel axis. These barforms are increasingly observed as intra-channel facies, forming large-scale tractional structures within channels, often indicating significant sediment bypass.

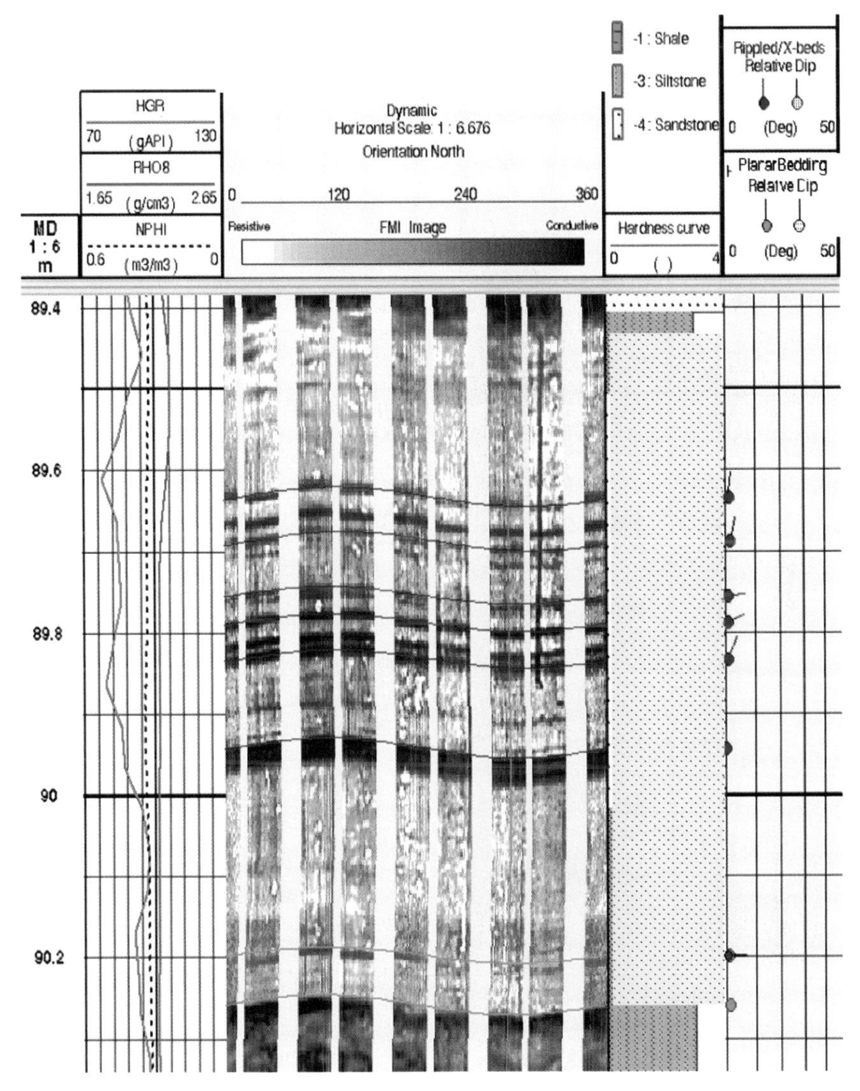

Fig. 6. Planar laminated sandstone as seen in a dynamically processed resisitivity image, laminations are highlighted by a more conductive image response possibly due to increased heavy mineral deposits or clays (89.4–90.24 m), Central Pukearuhe. Note dips are sub parallel and dipping towards the north and NE.

Convoluted laminated sandstones/siltstones. Convoluted laminated sandstone was only observed in the lower section of Pukearuhe Central. A good example is between 93.68 and 94.55 m (Fig. 10). The contorted laminations are bulbous in character and occur within a fairly thick sandstone unit (approximately 1 m). The greatest disruption was towards the top of the bed.

Convoluted sandstones are formed from the liquefaction of unconsolidated sediments caused by post-depositional disturbance. This suggests excessive pore fluids were trapped in the sediment characteristic of rapidly depositing turbidites and post-depositional loading.

Facies associations

The Pukearuhe Beach portion of the Mt Messenger Formation has been interpreted as a submarine slope fan sedimentary environment (Browne & Slatt 2002). The upper slope is typically a zone dominated by sediment bypass processes (abundant 'high-energy' features, including resedimented facies,

Fig. 7. Rippled sandstones in core (40.0–42.0 m), Pukearuhe North. Scale = 2 cm per colour unit (courtesy of Greg Browne).

slide scars, mudstone clast conglomerates at the base of erosional gullies and channels), with local sediment ponding, shelf-edge progradation and channel filling. The lower slope–apron is characterized by 'lower energy' features, with greater frequency of fine-grained turbidites, isolated submarine channel fills, debris flows, slide and slump scars, and local interfingering with contourite drifts and/or submarine fan deposits (Stow 1986; Pickering *et al.* 1989). A definitive facies model has been difficult to determine due to the apparent randomness of sedimentation. However, the Markov cycle results in Pukearuhe do suggest some order to the vertical stacking patterns, but this order is not continuous laterally. In Pukearuhe wells, three slope facies associations have been identified from the microimaging log. These facies associations comprise channel-levee, gully and overbank deposits, and channel-fill.

Slope system channel-levee facies associations

The vertical section between 58.0 and 112.0 m (total depth) in Pukearuhe Central is interpreted as a high energy channel facies association. The facies comprises predominantly stacked, thick-bedded (1 m thick), massive and planar laminated sandstones (Figs 3–6). Some of the beds exhibit post-depositional disturbance (Fig. 10). The beds dip at a fairly low angle and display a variety of dip azimuth directions. Towards the NE, between 58.0 and 70.0 m at Pukearuhe North, the proximal facies are completely absent, and mudstone with thin intercalations of siltstone predominates. This dip direction suggests a levee complex towards the NW. The dip data in this lower section exhibits a variety of directions, but the dominant trend is to the north and NW, which is consistent with the orientation of the palaeoslope.

Slope system gully and overbank facies associations

The vertical section between 50.0 and 58.0 m at Pukearuhe Central and 47.0 and 58.0 m at Pukearuhe North is interpreted as slope gullies and overbank facies associations (Fig. 11). Both wells exhibit a crude coarsening-upward signature. Pukearuhe Central coarsens from intercalated mudstone units with thin siltstones to a 3 m thick sandy unit capping the succession, whereas Pukearuhe North coarsens from a thick mudstone unit, to a siltstone and is capped by a 0.2 m sandstone. Most of the sediments are highly bioturbated, which is confirmed from core sections. The sandstones and siltstones dip around 10° towards the NNE, suggesting onlap onto some localized scours possibly gullies. Towards the NE, Pukearuhe North is devoid of any coarse clastic material in the lower section; instead, a thick unit of moderately bioturbated, laminated mudstone was deposited, and is interpreted as overbank deposits. Dip data is irregular and fairly high angle (10–18°), suggesting some sort of deformation in the muds, possibly caused by a muddy debris flow. The contrasting facies between the wells may be related to localized gullying at Pukearuhe Central incising into the slope. These gullies are laterally discontinuous.

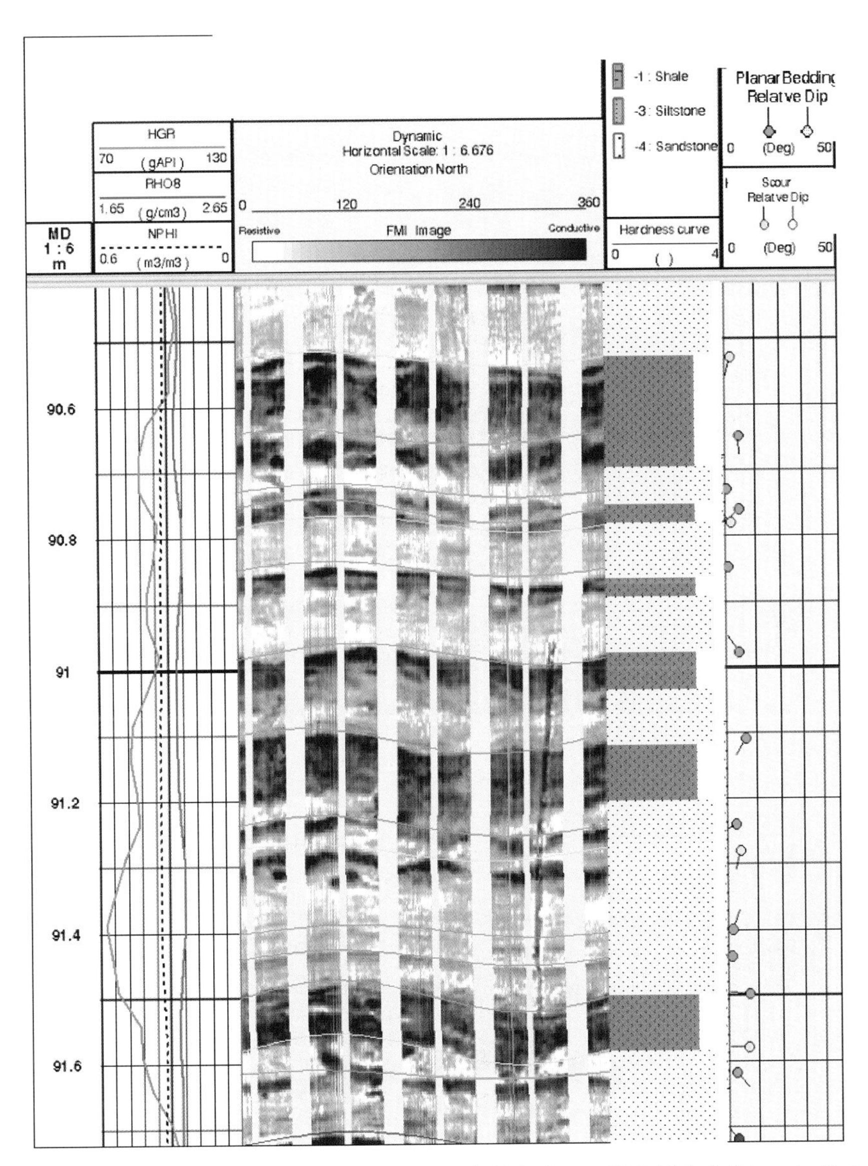

Fig. 8. Rippled sandstone as seen in a dynamically processed resistitivity image (90.5–91.4 m), Pukearuhe Central. Note stacked beds of starved ripples (resistive sediments) overlain by siltstone (more conductive sediments). The dips are bed boundaries and exhibit a variety of dip orientations.

Slope system channel levee facies associations

The vertical section between 42.0 and 50.0 m at Pukearuhe Central and 42.0 and 47.0 m at Pukearuhe North is interpreted as a slope channel-levee facies association (Fig. 11). A thick unit of mudstone, intercalated with thin siltstones, characterizes the facies at Pukearuhe Central. The sediments are bioturbated, and this has disturbed much of the primary depositional fabric. Some bedding planes are preserved, and these dip towards the SE, possibly infilling some localized topographic feature. At Pukearuhe North, the facies comprise a thick unit (7.5 m) of interbedded siltstones with minor intercalations of sandstones. The dip data at the base of the section exhibit a pattern of decreasing dip magnitude up section from 14–5°, oriented towards the SE. This also suggests onlap sedimentation on to a pre-existing scoured surface.

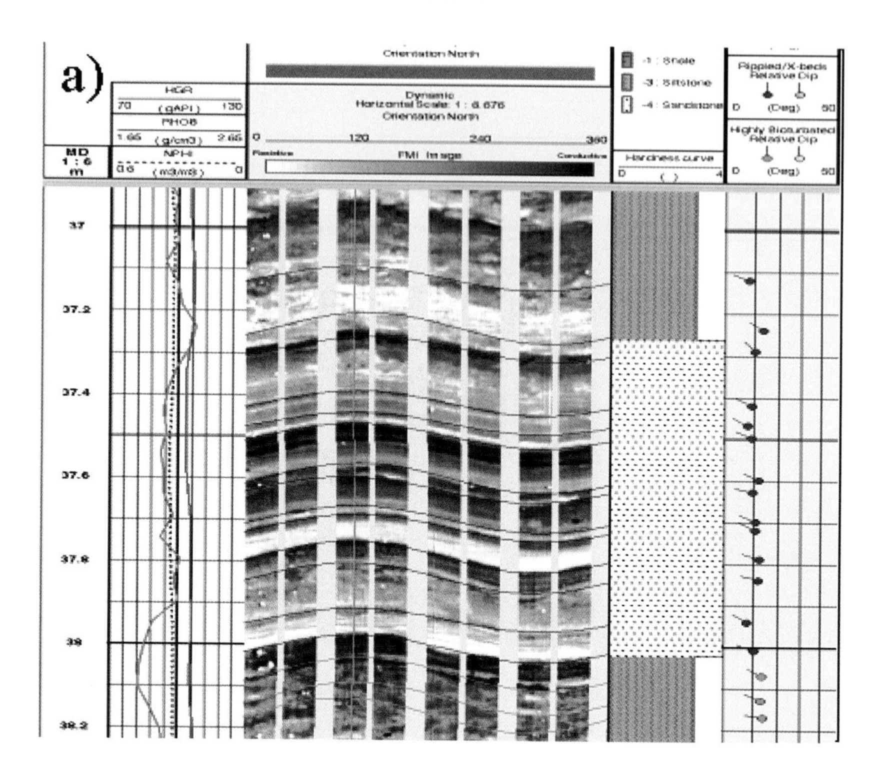

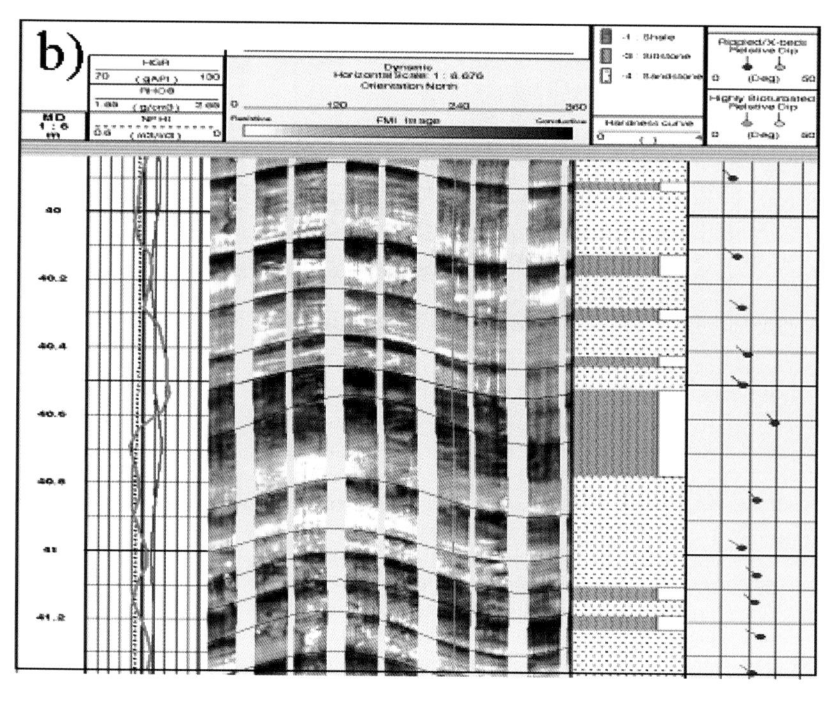

Fig. 9. Inclined-bedded sandstones in a dynamic processed resistivity image dipping consistently towards the NW (**a**) Pukearuhe Central (37.2–38.0 m), (**b**) Pukearuhe North (39.9–41.2 m).

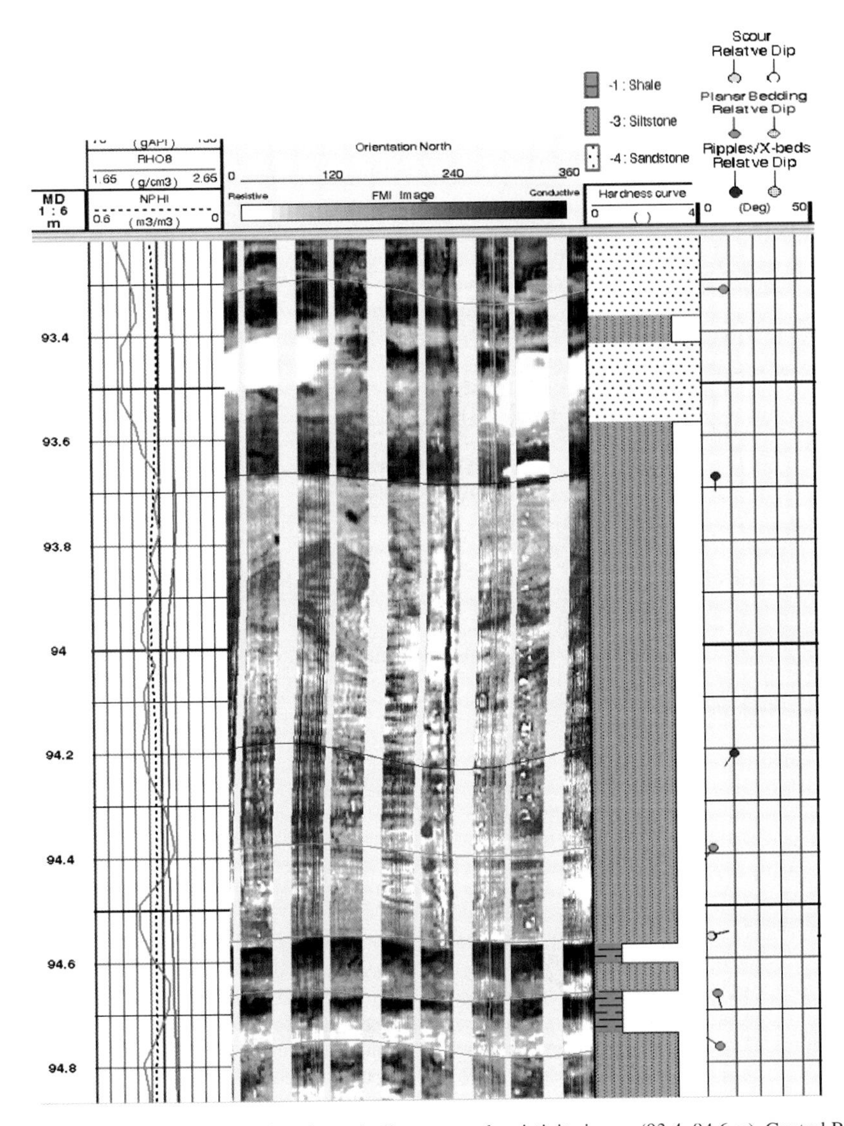

Fig. 10. Convoluted sandstones as seen in a dynamically processed resistivity image (93.4–94.6 m), Central Pukearuhe. Note dips are orientated towards the south.

Slope system channel axis facies associations

The vertical section between 36.0 and 42.0 m in Pukearuhe Central and 36.0 and 42.0 m in Pukearuhe North has been interpreted as a slope channel facies association (Fig. 11). The base of this section was delineated by a major erosional scour infilled by a conglomeritic interval (Fig. 12). The facies observed in both wells consist of thin (around 0.1–0.2 m thick) beds, forming fining-up sandstone to siltstone units. The beds are observed dipping at around 10° to the NW, with both wells displaying a higher-magnitude dip towards the base of the unit: 17° at Pukearuhe Central and 35° at Pukearuhe North. This facies association has been interpreted as having been deposited within waning turbidity currents which were back-filling a pre-existing slope channel during sea-level rise.

Conclusions

The late Miocene Mt Messenger Formation at Pukearuhe Beach is dominated by a major channel that incised into a lower channel-levee and overbank facies. This scour surface, infilled by a distinctive

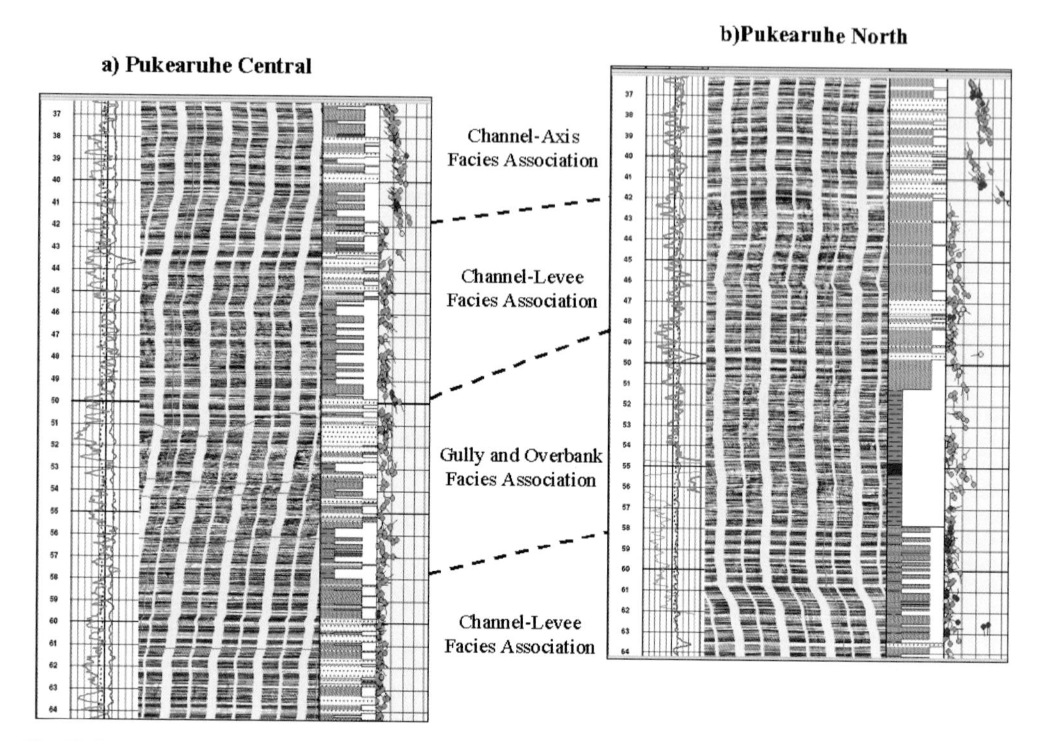

Fig. 11. Correlation of the high resolution image logs from Pukearuhe Central and North, illustrating the correlation of the interpreted facies associations (1:200 Scale). Track 1, Depth in metres; Track 2, Green curve = gamma-ray scaled 70–130 g API, black dashed curve = neutron scaled 0.0–0.5 $m^3/m^3$and red solid curve = density1.65–2.65g cm^{-3}; Track 3, Static high resolution resistivity image; Track 4, facies, sandstone = yellow & stippled, siltstone = orange & stippled, and mudstone = green & dashed.

conglomeritic interval allowed a confident correlation of the two wells, Pukearuhe Central and Pukearuhe North and the outcrop. In comparison to the core, the image yielded a much more detailed facies definition. This was due to the very fine-grained nature of the sedimentation, which obscured the bedding surfaces in the core, but they were highlighted in the image. This additional resolution allowed a more detailed lithological interpretation to be determined. In addition, the dip data derived from the image provided important characteristics, which assisted in interpreting the transport direction and thus the mode of deposition of each facies.

The sedimentary deposits were divided into three slope facies associations: channel-levee, gully and overbank, and channel-fill. The overbank and channel levee facies cycles between the two adjacent wells were uncorrelatable along the strike of the palaeoslope. This marginal channel system, located below the major channel axis was probably associated with a different channel body. In the channel facies, however, above the erosive scour, similar facies were observed in both wells; only the magnitude of the erosive scour differed in this interval (Figs 11 & 12). The dip data indicated that the sandstone channel-fill was dipping NW down palaeoslope. Based on this data, the sediment is thought to be unrelated to the formation of the scour surface, but instead to the back-filling of the channel.

From this study, it is evident that the lateral extent of the thin beds in this slope setting is limited and that the thicker channel sandstones are a better reservoir play. Detailed facies and dip data analyses were important in determining whether the coarse-grained clastic body migrated across or prograded down the palaeoslope. This information is critical in positioning successful offset wells.

I would like to thank both editors of this paper, Vincent Hilton, Stefan Luthi, and Dave Hodgson whose contributions were essential in improving this manuscript. In addition, I am indebted to Greg Browne (Institute of Geological & Nuclear Sciences) for his photo contributions and careful editing and Roger Slatt (University of Oklahoma) for providing the inspiration for this paper. I would also like to give thanks to the original image processor and dip picker, Steve Hansen of Schlumberger, and Schlumberger in general for giving me the time and funding to write and present this work.

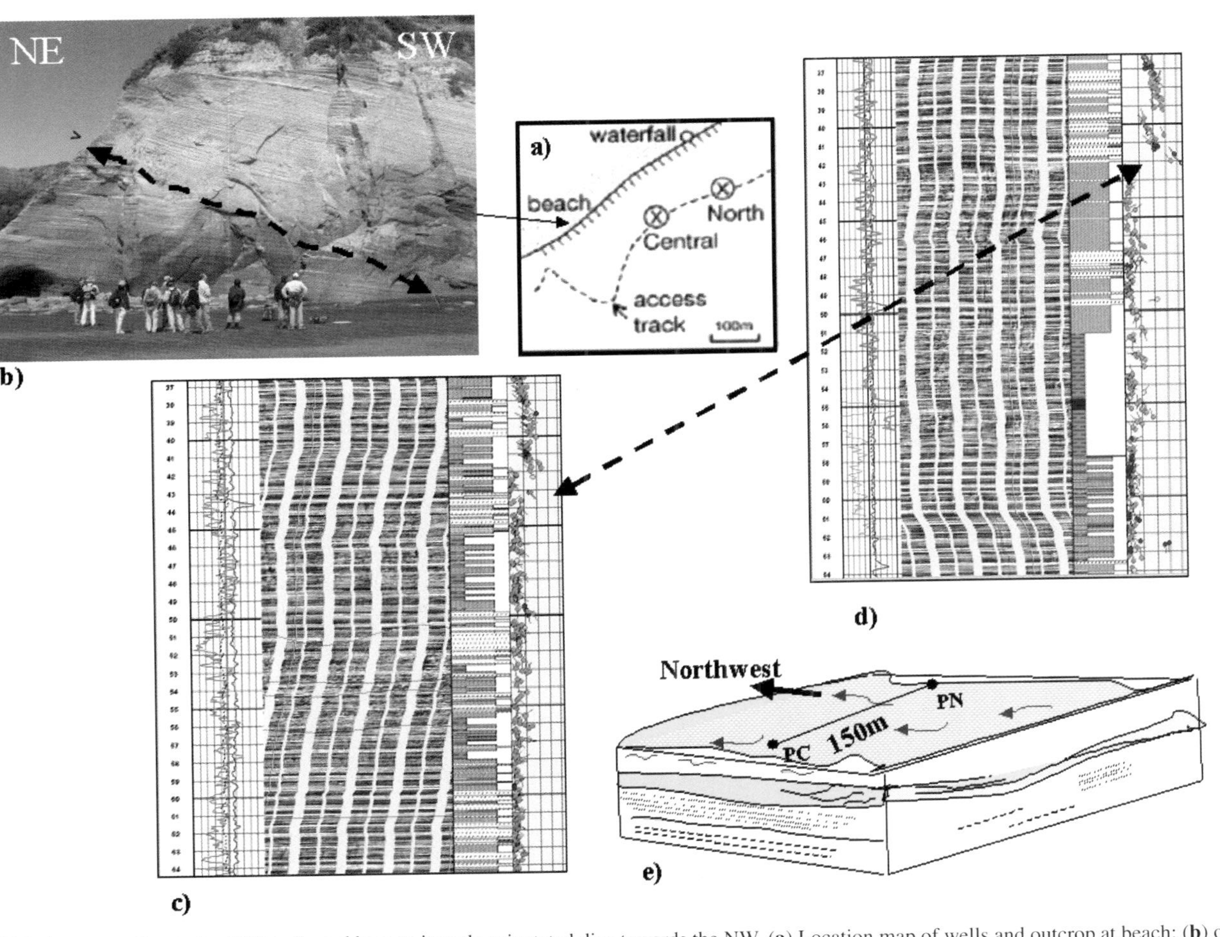

Fig. 12. Channel-fill facies prograding to the NW, indicated by consistently orientated dips towards the NW. (**a**) Location map of wells and outcrop at beach; (**b**) outcrop of the channel identified on the image logs on Pukearuhe Beach (Mt Messenger Formation). The channel base is delineated by a black dashed line on the photograph (courtesy of Greg Browne); (**c**) Pukearuhe Central, erosive scour at 42.0 m indicated by high angle (20°) dips; (**d**) Pukearuhe North, erosive scour at 42.0 m as indicated by high angle (40°) dips; (**e**) Schematic model of channel axis indicating relative position of wells, Pukearuhe Central (PC) and Pukearuhe North (PN).

References

Browne, G.H. & Slatt, R.M. 2002. Outcrop and behind-outcrop characterization of a late Miocene slope fan system, Mt Messenger Formation, New Zealand. *American Association of Petroleum Geology Bulletin* , **86**, 841–862.

Hansen, S.M. & Fett, T. 1998. *Turbidite identification and evaluation for hydrocrbon production using open hole logs and borehole images*. Gulf Coast Association Geological Society Transactions, **48**.

King, P.R. & Thrasher, G.P. 1996. Cretaceous–Cenozoic geology and petroleum systems of the Taranaki Basin, New Zealand. *Institute of Geological and Nuclear Sciences Monograph*, **13**, 243.

King, P.R., Scott, G.H. & Robinson, P.R. 1993. Description, correlation and depositional history of Miocene sediments outcropping along the north Taranaki coast. *Institute of Geological and Nuclear Sciences Monograph*, **5**, 199.

King, P.R., Browne, G.H. & Slatt, R.M. 1994. Sequence architecture of exposed late Miocene basin floor fan and channel levee complexes (Mt Messenger Formation), Taranaki Basin, New Zealand. *In*: Weimer, P., Bouma, A.H. & Perkins, B.F. (eds) *Submarine fans and turbidite systems*. Gulf Coast Section SEPM 15th Annual Research Conference, 177–192.

Luthi, S.M. 2000. *Geological Well Logs: their use in reservoir modelling*. Springer Verlag, Berlin.

Pickering, K.T., Hiscott, R.N. & Hein, F.J. 1989. Slope aprons and slope basins. *In*: Pickering, K.T., Hiscott, R.N. & Heins, F.J. (eds) *Deep Marine Environments: Clastic sedimentation and tectonics*. Unwin & Hyman, 91–108.

Pickering, K.T., Hodgson, D.M., Platzman, E., Clark, J.D. & Stephens, C. 2001. A new type of bedform produced by backfilling processes in a submarine channel, late Miocene, Tabernas-Sorbas basin, SE Spain. *Journal of Sedimentary Research*, **71**, 692–704.

Stow, D.A.V. 1986. Deep clastic seas: where are we and where are we going? *In*: Brenchley, P.J. & Williams, B.P.J. (eds) *Sedimentology: recent developments and applied aspects. Geology Society, London, Special Publication*, Blackwell Scientific, Oxford, **18**, 67–93.

Tucker, M.E. 1986. Collection and analysis of field data. *In*: *Techniques in Sedimentology*. Blackwell Scientific Publications, Oxford, 5–62.

Architecture and stratigraphic evolution of multiple, vertically-stacked slope channel complexes, Tanqua depocentre, Karoo Basin, South Africa

RICHARD J. WILD, DAVID M. HODGSON & STEPHEN S. FLINT

Stratigraphy Group, Department of Earth & Ocean Sciences, University of Liverpool, 4 Brownlow Street, Liverpool L69 3GP, UK. (e-mail: rwild@liv.ac.uk)

Abstract: Early Permian deep-water deposits of the Tanqua depocentre, SW Karoo Basin, South Africa, include Unit 5, an extremely well-exposed 100 m-thick lower slope succession. Within the study area, Unit 5 comprises two partially-synchronous, vertically stacked, sub-parallel channel complex sets that lie 8 km apart along strike (the east-trending Klein Hangklip complex set and the NE-trending Groot Hangklip complex set). The detailed time-stratigraphic relationship between deposition in the interchannel areas and channel fill aggradation remains unresolved due to exposure limitations; however, it is suggested that most of the turbidite sheet deposits between the channels represent frontal lower slope splays from earlier slope feeder systems and are not genetically related to the channels. Gravitational instability in the sheet deposits drove a range of deformation processes from low velocity 'slope creep' to complete failure and slumping during times of maximum incision and bypass within the slope channels. Following the main phase of aggradation within the channels, periods of spill led to the formation of lateral splays and splay channels, which are distinct from the older frontal splay deposits. Each channel complex comprises two composite channel bodies and is interpreted to represent a fifth order sequence. In the absence of evidence of local (intraslope) tectonic controls, the vertical stacking of the channel complexes is interpreted to be due to fixed shelf edge entry points. Abrupt lateral facies changes along depositional strike, the ubiquity of instability features, the high proportion of sandstone preserved in the channel complexes and the absence of levees supports the interpretation that Unit 5 in the Hangklip area was deposited in a lower slope setting.

Although in recent years the acquisition and interpretation of increasingly high-resolution 3D seismic data has led to a greater understanding of slope turbidite systems (Mayall & Stewart 2000; Kolla *et al.* 2001; Samuel *et al.* 2003; Abreu *et al.* 2003), relatively little is known about the detailed internal architecture below seismic resolution. This is exemplified in fine-grained systems (Stelting *et al.* 2000), which provide a challenge to exploration as potential reservoir sandstones are relatively thin, commonly difficult to detect on seismic and their stratigraphic position may be unpredictable (Martinsen *et al.* 2003).

Outcrop analogue studies help to address these issues and provide a means to test the seismic-based models, to reduce uncertainty in lithology prediction and sub-seismic connectivity, and to assess the predictive ability of these models critically. Some of the more widely known outcrop analogues are the Permian Upper Brushy Canyon Formation in the Delaware Mountains of West Texas (Beaubouef *et al.* 1999; Gardner *et al.* 2003), the Eocene deposits of Svalbard (e.g. Plink-Björklund *et al.* 2001; Mellere *et al.* 2002; Plink-Björklund & Steel 2002), the Carboniferous succession of western Ireland (Elliott 2000; Martinsen *et al.* 2003; Lien *et al.* 2003) and the Late Cretaceous Pab Range outcrops of Pakistan (Eschard *et al.* 2003). These four examples differ in age, basin type, grain size range and in length and geometry of the shelf to slope profile. This paper presents a new, outcrop-based dataset on the architecture and stratigraphic development of lower slope channel complexes in a delta-fed, progradational, relatively low relief margin setting with a narrow grain size range (fine sand to clay) in the Tanqua depocentre, SW Karoo Basin, South Africa (Fig. 1).

Geological setting

The major Gondwana foreland basins (Paranà, Karoo, Beacon and Bowen Basins) developed in response to accretion tectonics along the southern margin of Gondwana during the Late Palaeozoic (De Wit & Ransome 1992; Veevers *et al.* 1994; López-Gamundí & Rossello 1998). Continued subduction resulted in northward compression and the development of a fold-thrust belt inboard of the magmatic arc (Visser 1987; Veevers *et al.* 1994). Most previous authors have considered that the Karoo Basin developed as a retroarc foreland basin with subsidence solely due to loading by the fold-thrust belt, which lies along the southern and southwestern margin of the basin (e.g. Johnson 1991; Visser 1993; Cole 1992; Veevers *et al.* 1994). However, petrographic and geochemical studies of the Karoo turbidites have shown that they were not derived from Cape Fold Belt rocks, indicating that the fold belt was not

From: HODGSON, D.M. & FLINT, S.S. (eds) 2005. *Submarine Slope Systems: Processes and Products*. Geological Society, London, Special Publications, **244**, 89–111. 0305–8719/$15.00

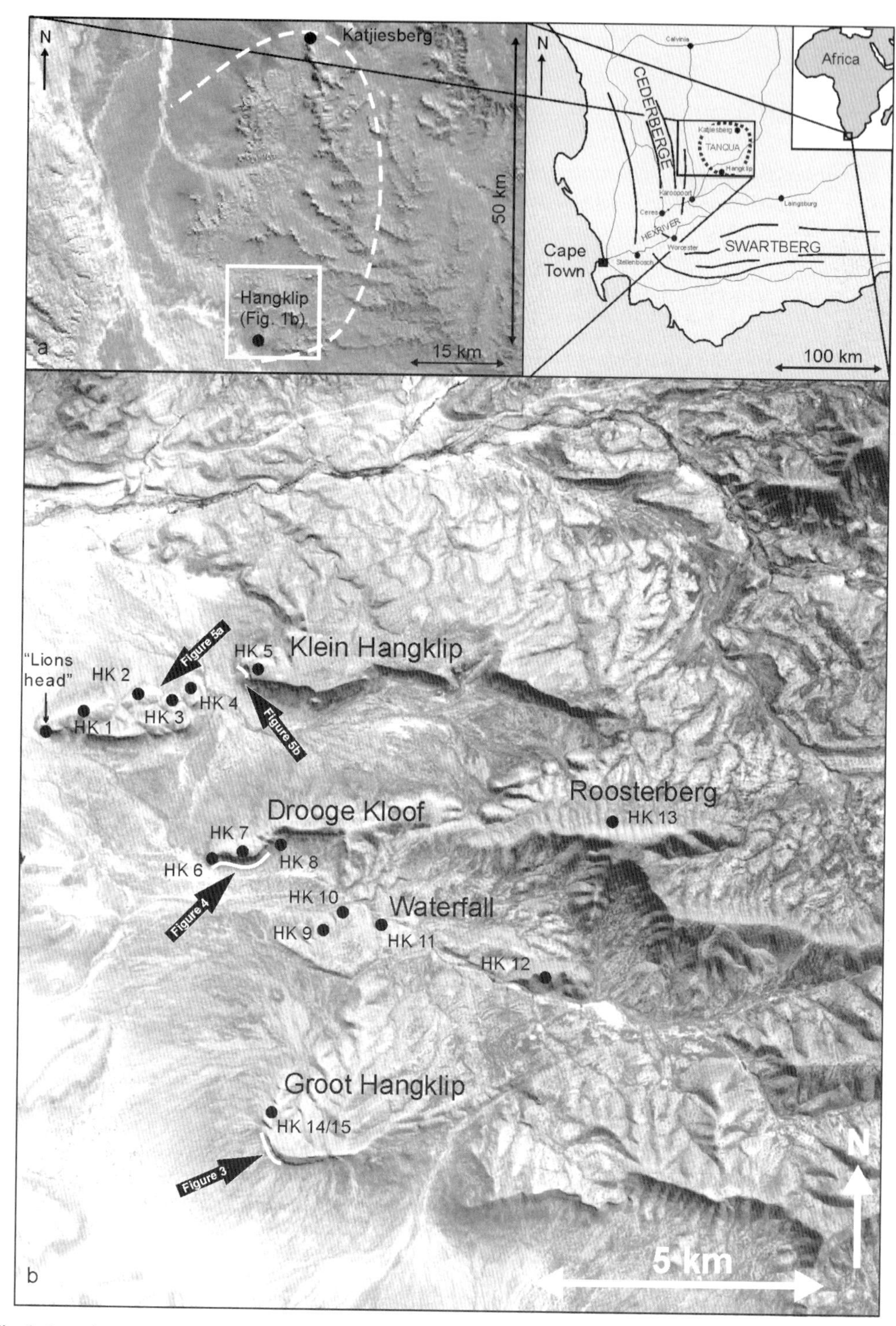

Fig. 1. Location map. (**a**) Landsat image of the Tanqua depocentre showing the position of the Hangklip study area (boxed) in relation to southwestern South Africa. The regional mapped extent of Unit 5 is outlined (dashed line). (**b**) Aerial photograph of the Hangklip study area showing the positions of the outcrops studied, the main logged sections and interpreted outcrop photographs (white line).

substantially emergent at the time of deep-water deposition. These interpretations have been synthesized by van Lente (2004) into a model that calls for derivation of the deep-water deposits from the Patagonian batholith.

Stratigraphy of the Tanqua depocentre

The stratigraphy of the Karoo Supergroup is divided into the Dwyka Group (Westphalian to early Permian glacial deposits), the Ecca Group (Permian) and the Beaufort Group (Permo-Triassic fluvial sediments). In the southwestern Karoo Basin, the 1400 m-thick Ecca Group comprises the basal Prince Albert Formation (shale and cherty shale beds; 288 ±3 Ma; Bangert *et al.* 1999), the Whitehill Formation (black, carbonaceous shales with pelagic organisms; Visser 1992) and the Collingham Formation (fine-grained sheet turbidites and intercalated ashes; 270 ± 1 Ma; Turner 1999), all-indicative of post-glacial, long-term sea level rise. The Collingham Formation is overlain by several hundred metres of dark basinal shales (Tierberg Formation) and then the sand-prone deep-water Skoorsteenberg Formation (Fig. 2). Previous researchers have identified four basin-floor and one intraslope sand-rich submarine fan systems ('Fans' 1–5) in the Skoorsteenberg Formation (e.g. Bouma & Wickens 1991; Wickens 1994; Wickens & Bouma 2000; Johnson *et al.* 2001). A 100 m-thick sand-prone interval that outcrops in the SW of the Tanqua depocentre, Unit 5, is the focus of this study.

Recent integrated outcrop and subsurface study on the Skoorsteenberg Formation has clarified this stratigraphy (Hodgson *et al.* 2005). Unit 5 encompasses the stratigraphy from the top of two regional mudstone intervals above the uppermost basin-floor fan (Fan 4) (Fig. 2), to the base of a regional, 12 m-thick mudstone interval that can be mapped into the top of the 'Hangklip Fan'. A unit previously referred to as Fan 6 or the 'Hangklip Fan' in the south of the Tanqua area (Wickens 1994; Wach *et al.* 2000) is now recognized as comprising the most proximal exposed part of Unit 5. Regional mapping indicates that Unit 5 is the thickest (80–100 m) and most consistently sand-prone unit within the Skoorsteenberg Formation (Fig. 2). Unit 5 comprises several channel, sheet and overbank elements at different stratigraphic intervals with numerous abrupt lateral lithofacies changes (Hodgson *et al.* 2005), and is exposed across an 800 km^2 area within the depocentre (Fig. 1a). The largely north–south orientation of the outcrop belt, coupled with the dominantly SW–NE palaeoflow indicators, provides exposures in a dominantly oblique strike orientation. Evidence of instability (convolute lamination, centimetre-scale dishes and pipes, overturned flame structures and slumps) is common in the south (up-dip), and is less developed obliquely down-dip to the north. The combination of facies associations, instability features and stratigraphic context are in accord with a lower slope to base-of-slope depositional setting for Unit 5 (Hodgson *et al.* 2005). This paper focuses on the detailed architecture and stratigraphic evolution of Unit 5 in a 10 km^2 area in the Hangklip region (Fig. 1), within this new regional context.

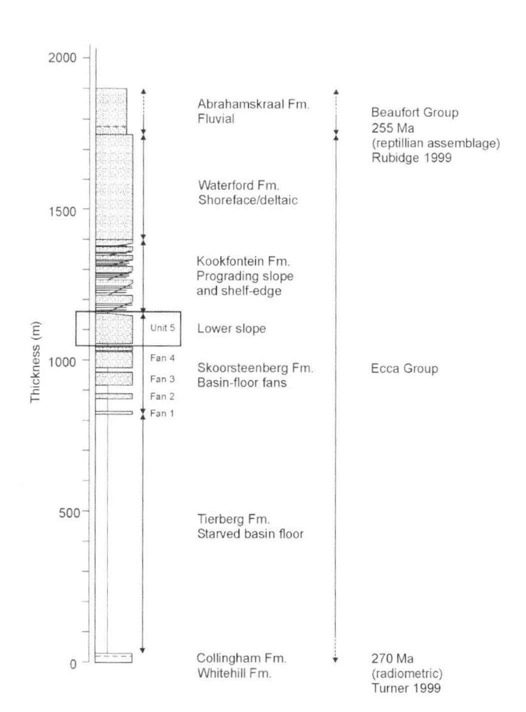

Fig. 2. Simplified stratigraphy of the Tanqua depocentre showing the position of Unit 5 (boxed).

The overlying upper submarine slope and shelf-edge (Kookfontein Formation), shoreface/deltaic (Waterford Formation) and fluvial (Abrahamskraal Formation, Beaufort Group) successions mark the overall progradation of the sedimentary system to the north and east during the mid to late Permian. A radiometric date of 270 +/− 1 Ma from ashes in the underlying Collingham Formation (Turner 1999) and a 255 Ma date from early reptile fossils in the overlying Beaufort Group (Rubidge *et al.* 1999) bracket the whole deep-water, shelf and basal fluvial deposits to a 15 Ma period (Fig. 2).

Dataset and methods

Outcrop sedimentological logging was undertaken at a centimetre-scale and combined with land- and helicopter-based oblique photomontages and 1:30 000 conventional aerial photographs to correlate boundaries of genetic units and to constrain the large-scale architecture of Unit 5. Key surfaces were walked-out between logged sections and trends in sediment dispersal were reconstructed using measured palaeocurrent indicators (mainly foresets of current-ripples, sole marks and wave-modified bed tops). This enabled the spatial and temporal distribution of lithofacies, and their geometries and depositional environments to be interpreted at a variety of scales from the individual architectural element (channel, sheet or lobe) to the entire thickness of Unit 5 in the Hangklip area (multiple channel complex sets). The location of the Hangklip study area, key sections and outcrop logs are shown in Figure 1b.

Lithofacies and depositional process

The descriptions and interpretations of the facies encountered within the Hangklip study area are detailed in Table 1. Derivation of this facies classification scheme is based on composition, grain-size and sedimentary structures and are related to depositional process.

Stratigraphy of Unit 5 in the Hangklip area

Unit 5 is well exposed along three west–east trending ridges in the Hangklip study area (Fig. 1b). Physical correlation and bed/horizon tracing from helicopter mosaics were complemented by the recently revised understanding of the stratigraphy underlying Unit 5 (Hodgson *et al.* 2005). A 12 m-thick regional shale above a package of thin-bedded siltstone turbidites that reflect the retrogradation of the sedimentary system at the top of Unit 5 is used as a correlation datum. The descriptions and interpretations below are presented geographically in terms of the key localities and then synthesized into a palaeogeographic model.

Groot Hangklip

Groot Hangklip forms a cliff-face at the western end of the most southerly west–east trending ridge in the study area (Figs 1b & 3a). The complete Unit 5 succession is represented by 30 m of siltstone–sandstone interbeds and interbedded sandstone (lithofacies Sl 1 and Sl 2, Table 1) with intercalated claystone (lithofacies B 1, Table 1), sharply overlain by a 60 m-thick body of thick-bedded structureless and dewatered sandstones (lithofacies Sl 4, Table 1). There is one persistent break (0.01–0.05 m) of thin-bedded sandstones and siltstones (lithofacies Sl 1 and Sl 2, Table 1) within the sandstone body. Beneath Unit 5 is a 100 m-thick exposure of shales with 'ribs' of thin-bedded siltstones and very fine-grained sandstones (lithofacies Sl 1 and Sl 2, Table 1) that are interpreted as oblique up-dip expressions of basin-floor Fans 2, 3, and 4 (Fig. 2).

Most of the thin-bedded facies within the lower 30 m of Unit 5 are sheet-like siltstones and very fine-grained sandstones (lithofacies Sl 1 and Sl 2, Table 1). Ripple lamination is common, and rare deformed siltstone and sandstone units occur (<0.2 m-thick). Deformation structures include convolute lamination, centimetre-scale dishes and pipes and loaded bed bases. At outcrop, individual beds can be traced out for hundreds of metres with no change in thickness or evidence for onlap or truncation. These observations are backed up by analysis of extensive helicopter-based photographs. Palaeocurrent measurements for this interval indicate that palaeoflow was towards the NE.

The upper 60 m of Unit 5 at Groot Hangklip comprises thick-bedded structureless and dewatered very fine- and fine-grained sandstones (lithofacies Sl 4, Table 1) that can be divided into two 15–45 m-thick units with significant composite basal incision surfaces (Fig. 3a–e). These thick-bedded sandstone packages are subsequently referred to in the text as GHK A (older) and GHK B (younger).

GHK A

The base of the lower thick-bedded sandstone unit consists of 5–8 m of interbedded siltstones and fine-grained lenticular sandstones with current- and climbing-ripple lamination and erosive bases (lithofacies Sl 1 and Sl 2, Table 1). A composite basal erosion surface (Fig. 3b) with less than 6 m of incision is marked by thin-bedded siltstones and very fine-grained sandstones (lithofacies Sl 1 and Sl 2, Table 1) truncated by numerous scour surfaces that are mantled with claystone clasts (lithofacies Sl 5, Table 1). The overlying thick-bedded structureless and dewatered sandstones (lithofacies Sl 4, Table 1) exhibit a wide range of soft-sediment deformation structures such as convolute lamination, dish and pillar structures, loaded bed bases and large (>1 m high) flame structures, which are also cut by 2–3 m-deep erosion surfaces. The degree of amalgamation and dewatering decreases towards the margins of these erosion surfaces. Palaeocurrent measurements for GHK A (sole marks) indicate a NNE palaeoflow (Fig. 3a).

GHK B

The upper thick-bedded sandstone unit is also bounded at the base by a composite erosion surface

Table 1. *Characteristics of the lithofacies defined in this paper.*

Lithofacies number	Lithology	Sedimentary structures	Turbidite divisions	Bounding surfaces	Thickness	Geometry	Trace fossils and other notable features	Depositional process
B 1	Claystone	Structureless	–	Gradational	0.02 m + packages	Often laterally extensive sheets	Common concretionary horizons. Rare to present *Chondrites*	Hemi-pelagic suspension
B 2	Siltstone-claystone interbeds	Generally massive to parallel lamination, starved ripple lamination	T_{de} rare T_{cde}	Laminae have sharp base and gradational top	Laminae 1–5 mm, 0.01–0.04 m packages	Laminae tabular to lenticular. Units often sheet like	Rare to moderate *Chondrites, Gordia sp.*	Low concentration turbidity currents and minor hemi-pelagic suspension
Sl 1	Siltstone-sandstone interbeds	Silt to vfs have starved ripples, parallel lamination and massive nature. Prods and grooves on base	Variable. Common T_{cde}, T_{de} and T_{bc}	Sands have sharp base, tops gradational to sharp	0.01–0.05 m	Individual beds tabular at the outcrop scale. Units display a sheet geometry	Common *Chondrites, Helminthopsis, Helminthoida, Gordia sp. Lorenzinia, Lophoterium, Cosmorhaphe, Palaeodyctyon*	Low to medium concentration turbidity currents
Sl 2	Interbedded sandstone	Variable. Climbing ripples, parallel lamination, massive. Local sigmoid geometry and pinch and swell	T_{cde}, T_{ab}, (former more common)	Sharp bases to sands. Sharp to gradational tops. Upper fine layer (Te) can be absent	Sandstones usually form units dominated by bedding of 0.05–0.1 m, 0.1–0.2 m and 0.20 m +	Beds tabular. Sheet geometry to units	–	Low to high concentration turbidity currents
Sl 3	Bedded sandstone	Common massive base, parallel, climbing ripples. Some scour and fill. Dewatering	T_{ab} and T_{ac} common	Bases sharp. Rarely erosional	0.2–0.6 m	Tabular to locally lenticular. Units form sheet and channel geometries	–	High concentration turbidity currents
Sl 4	Structureless sandstone	Massive, local parallel lamination. Local scour and fill. Dewatering fabrics	T_a	Sharp to erosive base. Sharp tops	0.6–2 m > 2 m packages due to amalgamation	Sheet and channel geometries	Wood fragments occur	High concentration turbidity currents
Sl 5	Lag	Clast and matrix supported	–	Sharp to erosional base, gradational to sharp top	Up to 0.5 m	Lenticular pockets. Local scour and fill	Very angular to sub-rounded clasts of siltstone and very fine-grained sandstone. Commonly siltstone clasts < 0.005–0.02 m	Deposition from erosive sediment-laden flows, channel/point bar migration

Continued

Table 1. (Continued)

Lithofacies number	Lithology	Sedimentary structures	Turbidite divisions	Bounding surfaces	Thickness	Geometry	Trace fossils and other notable features	Depositional process
Pd 1	Deformed siltstone and sandstone	Small and large scale soft-sediment deformation. Dishes, pipes and flame structures <1 m to 2 m	–	Loaded to sharp	Up to 2 m	Disturbed sheets, lenticular pockets up to 50 m wide	–	Range of shelfal and slope depositional processes. Abrupt loading and expulsion of fluid, creep
Pd 2	Concretionary horizon	Isolated nodules and concretionary horizons	–	Sharp	Up to 0.5 m	Lenticular to localized pans	–	Diagenetic concretions at times of maximum sediment starvation

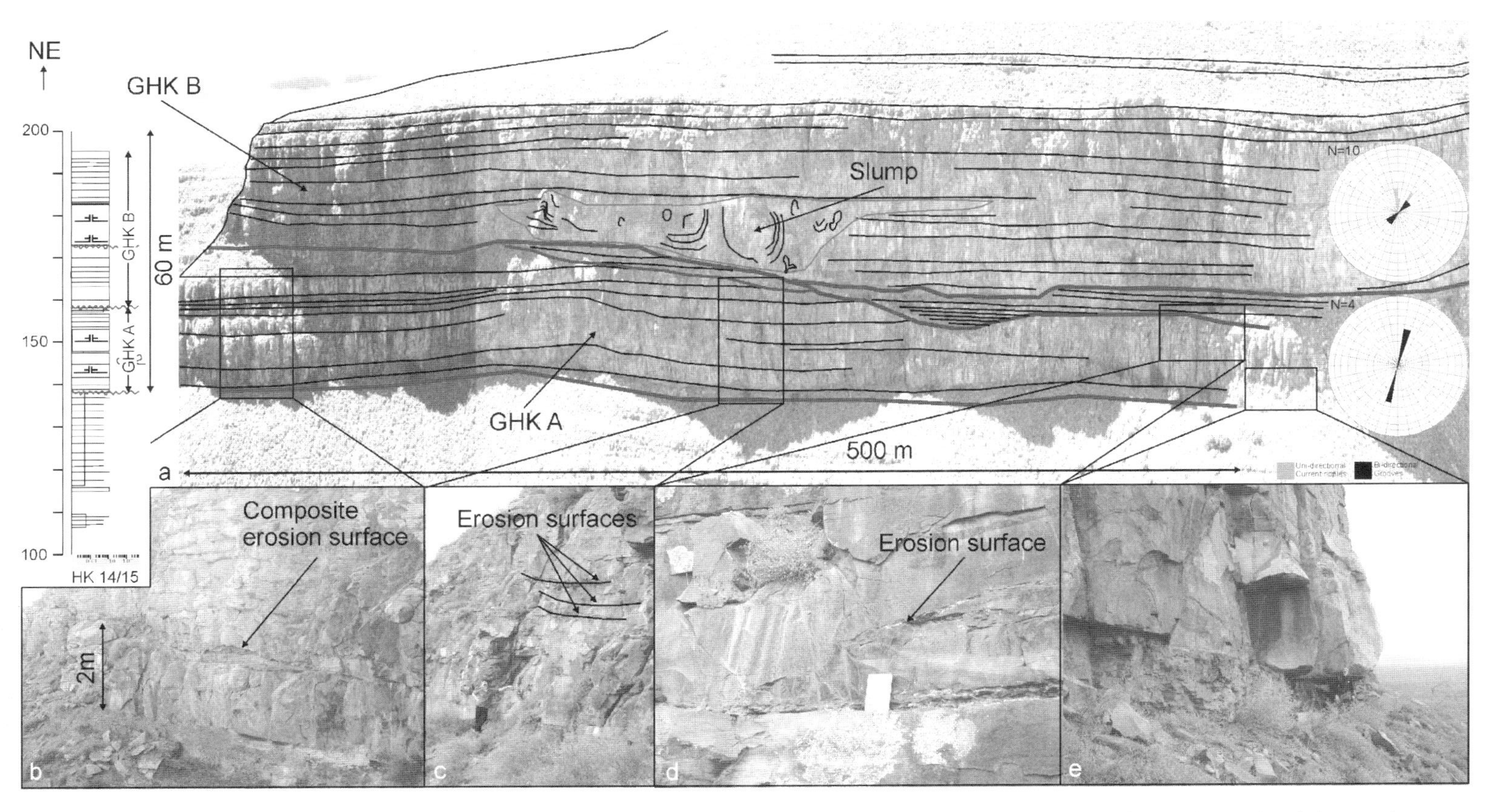

Fig. 3. Groot Hangklip slope channel complex set. (**a**) Photomontage and stretched (×2 vertical exaggeration) interpretive line drawing from helicopter-based photographs (courtesy of Asle Strøm, Statoil) of the upper part of Unit 5 at Groot Hangklip, composite sedimentary log (HK 14/15) (log location relative to the outcrop photograph is shown in Fig. 1b) and reconstructed palaeocurrent trends for GHK A (older) and GHK B (younger) channel complexes. (**b**) Composite erosion surface with more than 6 m of incision around the outcrop. Note the recessive interval between erosion surfaces that is composed of claystone clasts, which represent active bypass. (**c**) Low amplitude erosion surfaces that typically have an incision depth of 2–4 m, and are overlain by thick-bedded structureless sandstones. (**d**) Close-up of erosion surface mantled with claystone clasts. (**e**) Major erosion surface (GHK A), level with the geologist's head. The underlying thin-bedded facies contain numerous scours.

with more than 15 m of incision that forms a recessive break marked by thin-bedded siltstones and very fine-grained sandstones, cut by numerous scour surfaces mantled with clast-rich horizons (Fig. 3a & d). Unlike the composite erosion surface at the base of GHK A, the thickness of the associated fine-grained sediments rarely exceeds 1 m. Pervasive soft-sediment deformation structures occur in the overlying sandstones, including convolute lamination, dish and pillar structures and flame structures. A 10 m-thick sand-prone slump interval occurs above the fine-grained sediments associated with the composite basal erosion surface (Fig. 3a). Overturned flame structures and current-ripple foresets within thick-bedded sandstone units occur towards the base of GHK B and indicate a component of northerly palaeoflow, whereas current-ripple foresets within the uppermost thin-bedded sandstones and siltstones suggest that palaeoflow was to the NE (Fig. 3a).

At log location HK 12, which is 5 km down dip from Groot Hangklip (Figs 1b, 8a–d), the lower 25 m of the outcrop consists primarily of thick-bedded, dewatered very fine- and fine-grained sandstones (lithofacies Sl 4, Table 1), intercalated with packages of thin-bedded ripple-laminated sandstone and siltstone turbidites (lithofacies Sl 1 and Sl 2, Table 1). As at Groot Hangklip, these heterolithic intervals typically occur immediately above erosion surfaces and commonly contain siltstone-rich rip-up horizons. Slumped intervals are more prevalent at this locality than at Groot Hangklip. Palaeocurrent measurements (grooves and wave-modified bed tops) indicate a NE–SW trend in palaeoflow.

A change in depositional style is marked at Groot Hangklip by a recessive break at the top of the cliff-forming structureless sandstones (Fig. 3a). Sheet-like, planar laminated, medium-bedded fine-grained sandstone (lithofacies Sl 3, Table 1) and ripple laminated, very fine- and fine-grained sandstone interbeds (lithofacies Sl 2, Table 1), fine- and thin-upward into siltstone–sandstone and siltstone–claystone interbeds (lithofacies Sl 1 and B 2, Table 1).

Interpretation

The two 15–45 m-thick, structureless thick-bedded sandstone units, with significant composite basal incision surfaces and numerous internal 2–4 m erosional surfaces, are interpreted as a submarine channel complex set (*sensu* Campion *et al.* 2000), with individual channel complexes GHK A and GHK B stacked vertically. The composite nature of the basal incision surface reflects successive phases of channel aggradation and erosive flushing of the conduit and suggests bypass of sediment into the deeper basin to the NE. Similar composite channel margins associated with bypass and with similar sand-prone fills have been described from lower slope and base of slope channel complexes in the Permian Upper Brushy Canyon Formation deposits of West Texas (Beaubouef *et al.* 1999). Palaeocurrents and facies distributions at outcrop show that the local palaeoflow switched from the NNE (GHK A) to the NE (GHK B). The fining- and thinning-upward turbidite package, marked by the recessive break at the top of the thick-bedded sandstones of GHK B is present across the top of Unit 5 throughout the Hangklip area and is interpreted to reflect the retrogradation of the system.

Drooge Kloof

Drooge Kloof is the middle ridge in the Hangklip study area (Figs 1b & 4a). The lower stratigraphy of Unit 5 is well exposed, but the upper stratigraphy is only preserved at the eastern limits of the Hangklip area near Roosterberg (Fig. 1b).

At the base of Unit 5 at Drooge Kloof, interbedded siltstone-claystone (lithofacies B 2, Table 1) and siltstone-sandstone (lithofacies Sl 1, Table 1) heteroliths with tabular geometries form aggradational packages. Also present are fining- and thinning-upward packages (0.5–1 m thick) of very fine-grained, current-ripple laminated, normally graded sandstones (lithofacies Sl 2, Table 1). Bed bases are typically

Fig. 4. Sheet turbidites, Drooge Kloof. (**a**) Photomontage and stretched (×2 vertical exaggeration) interpretive line drawing of Unit 5 at Drooge Kloof with reconstructed palaeocurrent trends. Note the two sedimentary logs that pass through a basal simple channel (very oblique view), into a dominantly thin-bedded facies and finally into an upper, channelized unit. (**b**) Highly dewatered and deformed unit with a thick siltstone cap at the top of a coarsening-upward package (approximately 0.5 m below the geologist's feet). Undisturbed thin-bedded strata overlie this unit. (**c**) Scour surface at the Waterfall section, mantled with ripple forms. These scours are interpreted to represent erosion from non-depositional turbidity currents that spilled from the Groot Hangklip (GHK A) and Klein Hangklip (KHK B) channel complexes and occur at the equivalent stratigraphic interval to that of the geologist's feet in Fig. 4b. (**d**) Flame structure from a dewatered interval at the Waterfall section. This dewatered interval occurs at the equivalent stratigraphic horizon to the deformed unit shown in Fig. 4b. (**e**) Top surface of a T_c bed, reworked with symmetrical ripple forms. The palaeocurrents from the top surface ripples do not correspond with the 'internal' climbing-ripple measurements. (**f**) Helicopter-based photograph from the north side of Drooge Kloof where the basal channel is exposed. Also note the overlying erosion surface overlain by thick structureless sandstone in the dominantly thin-bedded succession. Photograph by courtesy of Asle Strøm, Statoil.

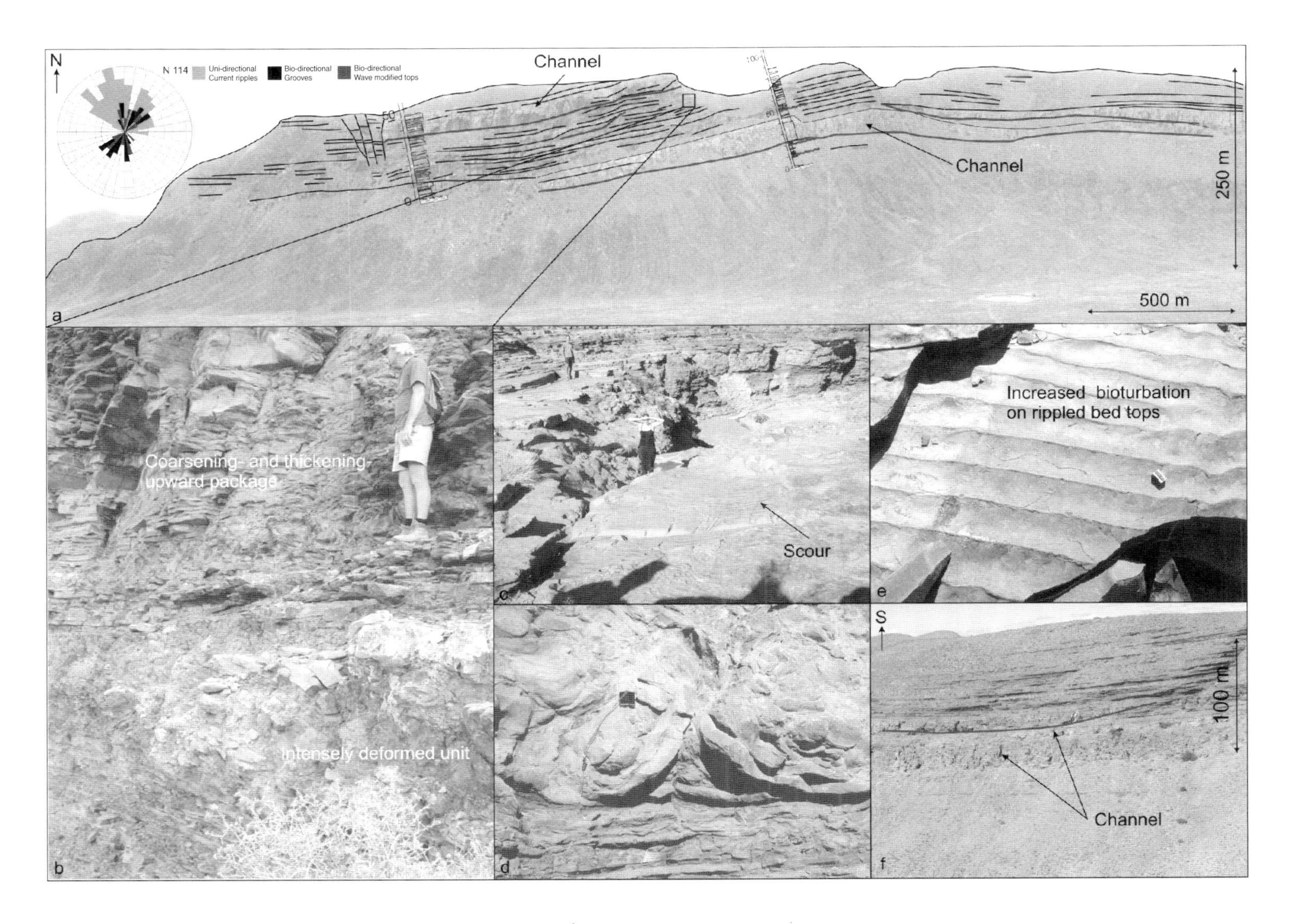

N
N 114
Uni-directional
Current ripples
Bio-directional
Grooves
Bio-directional
Wave modified tops
Channel
Channel
250 m
500 m
a
Coarsening- and thickening-
upward package
Intensely deformed unit
b
Scour
c
d
Increased bioturbation
on rippled bed tops
e
S
100 m
Channel
f

sharp and locally loaded. An isolated 16 m thick channel form obliquely intersects the Drooge Kloof ridge (Fig. 4a & f). Its base is marked by a 20 cm-thick matrix-supported mudstone rip-up clast interval (the matrix is fine-grained sandstone; lithofacies Sl 5, Table 1) and the channel form is filled with thick-bedded, structureless to planar laminated fine-grained sandstone, with pervasive soft-sediment deformation and dewatering fabrics (lithofacies Sl 3 and Sl 4, Table 1). Due to exposure limitations it is unclear whether the channel is bounded by a single simple cut or by a composite basal erosion surface. At the equivalent stratigraphic interval 2 km to the south (outcrop HK 9, Figs 1b & 8 a–d), siltstone-sandstone interbeds, ripple laminated interbedded sandstones and thin-bedded climbing-ripple laminated sandstones (lithofacies Sl 1, Sl 2 and Sl 3, Table 1) form coarsening- and thickening-upward packages (0.5–2.5 m-thick) capped by fine-grained thick-bedded deformed and dewatered sandstones (lithofacies Sl 4 and Pd 1, Table 1). The thick-bedded structureless sandstone beds are commonly erosively based and contain numerous plant fragments (concentrated towards the bed-bases). Where present, the dewatered sandstone intervals commonly exhibit loaded bases, dishes, pipes and flame structures. Internal palaeocurrent indicators (current-ripple foresets) indicate that palaeoflow was towards the ENE.

The stratigraphy above the isolated channel is dominated by sandstone and siltstone (lithofacies Sl 1, Sl 2 and Sl 3, Table 1) with parallel-, current- and climbing-ripple lamination, forming coarsening- and thickening-upward packages (Fig. 4a & b); symmetrical-ripples are commonly preserved on bed tops (Fig. 4e). These interbedded heteroliths are commonly intercalated with intensely dewatered coarse siltstones and fine-grained sandstones (lithofacies Pd 1, Table 1) that, when traced out down dip and along strike, pass into undeformed, bedded sandstones and siltstones (Sl 2 and Sl 3, Table 1). Sandstones commonly exhibit loaded bases, and dish, pipe and flame structures. The incidence of the deformed sandstone and siltstone intervals increase towards the top of the coarsening- and thickening-upward packages. Large-scale soft-sediment deformation affects beds up to 2 m in thickness with deformation occurring laterally for up to 300 m, metre-scale flame structures, sometimes overturned, occur at the bases of the deformed sandbodies. These bodies can be traced into non-deformed strata where deformation phenomena cease transitionally but relatively abruptly, without truncation. Intensely dewatered siltstones are commonly intercalated with undeformed sandstone beds.

The symmetrical-rippled bed tops (Fig. 4e) display wide-ranging palaeocurrent orientations on a bed-by-bed basis and in cross-section record the reworking of only the topmost laminae of each bed. However, when all data from these structures are grouped together, two trends in palaeoflow are revealed, one trending north–south the other NE–SW (Fig. 4a). Palaeocurrent measurements from internal climbing-ripple foresets and sole marks indicate two different, stratigraphically constrained trends in palaeoflow; one palaeoflow trend towards the NE and the other towards the NNW (minor ENE component). This change in palaeocurrent orientation within the beds occurs across a thin (< 0.5 m-thick) interval of interbedded siltstones and sandstones that overlies a 10–12 m-thick coarsening- and thickening-upward package and marks the base of another. At the equivalent stratigraphic level in the Waterfall section (Fig. 1b), several shallow scour forms and megaflutes truncate a deformed sandstone unit that caps a coarsening- and thickening-upward package. The largest and best-exposed scour displays a ripple-modified top and measures approximately 5 m wide by 0.5 m deep (Fig. 4c). Immediately below the horizon containing the flutes and scours, palaeocurrent data within the coarsening- and thickening-upward package indicate palaeoflow towards the NE, whereas above the horizon the dominant palaeoflow was towards the NNW.

In addition to the disparity in palaeoflow indicated from symmetrical-rippled bed tops and the internal climbing-ripple foresets of sandstone beds, an increase in the amount of bioturbation is observed between the symmetrical-rippled bed tops relative to the sandstone beds. Using the ichnofabric scheme of Droser & Bottjer (1989), an ichnofabric index of 3 is estimated for the symmetrical-rippled bed tops (horizontal traces) compared to an ichnofabric index of 1 for the sandstone beds.

A 10 m-thick channel form intersects the top of the Drooge Kloof ridge (Fig. 4a). Where exposed, its base is marked by a 0.5–1.5 m-thick package of interbedded sandstones and siltstones and thin-bedded ripple laminated sandstones (lithofacies Sl 2 and Sl 3, Table 1) cut by numerous low angle incision surfaces. The sandstone beds commonly contain claystone rip-up clasts and are rich in plant material. Above this, the fill comprises thick-bedded, structureless and ripple laminated, very fine- and fine-grained sandstones, commonly with pervasive soft-sediment deformation and dewatering and symmetrical-rippled bed tops (lithofacies Sl 3, Table 1). Foresets of current-ripples and sole marks indicate palaeoflow to the NNW whereas the symmetrical-rippled bed tops show a NE–SW trend (Fig. 4a).

Interpretation

Although the margins of the lower channel are poorly exposed and internal palaeocurrent indicators are absent (due to the predominantly structureless nature of the fill), axial positions have been identified on both sides of the ridge based on the deepest point of incision, which suggests that the channel was oriented WSW–ENE with palaeoflow towards ENE, based on regional palaeocurrent knowledge.

In the Drooge Kloof and Waterfall area, the heterolithic coarsening- and thickening-upward packages intercalated with deformed sandstones and siltstones are interpreted as a combination of frontal splay and lateral splay environments, the majority of sediment having been supplied by NE-prograding intraslope fans that deposited sand prior to incision of the slope channels. When deformation affects packages of sediment containing one or more different lithologies the style and extent of deformation is controlled by rheological contrasts. For example, rafts of sandstone are commonly separated from each other by siltstone pipes and flames and are supported within a structureless siltstone matrix. This upward injection of siltstone typically forms a finer-grained cap to the unit (Fig. 4b). It is proposed that formation was driven by violent dewatering, when unstable sandstone packages moved incrementally down slope (slope creep), leading to a build-up in basal pore pressures within the underlying lithology until failure occurred (Fig. 4b & d).

A subsidiary component of the stratigraphy in this area is genetically unrelated overbank splay channels and lobes (Figs 7 & 8), deposited during the late stage, and/or after, aggradation in the slope channels. Steep climbing-ripple lamination indicates rapid deposition and the NNW palaeocurrent orientation indicated by climbing-ripple lamination and grooves towards the top of the coarsening- and thickening-upward package immediately above the horizon containing the megaflutes and scours suggest periods of increasing spill (from GHK A).

The upper channel form differs from the lower channel form in a number of respects; its fill is thinner-bedded and contains more rip-up clast-rich horizons and plant material; it also exhibits a slight coarsening- and thickening-upward motif. Palaeocurrent measurements within the upper channel (Fig. 4a) indicate flow towards the NNW. This is approximately 60 degrees to overall palaeocurrent orientations observed in the Hangklip area channel complexes, and so the channel may represent an offshoot or overbank splay from GHK B.

Significance of wave modification of bed tops

The reworking of only the topmost lamina of each climbing- and current-ripple laminated turbidite sandstone bed, combined with the differences in palaeocurrent measurements from internal climbing-ripple lamination to symmetrical ripples (commonly more than 60 degrees) and the increase in the amount of bioturbation on the symmetrical-rippled bed tops relative to the climbing-ripple laminated turbidite sandstone beds indicates that these symmetrical ripples did not form in a shallow water setting. Additionally, Unit 5 overlies basin-floor submarine fans (Hodgson *et al.* 2005), and is immediately overlain by condensed deep-water shales followed by a 200 m-thick, progradational upper slope to shelf-edge succession. The symmetrical ripples are interpreted as the deep-water effect of large storm events that reworked the top surface of the turbidite beds by orbital bottom currents. The two dominant trends of symmetrical ripple crest orientations indicate that the strike of the palaeoslope was approximately NW–SE. An alternative interpretation that local orbital currents were generated from surrounding depositional topography off channel complex margin highs cannot be discounted. Fujioka *et al.* (1989) documented symmetrical ripples being generated at a present day water depth of nearly 3 km from the Yap Ridge, east of the Philippines. This highlights the potential danger of employing symmetrical ripples as an indication of water depth without fully taking into account additional evidence. This interpretation of the succession differs from that of Wach *et al.* (2000) who interpreted this lithofacies as representative of shallow water processes and ascribed it to a deltaic facies association, despite the abundance of otherwise deep-water structures.

Klein Hangklip

Klein Hangklip includes a westerly outlier separated from a more continuous ridge (Figs 1b & 5a, b); both ridges are separated from the southern outcrops by a valley. The upper part of Unit 5 is missing from the top of the Klein Hangklip ridge through weathering, preventing correlation of this part of the stratigraphy with the rest of the study area. In this region, Unit 5 comprises three packages of thick-bedded, structureless and dewatered sandstones (lithofacies Sl 4, Table 1) intercalated with thin-bedded, ripple-laminated units (lithofacies Sl 2 and Sl 3, Table 1). The three thick-bedded sandstone packages are subsequently referred to in this study as KHK A (oldest), KHK B and KHK C (youngest) and described in stratigraphic order. In north–south oriented exposures (across regional strike), numerous internal erosional surfaces (with depths of incision typically of 2–4 m) are common but these surfaces are rarely observed in east–west oriented dip exposures. Claystone clast-rich horizons and packages of thin-bedded, fine-grained material overlie erosion surfaces (lithofacies Sl 5, Table 1). Locally, thick-bedded amalgamated sandstones pass laterally into thin-bedded sandstones over distances of *c.* 100 m. Packages of interbedded

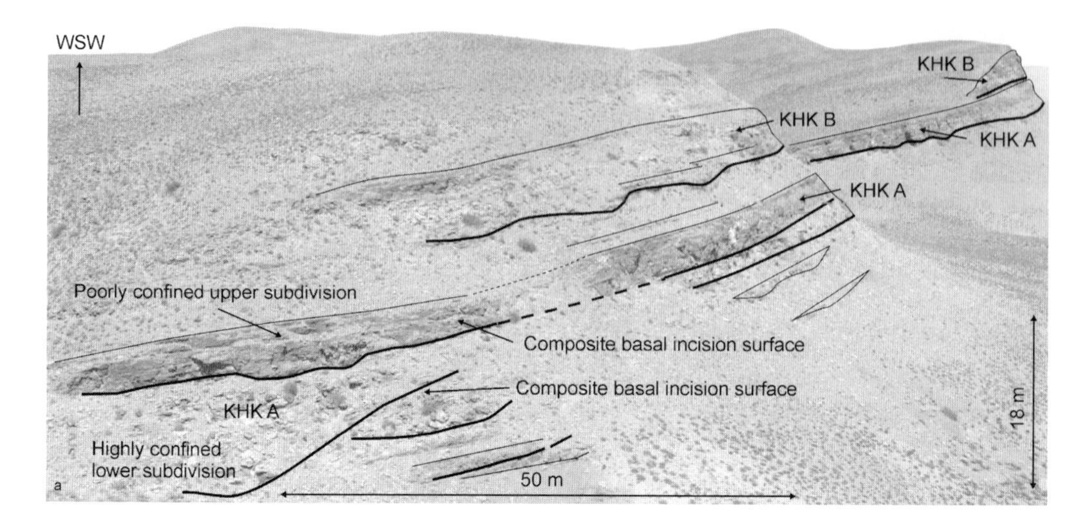

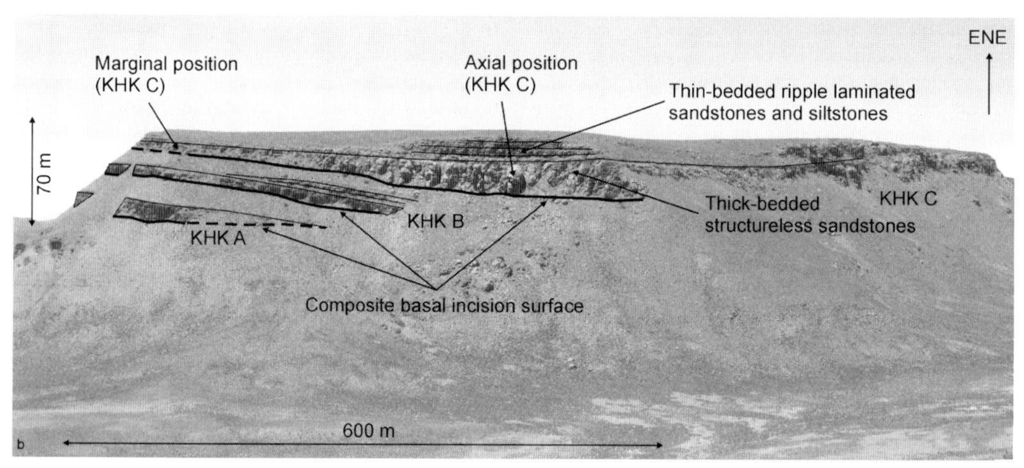

Fig. 5. Klein Hangklip slope channel complex set. (**a**) Outcrop photograph and interpretive line drawing of the north-facing outlier at Klein Hangklip (viewed perpendicular to palaeoslope). Note the bipartite nature to KHK A (outcrop HK3, Fig. 1b). (**b**) Outcrop photograph and interpretive line drawing of the west-facing end to the continuous ridge at Klein Hangklip (outcrop HK5, Fig. 1b). Note the obvious break in KHK C: thinning- and fining-upward, current- and climbing-ripple laminated sandstones and siltstones overlie thick-bedded amalgamated structureless and dewatered sandstones.

siltstone and claystone (lithofacies B 2, Table 1), siltstone and very fine-grained sandstone (lithofacies Sl 1, Table 1) and thin-bedded, very fine- and fine-grained sandstones (lithofacies Sl 2 and Sl 3, Table 1) stratigraphically separate the thick-bedded structureless and dewatered sandstone packages. The thickness of the heterolithic packages separating the structureless and dewatered sandstones, typically range from 1–5 m. Most of the thin-bedded siltstones and sandstones have sheet geometries and preserve climbing- and current-ripple lamination. Good exposures allow detailed observations to be made on the sedimentary architecture and internal organization of KHK A, KHK B and KHK C.

KHK A

The channel-fills exposed at outcrop HK 3 (Figs 1b & 5a) are dominated by thick-bedded structureless and dewatered sandstones containing numerous amalgamation and erosion surfaces (lithofacies Sl 4, Table 1). KHK A can be divided into two distinct units that are easily distinguished at outcrop due to differences in weathering style (Fig. 5a). The lowermost unit is composed of medium- to thick-bedded structureless and dewatered very fine- to fine-grained sandstones with numerous amalgamation surfaces (lithofacies Sl 4, Table 1). The erosive base of KHK A is composite with a maximum-recorded depth of incision of 3.5 m. The upper unit of KHK A comprises thick-bedded fine-grained sandstones rich in plant fragments (the organic material is typically found on amalgamation surfaces and the bases of the sandstone beds; lithofacies Sl 3, Table 1). It also has a composite basal erosion surface mantled with rip-up clasts (lithofacies Sl 5, Table 1), siltstones and very fine-grained sandstones (lithofacies Sl 1, Table 1) but it does not attain the same depth of incision as the lower division of KHK A (< 1.5 m) (Fig. 5a).

Approximately 0.3 km down palaeoslope to the east (outcrop HK 4, Fig. 1b), the lower unit of KHK A is still composed predominantly of medium- to thick-bedded structureless and dewatered sandstone (lithofacies Sl 4, Table 1), but the upper division is predominantly composed of thin-bedded, ripple laminated sandstones (lithofacies Sl 2 and Sl 3, Table 1). The break between upper and lower KHK A is marked by a fine-grained recessive interval. Lower KHK A exhibits a lateral facies change from thick, channelized structureless sandstones with numerous erosion surfaces and amalgamations (lithofacies Sl 4, Table 1) into thick-bedded structureless and thin-bedded, climbing-ripple laminated sandstones with dewatering fabrics (lithofacies Sl 3, Table 1) over 60 m. The basal erosion surface has a maximum depth of incision of 6 m. The upper division of KHK A is also bounded by a composite basal surface with rip-up clasts, siltstones and very fine-grained sandstones (lithofacies Sl 2, Table 1), but incision is minimal.

At locality HK 5 (Figs 1b & 5b), KHK A is bounded by a composite basal erosion surface mantled with rip-up clasts, and draped by siltstone and very fine-grained sandstone (lithofacies Sl 1, Table 1). It is not clear whether KHK A exhibits a bipartite architecture as observed elsewhere in the Klein Hangklip area; however, there is a change in the depositional style of the fill above the composite basal erosion surface. The lowest 3 m consists of thick-bedded structureless sandstone with planar laminations occurring infrequently towards the tops of beds (lithofacies Sl 3, Table 1). This lower thick-bedded interval is overlain by a 0.8 m-thick package of medium-bedded, ripple laminated sandstones with numerous erosion surfaces and rip-up clast horizons (lithofacies Sl 3, Table 1); above this the fill consists of thin-bedded, climbing-ripple laminated sandstones and siltstones (lithofacies Sl 2, Table 1). Palaeocurrent measurements from this interval indicate that palaeoflow was towards the NW.

KHK B

At the 'Lions Head' locality (Fig. 1b) a rapid lateral facies change is observed from north to south. Thin-bedded climbing-ripple laminated sandstones with dewatering fabrics (lithofacies Sl 2 and Sl 3, Table 1) pass into thick-bedded channelized sandstones with numerous erosion and amalgamation surfaces (lithofacies Sl 4, Table 1) over a distance of 70–80 m.

At outcrop HK 4 (Fig. 1b), when observed perpendicular to palaeoflow, the recessive interval of thin-bedded, ripple-laminated very fine-grained sandstones and siltstones (lithofacies Sl 2, Table 1) that typically overlie KHK A elsewhere in this part of the field area is cut out by KHK B (minimum observed depth of incision 5 m). Thick, channelized sandstones with numerous erosion surfaces and amalgamations (lithofacies Sl 4, Table 1) pass laterally into thick-bedded, structureless sandstones with dewatering fabrics (lithofacies Sl 3, Table 1) and thin-bedded, climbing-ripple laminated sandstones (lithofacies Sl 3, Table 1) over about 60 m.

At locality HK 5 (Figs 1b & 5b), KHK B is also confined by a composite basal erosion surface mantled with rip-up clasts, and draped by thin-bedded siltstone and very fine-grained sandstone beds (lithofacies Sl 1, Table 1). At this outcrop a bipartite division within KHK B is not readily distinguished; however, a change in the style of the fill is observed. The lower division of KHK B fines- and thins-upward from thick-bedded, structureless fine-grained sandstone with numerous erosion surfaces and rip-up clast horizons (lithofacies Sl 3, Table 1) to thin-bedded, ripple laminated, very fine-grained sandstone (lithofacies Sl 2, Table 1). Palaeocurrent measurements for this interval indicate that palaeoflow was typically towards the NE. The upper division of KHK B is predominantly thin-bedded climbing-ripple laminated sandstones and siltstones (lithofacies Sl 2, Table 1) although some medium-to-thick-bedded ripple laminated sandstones do occur; these typically exhibit loaded bases and dewatering fabrics.

KHK C

At the 'Lions head' locality an abrupt lateral facies change is observed from north to south in KHK C. Thin-bedded climbing-ripple laminated sandstones with dewatering fabrics (lithofacies Sl 2 and Sl 3, Table 1) pass into thick channelized sandstones with numerous erosion surfaces (lithofacies Sl 4, Table 1) over a distance of about 80 m.

Approximately 4 km down palaeoslope (locality HK 5, Figs 1b & 5b) KHK C attains a maximum thickness of about 35 m. A bipartite division of KHK C is easily distinguished at outcrop, as variations in the nature of the fill are highlighted by differences in the style of weathering. The lower 20 m of KHK C is confined by a composite basal erosion surface with a maximum-recorded depth of incision of 10 m. The fill consists of thick-bedded structureless and dewatered sandstones with numerous amalgamation and erosion surfaces, typically mantled with claystone rip-up clasts (lithofacies Sl 4, Table 1). This lower package is overlain by medium-bedded, fine-grained climbing- and current-ripple laminated sandstones (lithofacies Sl 3, Table 1) (bed bases are commonly erosive, mantled with claystone rip-up clasts and are rich in plant material) that thin- and fine-upward into thin-bedded ripple laminated siltstone and sandstone beds (lithofacies Sl 2, Table 1). The erosional base of the thinner-bedded upper 15 m of KHK C is also composite. An inclined erosion surface cuts out a package of thinly bedded siltstones and sandstones, (lithofacies Sl 1 and Sl 2, Table 1). Internal palaeocurrent indicators are absent from the lower 20 m of KHK C (due to the structureless nature of the fill); however, palaeocurrent measurements from current-ripple foresets indicate that palaeoflow in the upper division of KHK C was towards the NE.

Interpretation

Unit 5 in the Klein Hangklip area is interpreted as three sub-vertically stacked (offset by less than 50 m) submarine channel complexes (KHK A, KHK B and KHK C, Fig. 6a–d) that form a confined slope channel complex set (*sensu* Campion *et al.* 2000). Thick-bedded dewatered sandstones represent individual channel complex axis deposits; these pass laterally (but still within the incisional surface) into thin-bedded sandstone channel complex margin deposits. Pervasive dewatering structures are interpreted to have resulted from loading by rapid deposition. Palaeocurrent measurements, orientation of erosive surfaces and facies distributions demonstrate that the channel complexes are west–east trending. The data suggest that there were two distinct phases of incision within each channel complex (Fig. 7a & b). The first phase resulted in highly confined channels with no evidence of significant spill while the second phase of incision was less deep, and more spill deposits are identified. Each phase constitutes a composite channel (*sensu* Gardner *et al.* 2003) containing two or more single storey channels. When viewed perpendicular to palaeoflow, variations in the architecture and the nature and internal organization of the fill highlight the two phases within KHK A (Fig. 5a) and KHK C (Fig. 5b). The change from thick-bedded structureless sandstone to medium-bedded, ripple laminated sandstone with numerous erosion surfaces and rip-up clast horizons is interpreted to reflect the boundary between the lower highly confined composite channel and the upper poorly confined composite channel. Although not as easily demonstrated, it is suggested that the same bipartite division exists within KHK B (a steeply inclined composite basal erosion surface cuts out the thin-bedded facies separating KHK A from KHK B). The composite basal erosion surface of KHK C is deeper and wider than that of KHK A and KHK B, which is interpreted to reflect an increase in the magnitude and erosive capability of gravity flows at this time. The uppermost poorly exposed turbidites of Unit 5 are more sheet-like, fine- and thin-upward, and are interpreted to mark the retrogradation of the system.

Sequence stratigraphy

Stratigraphic relationship of the channel complexes and sheet turbidites

Outcrop limitations preclude interpretation of the precise time-stratigraphic relationship between the accumulation of the frontal (build) sheet turbidites across the Hangklip area, the incision of the Groot Hangklip and Klein Hangklip slope channel complexes, their filling, and the accumulation of lateral (spill) sheet turbidites in the intervening Drooge Kloof/Waterfall area. However, by correlating the outcrop-logged sections with the help of continuous oblique aerial photography, changes in channel complex architecture and changes in style and intensity of soft-sediment deformation allowed determination of the stratigraphic relationship between the axial and non-axial parts of the system.

The hypothesis that the accumulation of coarsening- and thickening-upward turbidite packages in the Drooge Kloof/Waterfall area reflects, to a large degree, deposition in an older (relative to channel incision) prograding intraslope fan environment is supported by the sheet-like nature to the bedding and the dominant NE direction to palaeoflow. In addition, the occurrence of the highly deformed sandbodies towards the tops of coarsening- and thickening-upward packages may indicate periods of depositional hiatus with dewatering and 'creep' down slope. These horizons are interpreted as deep-water 'interfluve' surfaces. Time 'stored' through deformation represents interesting alternative evidence for slope bypass.

Although poor exposure precludes direct observation of most channel margins, further evidence to support the supposition that the channels are younger and not genetically related to the surrounding turbiditic packages is the abrupt change in lithofacies from thick-bedded, amalgamated, structureless and dewatered sandstone in the lower, strongly confined phase of the channel complexes to the surrounding thin-bedded heterolithic strata, erosional truncation of these turbiditic packages, and the absence of evidence for levees. The composite nature of the basal erosion surfaces, the persistent

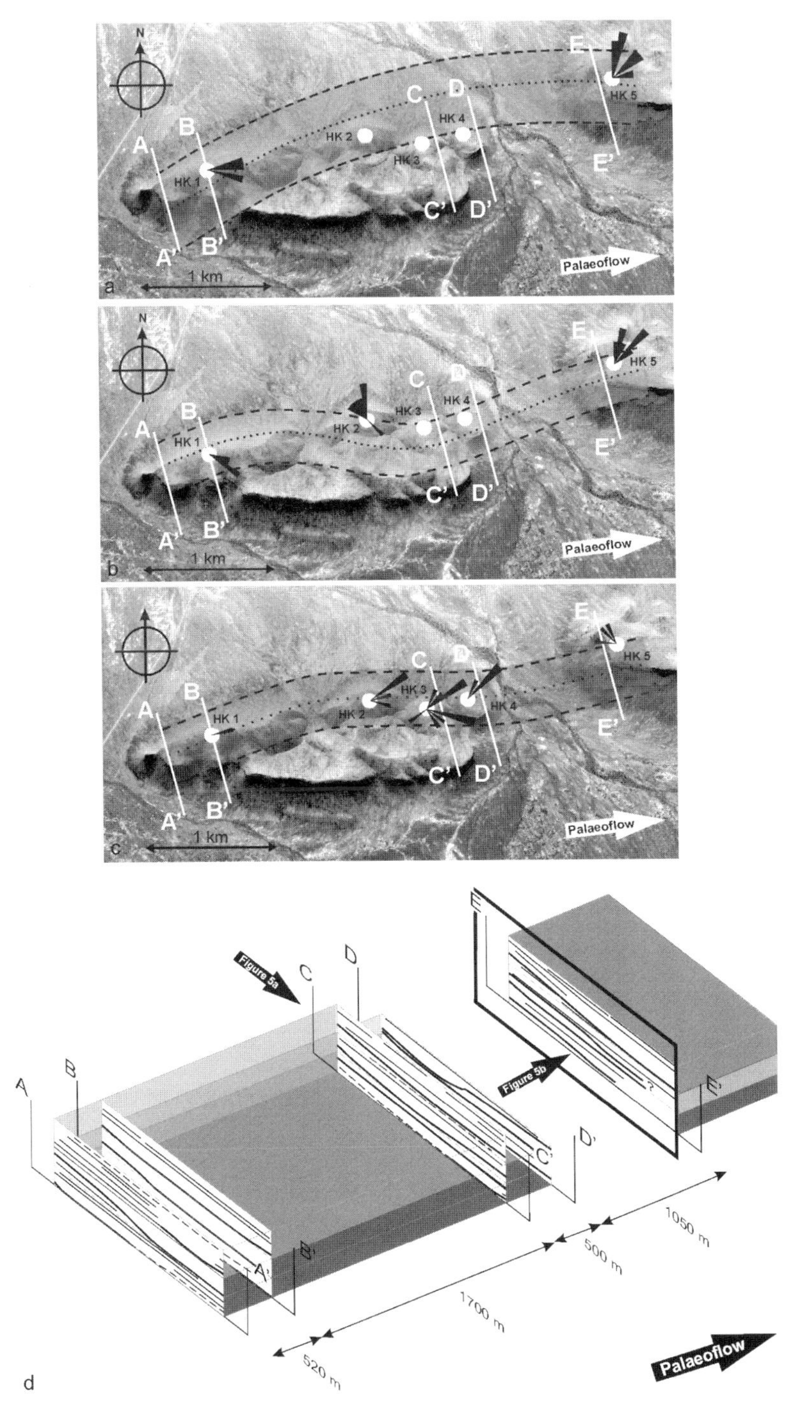

Fig. 6. Block diagram and interpreted aerial photograph of the Klein Hangklip outlier showing the position of the thick-bedded channelized sands with numerous erosion surfaces and amalgamations (axial position). Trends in sediment dispersal are indicated (see text for details) along with the associated log positions. The dotted line denotes the inferred centres of the channel complexes and the dashed lines depict the margins to the axial zones. (**a**) KHK C. (**b**) KHK B. (**c**) KHK A. (**d**) Block diagram of the Klein Hangklip stacked channel complex set. Note the slight lateral offset to the channel complexes. Arrows indicate the position of Fig. 5a & b.

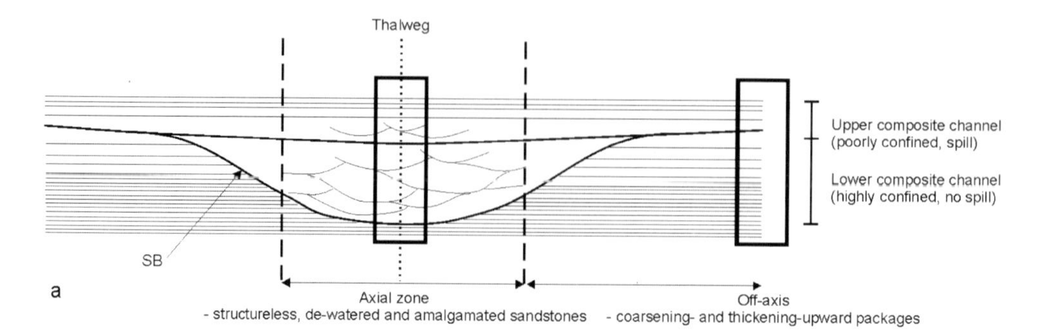

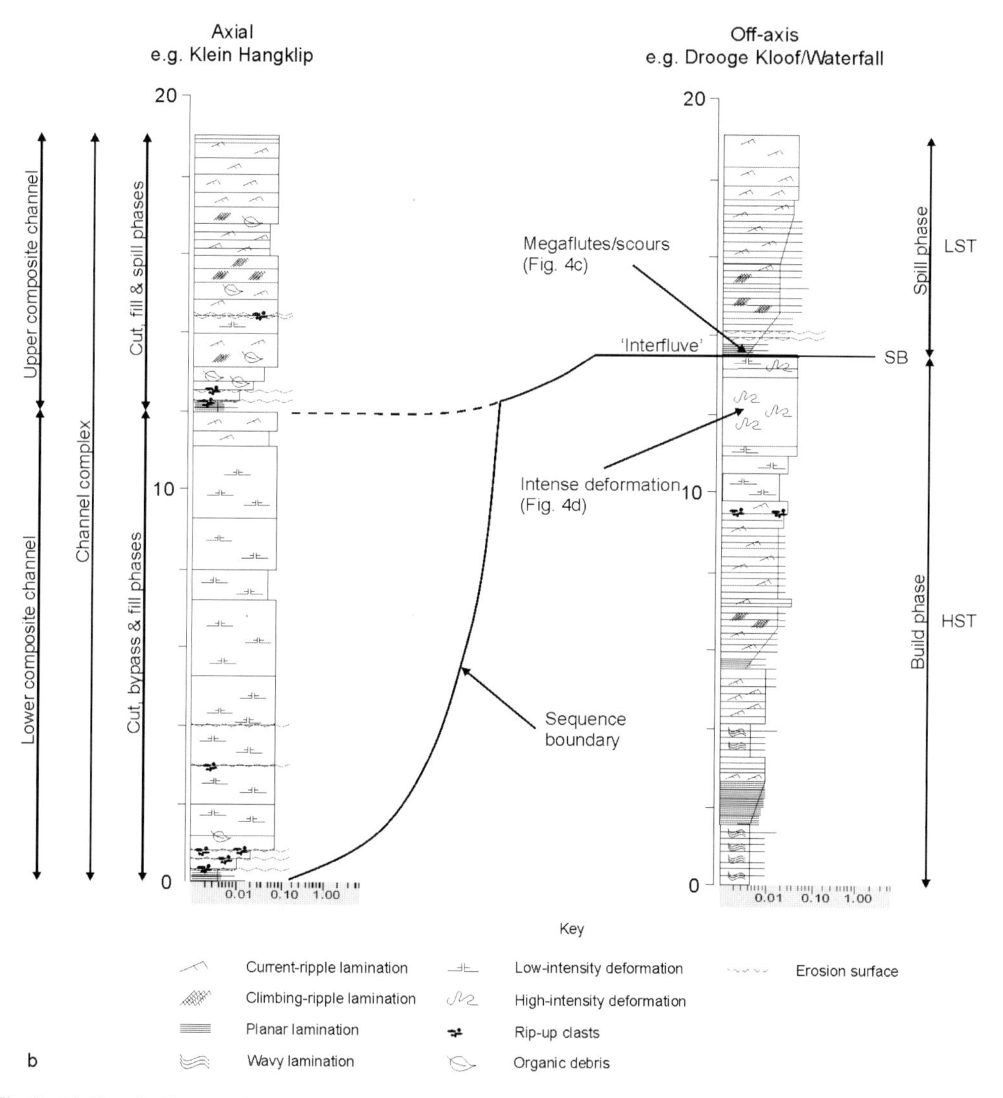

Fig. 7. (**a**) Generic diagram of a Klein Hangklip channel complex. Note the bipartite subdivision of the channel complex into a lower, highly-confined composite channel and an upper, poorly-confined composite channel. The inferred relationship between the two 'boxed' areas is shown in Fig. 7b. (**b**) Generic figure showing the relationship between an axial position within a Klein Hangklip channel complex and an off-axis position in the area of Drooge Kloof/Waterfall. See text for details.

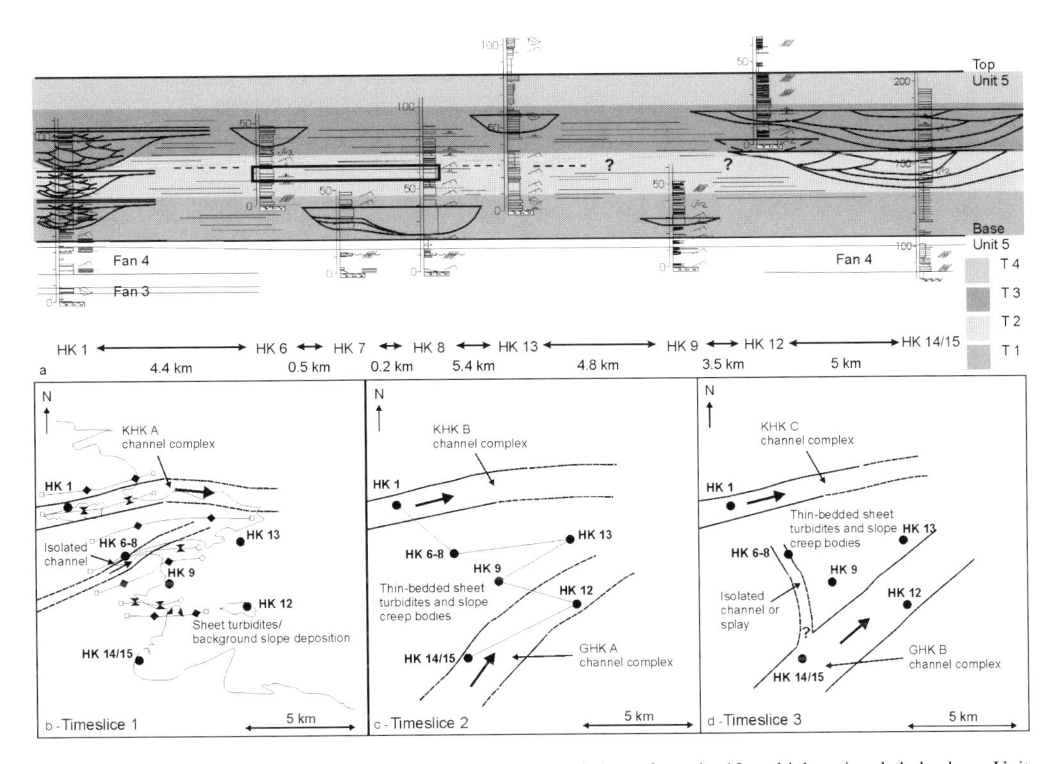

Fig. 8. (**a**) Cross-section of the Hangklip study area. The section is hung from the 12 m-thick regional shale above Unit 5. The horizon containing the megaflutes and scours interpreted to represent erosion from non-depositional turbidity currents that spilled from the Groot Hangklip (GHK A) and Klein Hangklip (KHK B) channel complexes is marked by the dashed line within T2. The boxed area corresponds to the deep-water 'interfluve' (zone of maximum deformation). Four timeslices (T1–T4) have been used to reconstruct the palaeogeographic evolution of Unit 5. T1, T2 and T3 are drawn at sequence boundary times and T4 represents retrogradation of the Unit 5 system. (**b–c**) Palaeogeographical reconstructions of the Hangklip area. (**b**) Timeslice 1 – Initiation of channelization. (**c**) Timeslice 2 - Channel complex development. 'Creep' bodies develop in the deep-water interfluve. (**d**) Timeslice 3 - Increased incision, overbank splay and lobe development.

bypass facies, and the numerous low-angle incision surfaces and amalgamations within the thick-bedded fill of the strongly confined phase of the channel complexes suggest efficient transport into the deeper basin to the NE and confinement during aggradational filling of the channel complex.

In the Drooge Kloof/Waterfall area, the interpretation that a proportion of the sheet turbidites accumulated in an overbank environment synchronous with late-stage channel complex aggradation and lateral spill is supported by the facies (coarsening- and thickening-upward packages of climbing-ripple laminated sandstones and siltstones), palaeocurrent data (oblique to the palaeoflow of the Groot Hangklip and Klein Hangklip channel complexes), high sandstone content, and the identification of a number of large scours or megaflutes above (older) thick-bedded dewatered sandstones (Figs 7 & 8a). These scours are interpreted to represent erosion from non-depositional turbidity currents that spilled from the Groot Hangklip (GHK A) and Klein Hangklip (KHK B) and channel complexes at the start of the spill stage (see below). This is an inferred relationship as the predominantly east–west orientation of the outcrops prevent the 'walking out' of the surface. This interpretation differs from that of Elliot (2000) who related megaflute erosion surfaces in the Upper Carboniferous Ross Formation to the initiation of turbidite channels whereas here it is proposed that the scours and megaflutes result from late-stage lateral spill.

Our preferred model for the time-stratigraphic development of the study area is similar to the build-cut-fill-spill (BCFS) model that Gardner & Borer (2000) proposed for single submarine channel/sheet cycles. In the Hangklip area it is only possible to apply the model reliably at a channel complex scale (Fig. 9). The build phase is represented by the widespread accumulation of frontal splay sheet heteroliths and very fine-grained sandstones. The highly confined amalgamated and dewatered sandstones within the lower bipartite channel complexes

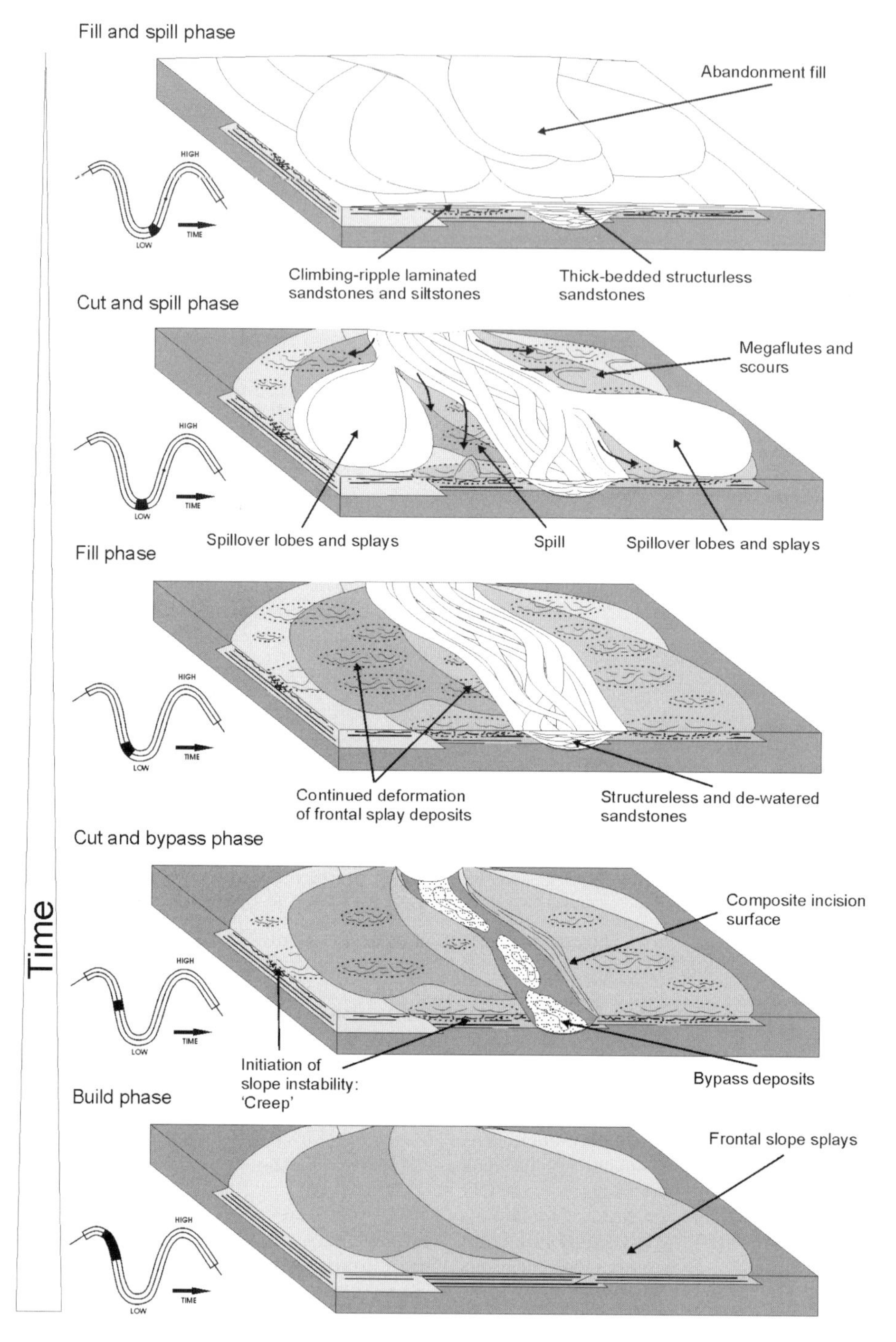

Fig. 9. Generic diagram for channel complex development in the Klein Hangklip area, based on the build-cut-fill-spill model of Gardner *et al.* (2003). Individual channel complexes are interpreted as representing fifth order sequences. Each fifth order sequence is composed of the cut (sequence boundary, SB), erosion and bypass phase (early LST), the fill phase (mid LST), the cut and spill phase (late LST) and a retrogradational fill and spill phase (early TST). The remainder of the TST and much of the HST are condensed, overlain by the next build phase (late HST/falling stage systems tract).

and the coeval deformation of the earlier build phase turbidites in the deep-water 'interfluve' correspond to the cut and bypass, and fill phases. The megaflutes and scours in the Drooge Kloof area relate to the early spill phase whereas the upper poorly confined fining- and thinning-upward ripple laminated sandstones and siltstones represent the main part of the spill phase (Figs 7 & 9). These spill deposits extend into the Drooge Kloof area and it was only at these times that Drooge Kloof was a 'genetically related' interchannel/overbank environment (Figs 7, 8 & 9).

Vertical stacking of channel complexes

The three channel complexes at Klein Hangklip (KHK A–C) and the two at Groot Hangklip (GHK A and GHK B) form vertically stacked channel complex sets. Tectonic and/or depositional confinement on the seabed is commonly invoked to explain vertical channel stacking patterns (e.g. Smith 2004). Present-day antiforms run parallel to and on either side of the Drooge Kloof ridge and the channel complex sets approximately trend along gentle synforms (Fig. 8b). However, currently, there is no conclusive evidence that these structures were active during sedimentation. Therefore the control on the long-term fixed positions of the slope channel complexes at Klein Hangklip and Groot Hangklip are interpreted as being due to long-lived (entrenched) shelf-edge entry point's up-dip. No mass transport complexes (MTCs) have currently been identified down-dip to infer shelf-edge collapse as the mechanism for positioning shelf entry points.

Channel and sequence hierarchy

In the absence of high-resolution chronostratigraphic data, Hodgson *et al.* (2005) employed modern pelagic sedimentation rates and 2:1 compaction estimates to interpret the four 30–60 m thick basin-floor fans that underlie Unit 5 as the lowstand systems tracts (LST) to fifth order sequences, each lowstand being a composite of higher-order intrafan cycles (Johnson *et al.* 2001). Based on its much greater stratigraphic thickness and sediment volume, Unit 5 is interpreted herein as a fourth order highstand systems tract (HST), a fourth order lowstand systems tract and a fourth order transgressive systems tract (TST). The fourth order HST is comprised of two fifth order sequences. Each fifth order sequence is composed of the cut (a sequence boundary, SB), erosion and bypass phase (early LST), the fill phase (mid LST), the cut and spill phase (late LST) and a retrogradational fill and spill phase (early TST). The remainder of the TST and much of the HST are condensed, overlain by the next build phase (late HST/falling stage systems tract, FSST) (Fig. 9). The fifth order sequences contain erosion and aggradation cycles (at the scale of individual channels and composite channels), that we tentatively interpret as sixth order sequences. The stacking pattern of the fifth order slope channel complexes within the fourth order Unit 5 sequence suggests that the incision-to-abandonment cycle for GHK B/KHK C was the most significant in terms of relative sea-level fall as these channel complexes are the deepest and widest. The incision surface at the base of GHK B/KHK C is therefore interpreted as the fourth order sequence boundary. This hypothesis is supported by the increasing sand content of successive build phases (T3 > T2 > T1, Fig. 8a), suggesting an overall increase in sediment flux coupled with increasing amounts of erosion.

The hierarchy of submarine channel sediment bodies is similar to that proposed for deep-water systems in general (Campion *et al.* 2000) and for the Permian Brushy Canyon Formation of West Texas (Gardner *et al.* 2003). Single-story channel-fills and composite channels (possibly sixth order) amalgamate to form channel complexes (fifth order). Multiple channel complexes form channel complex sets (channel fairways of Gardner *et al.* 2003) that stack vertically to form a sand-rich region that is reactivated after each abandonment phase.

Palaeogeographic reconstruction of the Hangklip area

Four composite timeslices (T1–T4) have been used to reconstruct the palaeogeographic evolution of Unit 5 in the Hangklip area. Each of these composite time slices includes build, cut, fill and spill components of interpreted fifth order sequences. It is not possible to depict the individual systems tracts in each composite timeslice so Fig. 8b–d shows T1, T2 and T3 at the time of maximum incision during three individual cycles of initiation, channel incision, channel aggradation, spill and abandonment.

Timeslice 1 (T1)

T1 (Fig. 8a, b) begins directly on top of the regional shale above Fan 4 with the widespread accumulation of sheet-like, thin-bedded ripple laminated siltstones and very fine-grained sandstones across the Hangklip area and is interpreted to represent deposition on the slope primarily from low-density turbidity currents, possibly during a time when the slope was below equilibrium grade and sediment was accreted to the slope as opposed to being bypassed into the deeper basin to the NE (Prather 2003). This low sediment supply period is interpreted to represent late highstand systems tract conditions with most of the sand being stored on the time-equivalent shelf, but some material being derived from the shelf edge to be deposited as frontal splays.

The isolated channel at Drooge Kloof and the Klein Hangklip channel complex KHK A represent the earliest fifth order sequence boundary incision within Unit 5. The upper boundary of T1 at Klein Hangklip and Drooge Kloof is marked by a fining- and thinning-upward package of interbedded very fine-grained sandstones and siltstones, interpreted to represent a reduction in sediment flux. At Groot Hangklip this interval has been cut out by facies interpreted to represent the early stages (erosion and bypass) in the formation of channel complex GHK A.

Timeslice 2 (T2)

T2 (Fig. 8a, c) starts with the widespread deposition of frontal splays within the falling-stage systems tract of the lowermost fifth order sequence. Development of synchronous channel complexes at Groot Hangklip and Klein Hangklip (GHK A and KHK B, Fig. 8a, c) mark the second fifth order sequence boundary. The basal incision surface (*c.* 6 m) overlain by thin-bedded rip-up clast-rich facies in the slope channel complexes identified across the outcrop belt suggest that significant amounts of sediment were bypassed down dip. In the Drooge Kloof/Waterfall area, the enhanced development of deformation is interpreted as reflecting an extended period of time when gravity flows were erosionally confined to the slope channels and this sediment starved area of the slope was the site of instability processes. Slope creep bodies are elongate parallel to the palaeoslope (NW–SE) and formed soon after deposition or near the surface. Occasionally, these slope creep bodies failed completely and transformed down slope into slumps or slides, which preserve large rafts of contorted turbidite sandstone beds. This horizon is interpreted as a deep-water 'interfluve', coeval to the fifth order sequence boundary, bypass and backfilling of the confined fill stage of the channel complexes. A number of large scours and megaflutes occur above the thick-bedded dewatered sandstones; these are interpreted to represent erosion from non-depositional (in the Hangklip area) turbidity currents that spilled outside of the partially filled poorly-confined Groot Hangklip (GHK A) and Klein Hangklip (KHK B) channel complexes during the spill stage (Fig. 8a).

Timeslice 3 (T3)

Late highstand to falling stage frontal splays of the second fifth order sequence are cut by the fourth order sequence boundary. This composite basal erosion surface at Groot Hangklip and Klein Hangklip (GHK B and KHK C) shows the greatest depth of incision recorded at any time across the area (> 15 m and > 10 m respectively) and it is clear that KHK C is wider and deeper than KHK A or KHK B (Figs 5b & 8a).

An increase in the net:gross and number of soft-sediment deformation structures within the Drooge Kloof/Waterfall areas (relative to T2) is interpreted to reflect an increase in sediment flux (related to the progradation of the system) and rapid deposition may have led to increased loading. As in T2, it is possible to pick an equivalent 'interfluve' horizon to the erosional sequence boundary, based on the maximum development of slope 'creep' bodies. Palaeocurrent measurements within the isolated channel and surrounding heterolithic strata imply that the dominant flow direction was towards the NNW. This is roughly 60 degrees to palaeocurrent orientations observed in single- or multi-storey channel bodies elsewhere within T3 and is interpreted to represent an offshoot or overbank splay from GHK B (Fig. 8a, d).

Timeslice 4 (T4)

A unit-wide change in depositional style is marked by a recessive break at the top of the cliff-forming structureless and dewatered sandstones of GHK B and KHK C (Fig. 8a). Sheet-like, planar-laminated, medium-bedded fine-grained sandstone (lithofacies Sl 3, Table 1) and sigmoidal, climbing-ripple laminated, very fine- and fine-grained sandstone interbeds (lithofacies Sl 2, Table 1) fine- and thin-upward into siltstone-sandstone and siltstone-claystone interbeds (lithofacies Sl 1 and B 2, Table 1). This fining- and thinning-upward turbidite unit is present across the top of Unit 5 throughout the Hangklip area and has been mapped regionally, over 40 km to the north (Hodgson *et al.* 2005; Van Der Merve, pers. comm.; Fig. 1a). T4 is interpreted as a retrogradation of the Unit 5 system, marking the fourth order transgressive systems tract, with increasing storage of sand in new shelf accommodation. The top of Unit 5 is marked by a regional 12 m-thick condensed deep-water claystone, which represents superimposed fourth order and third order maximum flooding surfaces (Hodgson *et al.* 2005).

Conclusions

Unit 5 in the Hangklip area is interpreted as the deposits of a lower slope environment with two partially-synchronous, unconformity-bounded, vertically stacked channel complex sets. The vertical stacking of the slope channel complexes into channel complex sets is interpreted to have been controlled by the fixed position of shelf-edge entry points rather than structural confinement in the Hangklip area. Each channel complex set comprises two or more channel complexes, which, in the Klein Hangklip area, contain readily discernible composite channels. The lower part of each composite channel is characterized by high confinement with no spill, while the upper part of the composite channel is characterized by low confinement.

The thin-bedded and deformed sandstone facies association in the Drooge Kloof and Waterfall area is interpreted as a combination of frontal splay and lateral splay environments. Most of the sediment was supplied by NE-prograding intraslope fans that deposited coarsening- and thickening-upward frontal splay packages as highstand to falling stage systems tracts that are not genetically related to the channel complexes. The occurrence of deformed sandbodies towards the tops of the frontal splay packages indicate periods of depositional hiatus during subsequent sequence boundary incision and bypass in the laterally adjacent slope channels, when 'interfluve' sediments were subjected to dewatering and down-slope creep.

Volumetrically subsidiary lateral splay channels and lobes were deposited during the late stages of channel complex aggradation and spill and are genetically related to the poorly-confined upper parts of the channel complexes. Large scours or megaflutes associated with the bases of spill packages are interpreted to represent erosion from single non-depositional (in the Hangklip area) turbidity currents that spilled from the Groot Hangklip (GHK A) and Klein Hangklip (KHK B) channel complexes.

Unit 5 is interpreted as part of two fourth order sequences, that include three superimposed *c.* 25 m-thick fifth order sequences. Each fifth order sequence is composed of the cut (SB) and bypass phase (early LST), the fill phase (mid LST), the cut and spill phase (late LST) and a retrogradational fill and spill phase (early TST) (Fig. 9). The remainder of the TST and much of the HST are condensed and the frontal splay build phase represents late HST/FSST. The stacking pattern of the fifth order slope channel complexes within the Unit 5 sequence suggests that the incision surface at the base of GHK B and KHK C represents a fourth order sequence boundary. This hypothesis is supported by the increasing sand content of successive build phases in the 'interfluve' areas of the fifth order sequences, suggesting an overall increase in sediment flux coupled with increasing erosion.

This work was undertaken within the SLOPE project at the University of Liverpool, which was funded by ChevronTexaco, ConocoPhillips, ExxonMobil and Statoil. RW acknowledges support by a Natural Environment Research Council research studentship (NER/S/A/2001/06302A). Dr DeVille Wickens is thanked for the provision of logistical support and Willem Van Der Merve and the NOMAD project workers for healthy discussion on the stratigraphy of the Tanqua depocentre. SLOPE project colleagues Ros King and Graham Potts provided structural geology support. The paper benefited from detailed and helpful reviews by Nick Drinkwater and Lorna Richmond.

References

ABREU, V., SULLIVAN, M., PIRMEZ, C. & MOHRIG, D. 2003. Lateral accretion packages (LAPs): an important reservoir element in deep water sinuous channels. *Marine and Petroleum Geology*, **20**, 631–648.

BANGERT, B., STOLLHOFEN, H., LORENZ, V. & ARMSTRONG, R. 1999. The geochronology and significance of ash-fall tuffs in the glaciogenic Carboniferous–Permian Dwyka Group of Namibia and South Africa. *Journal of African Earth Sciences*, **29**, 33–49.

BEAUBOUEF, R.T., ROSSEN, C., ZELT, F.B., SULLIVAN, M.D., MOHRIG, D.C. & JENNETTE, D.C. 1999. *Deep-water sandstones, Brushy Canyon Formation, West Texas.* American Association of Petroleum Geologists Continuing Education Course Note Series, **40**, American Association of Petroleum Geologists, Tulsa.

BOUMA, A.H. & WICKENS, H. DEV. 1991. Permian passive margin submarine fan complex, Karoo Basin. South Africa: possible model to Gulf of Mexico. *Gulf Coast Association of Geological Societies Transactions*, **41**, 30–42.

CAMPION, K.M., SPRAGUE, A.R., MOHRIG, D., ET AL. 2000. Outcrop expression of confined channel complexes. *In:* WEIMAR, P., SLATT, R.M., COLEMAN, J., ROSEN, N.C., NELSON, H., BOUMA, A.H., STYZEN, M.J. & LAWRENCE, D.T. (eds) *Deep-water reservoirs of the world.* Gulf Coast Section Society of Economic Palaeontologists and Mineralogists, 127–150.

COLE, D.I. 1992. Evolution and development of the Karoo Basin. *In:* DE WIT, M.J. & RANSOME, I.G.D. (eds) *Inversion Tectonics of the Cape Fold Belt, Karoo and Cretaceous Basins of Southern Africa.* Balkema, Rotterdam, 87–99.

DE WIT, M. & RANSOME, I.G.D. 1992. Regional inversion tectonics along the southern margin of Gondwana. *In:* DE WIT, M. & RANSOME, I.G.D. (eds) *Inversion Tectonics of the Cape Fold Belt, Karoo and Cretaceous Basins of Southern Africa.* Balkema, Rotterdam, 15–21.

DROSER, M.L. & BOTTJER, D.J. 1989. Ordovician increase in the extent and depth of bioturbation: implications for understanding early ecospace utilization. *Geology*, **17**, 850–852.

ELLIOTT, T. 2000. Megaflute erosion surfaces and the initiation of turbidite channels. *Geology*, **28**, 119–122.

ESCHARD, R., ALBOUY, E., DESCHAMPS, R., EUZEN, T. & AYUB, A. 2003. Downstream evolution of turbiditic channel complexes in the Pab Range outcrops (Maastrichtian, Pakistan). *Marine and Petroleum Geology*, **20**, 691–710.

FUJIOKA, K., WATANABE, M. & KOBAYASHI, K. 1989. Deep-sea photographs of the Northwestern and Central Pacific Ocean—An invitation to deep-sea environment. *Bulletin of the Ocean Research Institute, University of Tokyo*, **27**, 1–214.

GARDNER, M.H. & BORER, J.A. 2000. Submarine channel architecture along a slope to basin profile, Permian Brushy Canyon Formation, West Texas. *In:* BOUMA, A.H. & STONE, C.G. (eds) *Fine-Grained Turbidite Systems.* American Association of Petroleum Geologists Memoir **72**/Society of Economic Palaeontologists and Mineralogists Special Publication, **68**, 195–215.

GARDNER, M.H., BORER, J.A., MELICK, J.J., MAVILLA, N., DECHESNE, M. & WAGERLE, R.N. 2003. Stratigraphic process-response model for submarine channels and related features from studies of Permian Brushy Canyon outcrops, West Texas. *Marine and Petroleum Geology*, **20**, 757–787.

HODGSON, D.M., FLINT, S.S., HODGETTS, D., DRINKWATER, N.J., JOHANNESSON, E.J. & LUTHI, S.M. 2005. Stratigraphic evolution of Permian submarine fan systems, Tanqua depocentre, South Africa. *Journal of Sedimentary Research* (in press).

JOHNSON, M.R. 1991. Sandstone petrography, provenance and plate tectonic setting in Gondwana context of the southeastern Cape-Karoo Basin. *South African Journal of Geology*, **94**, 137–154.

JOHNSON, S.D., FLINT, S., HINDS, D. & WICKENS, H. DEV. 2001. Anatomy of basin floor to slope turbidite systems, Tanqua Karoo, South Africa: sedimentology, sequence stratigraphy and implications for subsurface prediction. *Sedimentology*, **48**, 987–1023.

KOLLA, V., BOURGES, P., URRUTY, J.M. & SAFA, P. 2001. Evolution of deep-water Tertiary sinuous channel offshore Angola (West Africa) and implications for reservoir architecture. *American Association of Petroleum Geologists Bulletin*, **85**, 1371–1405.

LIEN, T., WALKER, R.G. & MARTINSEN, O. J. 2003. Turbidites in the Upper Carboniferous Ross Formation: reconstruction of a channel and spillover system. *Sedimentology*, **50**, 113–148.

LÓPEZ-GAMUNDÍ, O.R. & ROSSELLO, E.A. 1998. Basin-fill evolution and paleotectonic patterns along the Samfrau geosyncline: the Sauce Grande basin — Ventana foldbelt (Argentina) and Karoo basin - Cape foldbelt (South Africa) revisited. *Geologische Rundschau,* **86**, 819–834.

MARTINSEN, O.J., LIEN, T., WALKER, R.G. & COLLINSON, J.D. 2003. Facies and sequential organisation of a mudstone-dominated slope and basin floor succession: the Gull Island Formation, Shannon Basin, Western Ireland. *Marine and Petroleum Geology*, **20**, 789–807.

MAYALL, M. & STEWART, I. 2000. The architecture of turbidite slope channels. *In:* WEIMAR, P., SLATT, R.M., COLEMAN, J., ROSEN, N.C., NELSON, H., BOUMA, A.H., STYZEN M.J. & LAWRENCE, D.T. (eds) *Deep-water Reservoirs of the World.* Gulf Coast Section Society of Economic Palaeontologists and Mineralogists, 578–586.

MELLERE, D., PLINK-BJÖRKLUND, P. & STEEL, R. 2002. Anatomy of shelf deltas at the edge of a prograding Eocene shelf margin, Spitsbergen. *Sedimentology*, **49**, 1181–1206.

PLINK-BJÖRKLUND, P. & STEEL, R. 2002. Sea-level fall below the shelf edge, without basin-floor fans. *Geology*, **30**, 115–118.

PLINK-BJÖRKLUND, P., MELLERE, D. & STEEL, R.J. 2001. Turbidite variability and architecture of sand-prone, deep-water slopes: Eocene clinoforms in the Central Basin, Spitsbergen. *Journal of Sedimentary Research*, **71**, 895–912.

PRATHER, B.E. 2003. Controls on reservoir distribution, architecture and stratigraphic trapping in slope settings. *Marine and Petroleum Geology*, **20**, 529–545.

RUBIDGE, B.S., MODESTO, S., SIDOR, C. & WELMAN, J. 1999. Eunotosaurus africanus from the Ecca-Beaufort contact in Northern Cape Province, South Africa — implications for Karoo Basin development. *South African Journal of Science*, **95**, 553–555.

SAMUEL, A., KNELLER, B., RASLAM, S., SHARP, A. & PARSONS, C. 2003. Prolific deep-marine slope channels of the Nile Delta, Egypt. *American Association for Petroleum Geologists Bulletin*, **87**, 541–560.

SMITH, R. 2004. Turbidite systems influenced by structurally induced topography in the multi-sourced Welsh Basin. *In:* LOMAS, S.A. & JOSEPH, P. (eds) *Confined Turbidite Systems.* Geological Society, London, Special Publications, **222**, 208–209.

STELTING, C.E., BOUMA, A.H. & STONE, C.G. 2000. Fine-grained turbidite systems: Overview. *In:* BOUMA, A.H. & STONE, C.G. (eds) *Fine-grained turbidite systems.* American Association of Petroleum Geologists Memoir **72**/Society of Economic Palaeontologists and Mineralogists Special Publication, **68**, 1–7.

TURNER, B.R. 1999. Tectonostratigraphical development of the Upper Karoo foreland basin: orogenic unloading versus thermally-induced Gondwana rifting. *Journal of African Earth Sciences*, **28**, 215–238.

VAN LENTE, B. 2004. *Chemostratigraphic trends and provenance of the Permian Tanqua and Laingsburg depocentres, southwestern Karoo basin, South Africa.* Unpubl. Ph.D. thesis, University of Stellenbosch.

VEEVERS, J.J., COLE, D.I. & COWAN, E.J. 1994. Southern Africa: Karoo Basin and Cape Fold Belt. *In:* VEEVERS, J.J. & POWELL, C.MCA. (eds) *Permian–Triassic Pangean Basins and foldbelts along the Panthalassan Margin of Gondwanaland.* Geological Society of America Memoir, **184**, 223–279.

VISSER, J.N.J. 1987. The palaeogeography of part of southwestern Gondwana during the Permo-Carboniferous glaciation. *Palaeogeography, Palaeoclimatology, Palaeoecology*, **61**, 205–219.

VISSER, J.N.J. 1992. Deposition of the Early to Late Permian Whitehill Formation during a sea-level highstand in a juvenile foreland basin. *South African Journal of Geology*, **95**, 181–193.

VISSER, J.N.J. 1993. Sea-level changes in a back-arc foreland transition — The Late Carboniferous–Permian Karoo Basin of South Africa. *Sedimentary Geology*, **83**, 115–131.

WACH, G.D., LUKAS, T.C., GOLDHAMMER, R.K., WICKENS, H. DEV. & BOUMA, A.H. 2000. Submarine fan through slope to deltaic transition basin-fill succession, Tanqua Karoo, South Africa. *In:* BOUMA, A.H. & STONE, C.G. (eds) *Fine-Grained Turbidite Systems.* American Association of Petroleum Geologists Memoir **72**/Society of Economic Palaeontologists and Mineralogists Special Publication, **68**, 173–180.

WICKENS, H. DEV. 1994. *Basin floor fan building turbidites of the southwestern Karoo Basin, Permian Ecca Group, South Africa*. Unpubl. Ph.D. thesis, University of Port Elizabeth, 233p.

WICKENS, H.DEV. & BOUMA, A.H. 2000. The Tanqua Fan Complex, Karoo Basin, South Africa – outcrop analog for fine-grained, deepwater deposits. *In:* BOUMA, A.H. & STONE, C.G. (eds) *Fine-Grained Turbidite Systems.* American Association of Petroleum Geologists Memoir **72**/Society of Economic Palaeontologists and Mineralogists Special Publication, **68**, 153–165.

Late Cenozoic evolution of the Nankai trench–slope system: evidence from sand petrography and clay mineralogy

MICHAEL B. UNDERWOOD[1] & CHRISTOPHER L. FERGUSSON[2]

[1] *Department of Geological Sciences, University of Missouri, Columbia, MO 65211, USA (e-mail: UnderwoodM@missouri.edu)*

[2] *School of Earth and Environmental Sciences, University of Wollongong, New South Wales 2522, Australia*

Abstract: Submarine slope systems in subduction zones evolve in response to a combination of tectonic and sedimentary forcing. It can be difficult to determine how and when tectonic forcing affects sedimentation, especially when investigating ancient rock successions, but one of the more reliable indicators is a change in sediment composition. During Leg 190 of the Ocean Drilling Program, sandy turbidites were recovered from a Quaternary trench wedge (Nankai Trough), a Pliocene–Pleistocene slope basin, the underlying Pliocene–Miocene accretionary prism, and a Miocene turbidite facies in the Shikoku Basin. Differences in detrital provenance between the sand and clay-sized fractions indicate that turbidity currents did not follow pathways of suspended-sediment transport during the past 10 Ma. During the middle and late Miocene, the sand probably was eroded from a newly exposed accretionary complex (Shimanto Belt). In contrast, high contents of detrital smectite in Miocene mudstones (>50 wt% of the <2 μm size fraction, relative to illite, chlorite+kaolinite, and quartz) point to a strong volcanic component of suspended-sediment input (Izu-Bonin island arc). The sand in accreted Pliocene turbidites was also eroded from the Shimanto Belt and transported by transverse flow down the insular slope. The trench-wedge facies then switched to axial flow during the Quaternary, when the sand supply tapped a mixed volcanic-metasedimentary provenance in the rapidly uplifted Izu-Honshu collision zone. Progressive depletion of smectite during the Pliocene and Pleistocene (<20 wt%) points to increased movement of illite- and chlorite-rich clay toward the east and NE from sources on Kyushu and Shikoku. That shift in mud composition coincides with intensification of the North Pacific western boundary current (Kuroshio Current) at approximately 3 Ma. Overall, the depositional system in the Nankai Trough and Shikoku Basin shifted its sand sources because of regional tectonics, whereas the suspended-sediment budget was modulated by hemispheric changes in ocean-water circulation.

Slope systems in subduction zones evolve in response to a complicated array of sedimentary, tectonic, and oceanographic factors (Underwood & Moore 1995). Eustatic forcing and autocyclic mechanisms play important roles in modulating the supply of sediment and moulding the character of lithofacies associations across all types of continental margins. In the case of subduction zones, however, several additional processes need to be considered: creation of ridges and intraslope basins via imbricate thrusting, fault-bend folding, and diapirism (Moore & Karig 1976); efficient sediment bypassing of forearc relief through deeply incised submarine canyons (Underwood & Karig 1980); mass wasting and severe warping of the forearc's structural grain during seamount subduction (Lallemand & Le Pichon 1987); gradual uplift of the forearc in response to underplating beneath the accretionary prism (Platt 1986); and punctuated uplift of new detrital sources during arc–trench or arc–arc collision (Kimura 1996). During geophysical surveys of modern systems, the products of tectonic activity can be imaged in impressive detail, and rates of uplift can be measured with GPS geodesy. The effects and rates of tectonism can be more difficult to quantify in the subaerial rock record, so other criteria need to be included in the geological interpretations. One of the more useful indicators of tectono-sedimentary change is sediment composition. The composition of turbidite sand or sandstone typically changes in response to uplift of new source areas and tectonically induced rerouting of delivery paths. Dispersal of hemipelagic mud is more complicated because of the added effects of deep-ocean thermohaline circulation and surface currents.

The Nankai subduction margin of SW Japan (Fig. 1) has been the site of considerable research activity, including recent drilling by the Ocean Drilling Program (ODP) and geophysical surveys (Moore *et al.* 2001; Mazzotti *et al.* 2002; Park *et al.* 2002; Underwood *et al.* 2003*a*). Nankai is a focus area for the MARGINS seismogenic zone experiment. In view of the large quantity of high-quality data, the Nankai margin provides a superior illustration of how tectonic evolution affects sediment dispersal and facies architecture. Previous workers (de Rosa *et al.* 1986; Taira & Niitsuma 1986; Marsaglia *et al.* 1992; Underwood *et al.* 1993) showed that sand in

From: HODGSON, D.M. & FLINT, S.S. (eds) 2005. *Submarine Slope Systems: Processes and Products*. Geological Society, London, Special Publications, **244**, 113–129. 0305–8719/$15.00

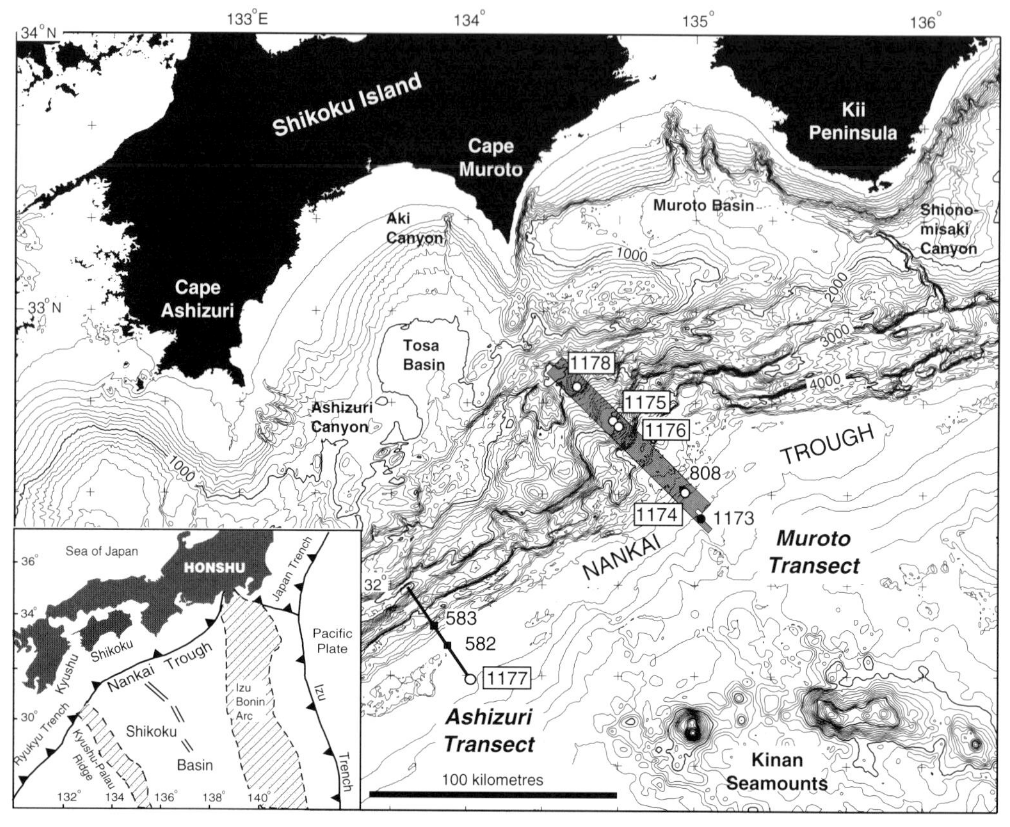

Fig. 1. Regional bathymetric map of the Nankai Trough and the northern edge of Shikoku Basin. Numbers refer to sites of the Deep Sea Drilling Project (DSDP) and the Ocean Drilling Program (ODP). Shaded region along the Muroto Transect corresponds to area of 3D seismic survey. Bathymetry is in metres. From Shipboard Scientific Party (2001).

the present-day Nankai Trough was eroded from a zone of arc–arc collision in central Honshu. However, illite-rich assemblages of detrital clay minerals from the trench wedge reflect a recycled metasedimentary source (Underwood *et al.* 1993). Older parts of the Nankai accretionary prism remained unsampled until ODP Leg 190. New data allow us to discriminate three sand petrofacies (volcanic-lithic, quartzose, sedimentary-lithic), and interpretations of detrital provenance for those petrofacies provide important new constraints on reconstructions of sediment dispersal during the Miocene and Pliocene (Fergusson 2003). We also show that the sources of detrital clay-sized sediment changed dramatically over the same span of the Miocene to Pliocene (Steurer & Underwood 2003; Underwood & Steurer 2003). The purpose of this paper is to summarize the new compositional data from the Nankai drill sites and build an integrated reconstruction of the margin's sediment-dispersal system. In doing so, we demonstrate that turbidite dispersal shifted because of regional tectonics; simultaneously, the suspended-sediment budget was driven by hemispheric changes in ocean-water circulation.

Tectonic and stratigraphic setting

The onland geology of central and SW Japan includes a wide variety of Mesozoic and early Cenozoic accretionary complexes (Taira *et al.* 1989; Isozaki 1996; Maruyama *et al.* 1997). The Inner Zone, which is located on the north side of the Median Tectonic Line (Fig. 2), contains low-pressure, high-temperature metamorphic rocks of the Ryoke Belt and related granitic rocks (Nakajima 1997). The Outer Zone (Fig. 2) consists of parallel bands of high-pressure metamorphic rocks and low-grade metasedimentary strata assigned to the Sanbagawa, Chichibu, and Shimanto Belts (Taira *et al.* 1988; Toriumi & Teruya 1988; Higashino 1990). Japan was connected to the Asian mainland prior to opening of the Japan Sea, which started at 15–18 Ma (Tamaki *et al.* 1992; Jolivet *et al.* 1994; Lee *et al.*

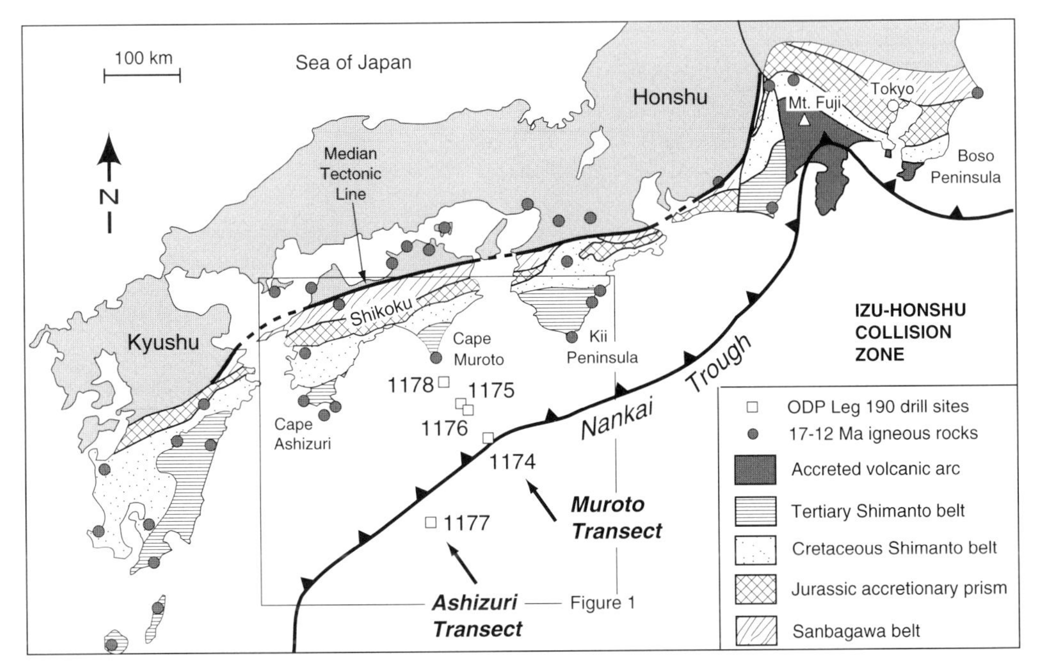

Fig. 2. Simplified geological map showing principal sources of sedimentary and metasedimentary detritus entering the Nankai Trough and forearc from the Outer Zone of SW Japan. The Izu-Honshu collision zone at the NE edge of Nankai Trough also contains neovolcanic source rocks. Numbers refer to ODP sites. Modified from Shipboard Scientific Party (2001).

1999). At approximately the same time, the Outer Zone was affected by rotation and widespread near-trench magmatic activity (Oba 1977; Hisatomi 1988; Terakado *et al.* 1988; Saito *et al.* 1997). The Izu-Bonin arc (Fig. 1) started to collide with Honshu at approximately 12 Ma, with four major phases of accretion occurring at 12, 7–9, 3–5, and 1 Ma (Niitsuma 1989; Amano 1991). A syntaxis of the Outer Zone belts (Fig. 2) is one obvious manifestation of the collision (Toriumi & Arai 1989; Kimura 1996; Takahashi & Saito 1997).

The submerged accretionary prism of Nankai Trough (Fig. 1) owes its origin to NW-directed subduction of the Philippine Sea plate beneath SW Japan (Eurasian–North American plate). The most recent phase of subduction–accretion began approximately 6 Ma as convergence accelerated (Itoh & Nagasaki 1996; Kamata & Kodama 1999). The convergence rate today is *c*. 40 mm/ar (Seno *et al.* 1993). The entire lithostratigraphic succession of the subducting plate was cored continuously at ODP Sites 808 (Taira *et al.* 1992) and 1174 (Fig. 1). The top of igneous basement consists of basalt (15 to 26 Ma), which formed by back-arc spreading in Shikoku Basin (Kobayashi *et al.* 1995). Miocene to Pleistocene sedimentary strata rest above the basalt. In the vicinity of ODP Site 1177 (Fig. 1), the lower Shikoku Basin facies was deposited on the flanks of the fossil spreading ridge, and strata there consist of a Miocene volcaniclastic unit overlain by Lower to Upper Miocene turbidites (Moore *et al.* 2001). However, these terrigenous sand layers do not exist throughout the basin. In the centre of Shikoku Basin (Muroto Transect), relief associated with the spreading ridge inhibited turbidite deposition, so the lower facies in that area is hemipelagic. The upper Shikoku Basin facies comprises mud interbedded with volcanic ash (Moore *et al.* 2001). The Nankai trench wedge is late Quaternary (<1 Ma) and thickens toward the base of the accretionary prism.

The upper (landward) slope of Nankai Trough contains several prominent forearc basins (Muroto, Tosa, and Kumano Basins), which intercept sediment emanating from small canyons and slope gullies (Blum & Okamura 1992). In deeper water, a fault-controlled ridge-and-trough landscape characterizes the frontal accretionary prism (Ashi & Taira 1992; Okino & Kato 1995). Two ODP sites (1175 and 1176) penetrated one of the small 'piggyback' basins on the lower slope (Fig. 3). Strata there include an upper unit of nannofossil-rich hemipelagic mud and volcanic ash with evidence of frequent submarine slides (Moore *et al.* 2001; Underwood *et al.* 2003*a*). Offscraped trench deposits were cored beneath the slope basin; these strata are mildly deformed, nearly flat lying, and late

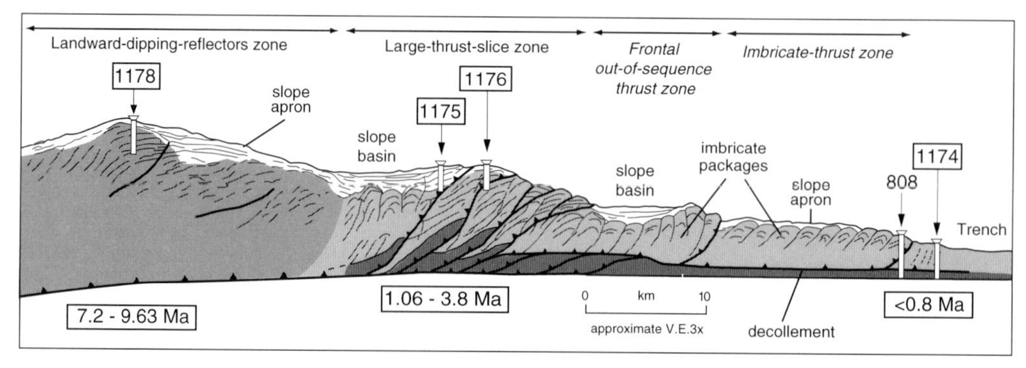

Fig. 3. Interpretive cross section of the Nankai accretionary prism showing four zones of seismic-reflection structure within the Muroto Transect area (modified from Moore *et al.* 2001). Numbers refer to ODP drill sites. See Figure 1 for location of 3D seismic survey, which includes the plane of the cross section. Note ages of accreted trench-wedge deposits at each site in Ma.

Pliocene to early Pleistocene in age (1.06 to 3.8 Ma). The slope basin's architecture was created by a hanging-wall anticline that formed above a major out-of-sequence thrust (Fig. 3). Rapid uplift evidently cut off the supply of coarse-grained clastic debris soon after the basin formed. Higher up the slope at Site 1178 (Fig. 3), an apron of muddy slope sediment is 200 m thick. Those slope deposits are Pliocene to Quaternary in age (<7.2 Ma) and underlain by highly deformed thrust-imbricated trench sediments (6.8 to 9.63 Ma). Rotation of bedding created a series of landward-dipping reflectors on seismic profiles (Moore *et al.* 2001) (Fig. 3).

Sampling and laboratory methods

The samples used in this study were extracted from split cores that had been recovered via hydraulic piston corer, extended core barrel, and rotary core barrel drilling operations. The reported core depths are equal to maximum burial depths. All of the sand layers are uncemented, but some of the deeper specimens are moderately compacted. At Site 1174, the base of the sandy trench-wedge facies is 314.55 metres below seafloor (mbsf). The *in-situ* temperature at that depth is approximately 59 °C. At Sites 1175 and 1176, the maximum drilling depths are 435.40 mbsf and 440.36 mbsf, respectively, and the corresponding temperature maxima are only 25 °C and 27 °C. The total drilling depth at Site 1177 is 832.13 mbsf. Failure of the temperature probe at Site 1177 precludes an accurate estimate of the geothermal gradient, but heat-flow data from nearby Site 582 (Fig. 1) of the Deep Sea Drilling Project (Shipboard Scientific Party 1986) indicate that the maximum *in-situ* temperature is approximately 48 °C. At Site 1178, the maximum depth is 673.18 mbsf and the projected temperature maximum is 32 °C.

Fergusson (2003) and Underwood *et al.* (2003*b*) provided details of sample preparation, data acquisition, and error analysis. Briefly, the Gazzi-Dickinson method of point counting was followed using thin-sections stained for plagioclase and K-feldspar. Sand-sized crystals in lithic fragments (plagioclase phenocrysts, for example, in andesite clasts) were counted as the mono-mineral component. This method minimizes the effect of variable grain size (Ingersoll *et al.* 1984). X-ray diffraction analyses (Scintag PAD V diffractometer) were completed on oriented aggregates of the <2 μm size fraction, following ethylene glycol saturation. Clay-sized mineral abundances are reported here in units of relative wt%, where the sum of smectite, illite, chlorite+kaolinite, and quartz is equal to 100%. The calculations utilize integrated peak areas for the following reflections: smectite (001), illite (001), undifferentiated chlorite (002) + kaolinite (001), and quartz (100). The normalization factors were derived from analyses of standard mineral mixtures and matrix singular value deconvolution (Underwood *et al.* 2003*b*). No attempt was made to quantify the proportion of chlorite to kaolinite on a routine basis, but HCl boiling tests show that kaolinite typically makes up less than 20% of the chlorite+kaolinite contribution (Underwood *et al.* 1993; Steurer & Underwood 2003).

Sand composition

The sand samples recovered during ODP Leg 190 segregate into three major petrofacies (Fig. 4). These petrofacies are: volcanic-lithic (Site 1174), quartzose (Sites 1175 and 1176), and sedimentary-lithic (Site 1178). Samples from Site 1177 include both quartz-rich and sedimentary-lithic types.

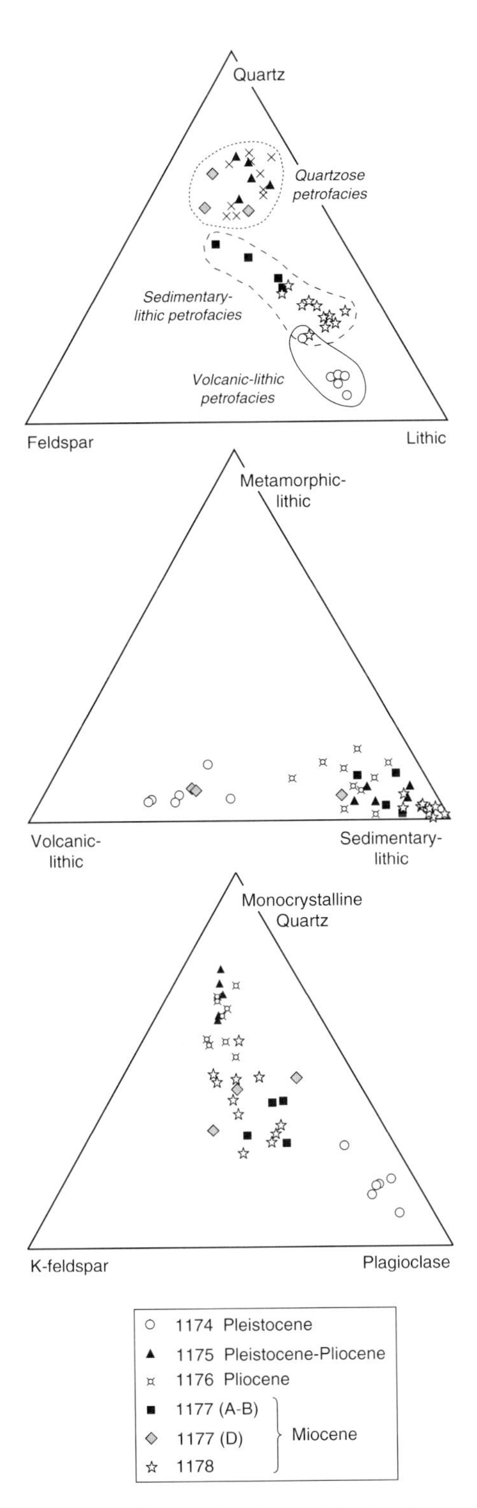

Fig. 4. Ternary diagrams showing modal values for turbidite sand samples from ODP Sites 1174, 1175, 1176, 1177, and 1178 (from Fergusson 2003).

Site 1174

The medium-grained to very coarse-grained sand samples from Site 1174 all come from the upper Quaternary axial trench-wedge facies of Nankai Trough (Fig. 3). Sample depths range from 20.03 mbsf to 220.28 mbsf. The sands are lithic rich; their modes plot near the L corner on a quartz-feldspar-lithic (Q-F-L) diagram and near the Lv corner on a metamorphic-volcanic-sedimentary lithic (Lm-Lv-Ls) plot (Fig. 4). High contents of plagioclase are also characteristic of this petrofacies (Fig. 4). Mafic to intermediate volcanic-rock fragments are abundant. Most such fragments contain phenocrysts and microphenocrysts of olivine, pyroxene, plagioclase, and (more rarely) hornblende in an altered groundmass of black or brown glass. Many of the porphyritic volcanic grains appear to be basaltic andesite. Felsic volcanic fragments are characterized by quartz, feldspar phenocrysts, and devitrification textures, although some such grains are difficult to discriminate from chert and sedimentary-lithic fragments. Fresh shards of colourless volcanic glass are relatively rare.

Sites 1175 and 1176

These sand samples come from accreted Pliocene–Pleistocene deposits beneath the slope-basin facies (Fig. 3). Sample depths range from 286.17 mbsf to 440.14 mbsf. The samples are medium-grained to very coarse-grained, poorly sorted sand and pebbly sand, with dominantly angular to subangular grains. They contain abundant quartz and sedimentary-rock fragments, but plagioclase contents are relatively low. Data from Site 1175 and 1176 cluster near the Q apex on the Q-F-L plot, whereas values on the Lm-Lv-Ls plot cluster near the Ls corner (Fig. 4). Some of the monocrystalline quartz grains exhibit undulose extinction, incipient polygonal shapes, and rare deformation bands, which suggests derivation from low-grade metamorphic rocks. Polycrystalline quartz and vein fragments with comb structure are also common. Grains of black and red chert contain recrystallized radiolarian tests. Sedimentary-lithic fragments include fine-grained mudstone and shale with thin quartz veins. Many of the fine-grained rock fragments are transitional to chert and polycrystalline quartz but contain more phyllosilicate impurities. Grains of fine-grained quartzose sandstone, lithic sandstone, and quartz siltstone are rare.

Site 1177

Samples from Site 1177 are distributed through the Miocene Shikoku Basin turbidite facies at depths ranging from 449.98 mbsf to 723.74 mbsf. Four sandy intervals (A–D) were cored, with interval D at the base (Shipboard Scientific Party 2001). The sands are poorly sorted with mostly angular to sub-angular grains. Samples from interval A, plus the top of interval B, contain approximately equal amounts of quartz, feldspar, and lithic fragments (Fig. 4). The lithic grains are dominantly sedimentary. On the Q-F-L diagram, data from intervals A and B plot close to values from Site 1178, whereas the Lm-Lv-Ls diagram shows overlap between data from Sites 1175 and 1176 (Fig. 4). Compared to intervals A and B, the three samples analysed from interval D have higher quartz contents and lower lithic contents. Their Q-F-L modes overlap those from Sites 1175 and 1176, but the Lm-Lv-Ls modes are more scattered (Fig. 4).

Site 1178

Compacted sand from the late Miocene accretionary prism (Fig. 3) is medium-grained to very coarse-grained and poorly sorted, with subrounded to angular grains. Sample depths at Site 1178 range from 272.96 mbsf to 663.15 mbsf. The most characteristic constituents in these deposits are sedimentary-lithic fragments (mudstone, siltstone, fine-grained sandstone, and siliceous claystone). On the Q-F-L plot, the field for Site 1178 lies near the modes for Site 1174, but this is only because of their low quartz contents (Fig. 4). The Lm-Lv-Ls plot is a better discriminator, with 1178 data plotting on or very close to the Ls corner (Fig. 4). Polycrystalline clast types are similar to those from Sites 1175, 1176, and 1177, but the overall proportion of lithic fragments is higher for 1178.

Designation of generic tectonic provenance

Ternary classifications of detrital modes (Dickinson & Suczek 1979; Dickinson *et al.* 1983) are popular tools for discriminating among generic categories of tectonic provenance. In applying this approach, the detrital modes for Quaternary sands from Site 1174 are similar to correlative trench-wedge deposits from other Nankai sites (de Rosa *et al.* 1986; Marsaglia *et al.* 1992; Underwood *et al.* 1993); the average modes plot in the undissected-arc to transitional-arc fields on the Q-F-L diagram (Fig. 5). On the Lm-Lv-Ls diagram, modes for Site 1174 are easily distinguished by their high content of volcanic-lithic fragments (Fig. 4). The modes of monocrystalline quartz, K-feldspar, and plagioclase (Qm-K-P) for Site 1174 cluster close to the plagioclase apex (Fig. 4), which is also consistent with a dissected-arc source. In comparison, Q-F-L values

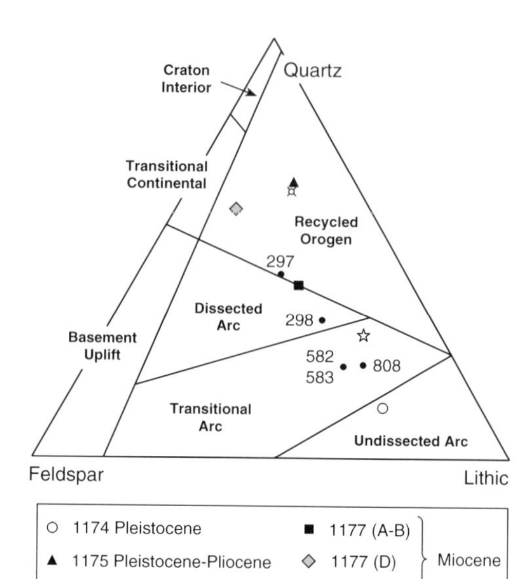

Fig. 5. Ternary diagram showing mean quartz-feldspar-lithic (QFL) values for ODP Sites 1174, 1175, 1176, 1177, and 1178 (from Fergusson 2003). Also shown are generic tectonic provenance fields of Dickinson *et al.* (1983) and comparisons with other data from the Nankai Trough trench-wedge facies. Mean values for Sites 297, 298 and 582/583 are from Marsaglia *et al.* (1992). The mean for Site 808 is from Underwood *et al.* (1993).

for Miocene and Pliocene to early Pleistocene strata (Sites 1175 and 1176, interval D at 1177) plot in the recycled-orogen field (Fig. 5). Modes for the late Miocene accretionary prism (Site 1178) plot in the transitional-arc and dissected-arc fields, whereas the mean for sand intervals A and B at Site 1177 plots on the boundary between recycled-orogen and dissected-arc provenance (Fig. 5).

Clay-sized mineral composition

Site 1174

Figure 6 shows that the most abundant clay-sized mineral in the Nankai trench-wedge facies is illite (average = 33 wt%, standard deviation (s) = 4%), followed by smectite (average = 27 wt%, s = 8%), chlorite+kaolinite (average = 25 wt%, s = 4%), and quartz (average = 15 wt%, s = 5%). Chamley *et al.* (1986) reported similar results for mud samples at DSDP Site 582, as did Underwood *et al.* (1993) for ODP Site 808. Contents of smectite increase slightly down-section (Fig. 6). X-ray diffraction measurements of (060) d-values show that

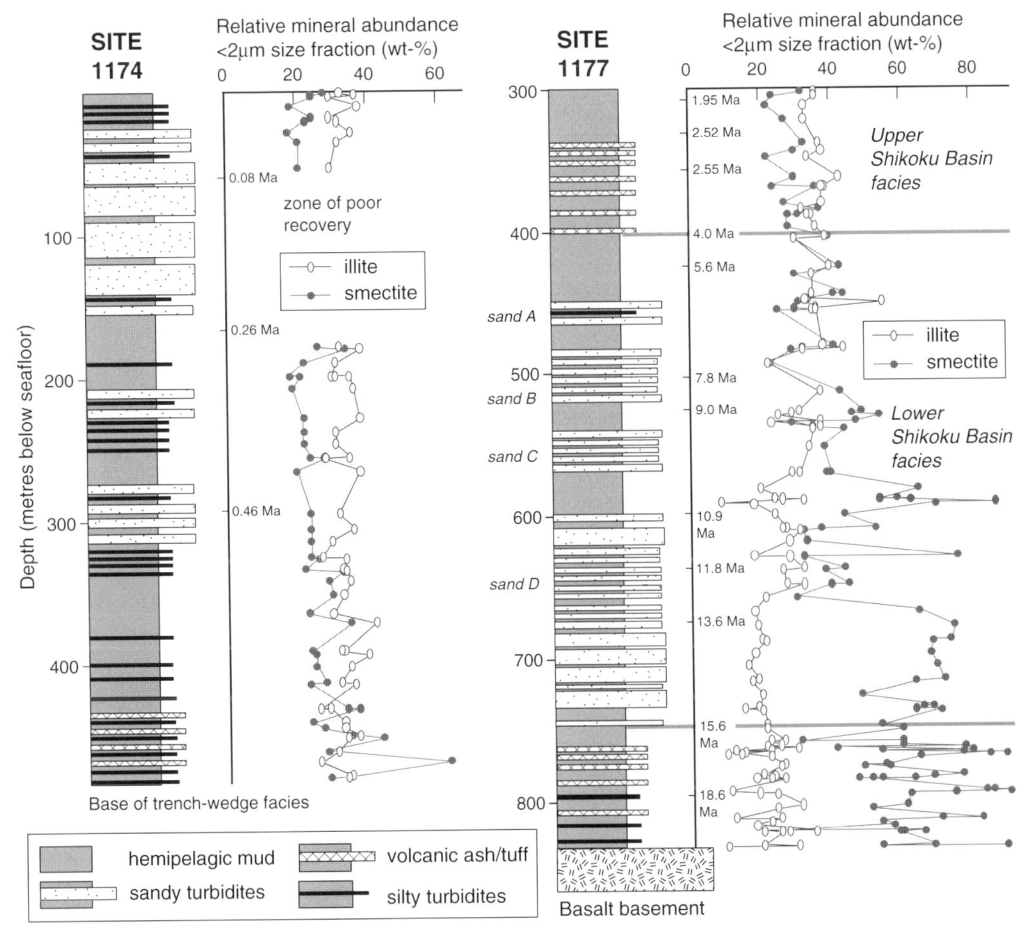

Fig. 6. Stratigraphic columns (from Shipboard Scientific Party 2001) and clay mineral abundances for ODP Sites 1174 and 1177 (from Steurer & Underwood 2003). Abundances of smectite and illite (wt%) are relative to a total assemblage of smectite + illite + (chlorite+ kaolinite) + quartz in the <2 μm size fraction. Note that the section at Site 1177 begins 300 m below seafloor. For Site 1174, the plot is limited to data from the trench-wedge facies because of clay diagenesis in the underlying Shikoku Basin facies.

the smectite is dioctahedral, either montmorillonite or beidellite (Steurer & Underwood 2003). A more detailed characterization of the detrital illite from Site 808 (crystallinity index, mica polytype, and b_o lattice values) points to source areas enriched in low-temperature, low-pressure meta-sedimentary rocks (Underwood *et al.* 1993). High heat flow, rapid burial beneath the trench wedge, and tectonic thickening at the toe of the accretionary prism have combined to overprint the underlying Shikoku Basin facies with progressive smectite-to-illite diagenesis (Underwood & Pickering 1996; Steurer & Underwood 2003). Because of that alteration, we did not include the Pliocene–Miocene deposits from Site 1174 in our assessment of detrital clay provenance.

Sites 1175 and 1176

Variations in clay-sized minerals are also minimal within and beneath the slope basin (Fig. 7). At Site 1175, relative percentages within the slope-basin facies average 37 wt% illite, 25 wt% smectite, 22 wt% chlorite (+kaolinite), and 16 wt% quartz. The corresponding values of standard deviation (s) are illite = 6%, smectite = 4%, chlorite+kaolinite = 4%, and quartz = 4%. Comparable slope-basin deposits at Site 1176 average 36 wt% illite (s = 5%), 25 wt% smectite (s = 5%), 24 wt% chlorite+kaolinite (s = 3%), and 16 wt% quartz (s = 5%). The underlying accretionary-prism mudstones at Site 1175 average 32 wt% illite (s = 3%), 32 wt% smectite (s = 9%), 25 wt% chlorite+kaolinite (s = 6%)),

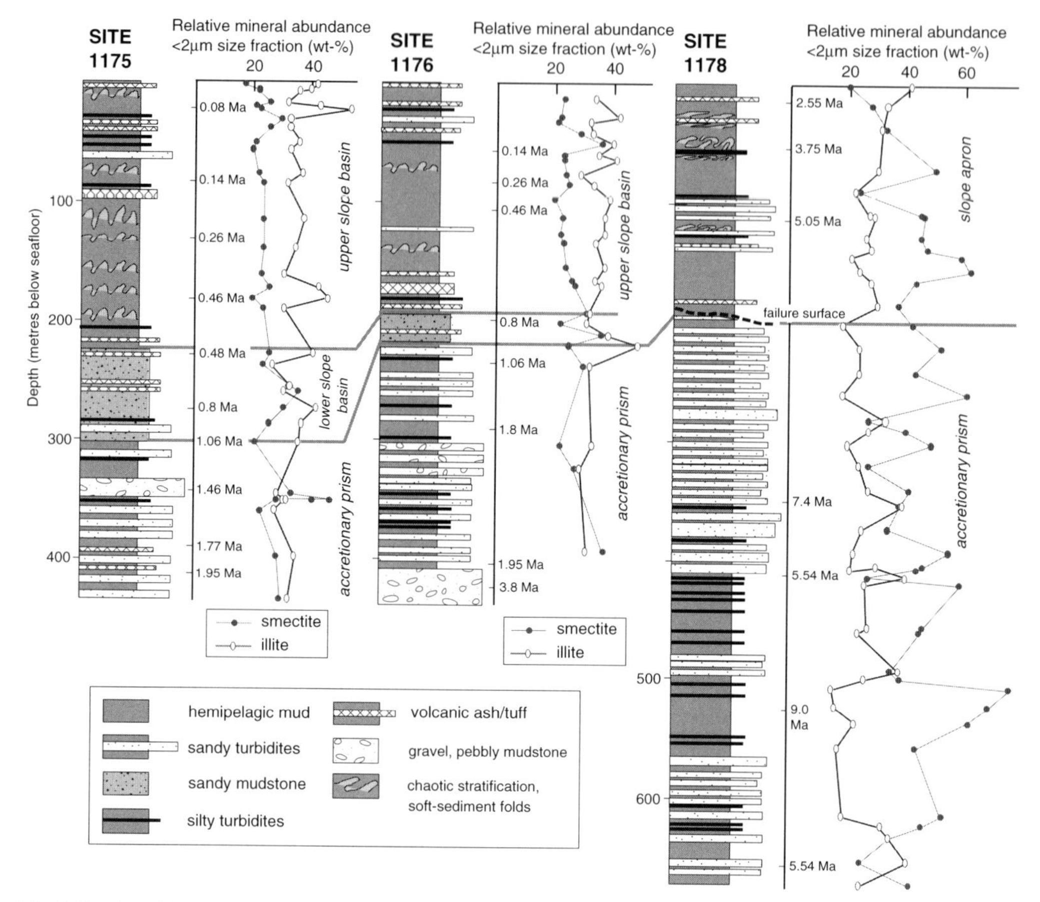

Fig. 7. Stratigraphic columns (from Shipboard Scientific Party 2001) and clay mineral abundances for ODP Sites 1175, 1176, and 1178 (from Underwood & Steurer 2003). Abundances of smectite and illite (wt%) are relative to a total assemblage of smectite + illite + (chlorite+ kaolinite) + quartz in the <2 μm size fraction.

and 11 wt% quartz ($s = 4\%$), whereas samples from Site 1176 average 31 wt% illite ($s = 2\%$), 29 wt% smectite ($s = 6\%$), 26 wt% chlorite+kaolinite ($s = 2\%$), and 14 wt% quartz ($s = 6\%$).

Site 1177

Compared to the trench-wedge facies, the amount of smectite is substantially higher and more scattered at Site 1177, with an overall average of 51 wt% and a standard deviation of 19% (Fig. 6). Illite averages 27 wt% ($s = 9\%$), chlorite+kaolinite averages 12 wt% ($s = 9\%$), and quartz is 11 wt% ($s = 7\%$). Smectite increases from 25 wt% at 300 mbsf (upper Shikoku Basin facies) to 45 wt% at 570 mbsf. Below 570 mbsf, the percentages vary from 27 wt% up to 91 wt%, with considerable heterogeneity among nearby interbeds. The variety of smectite is dioctahedral (montmorillonite or beidellite), and its expandability is generally between 65% and 85%, with random ordering (Steurer & Underwood 2003). As a frame of reference, a true bentonite (that is, clay formed through authigenic replacement of volcanic ash) would be expected to show expandability values close to 100% (Rettke 1981). Thus, the smectite at Site 1177 is probably detrital with some interlayers of illite crystallites.

Site 1178

When compared to the two slope-basin sites, the slope-apron facies at Site 1178 displays more scatter in relative clay-sized mineral abundances, and the contents of smectite are substantially higher (Fig. 7). The average values are 41 wt% smectite ($s = 13\%$), 28 wt% illite ($s = 5\%$), 21 wt% chlorite+kaolinite ($s = 4\%$) and 10 wt% quartz ($s = 7\%$). Mudstones within the underlying accretionary prism average

45 wt% smectite ($s = 12\%$), 26 wt% illite ($s = 7\%$), 20 wt% chlorite+kaolinite ($s = 6\%$), and 9 wt% quartz ($s = 5\%$). The highest content of smectite is 76 wt%, and smectite expandability ranges from 55 to 83% (Underwood *et al.* 2003*a*). These smectite values are similar to the Miocene data from Site 1177.

Generic clay provenance

The composition of detrital clay-sized mineral assemblages will change in deep-marine sediments in response to several first-order factors. The ratio of chlorite-to-kaolinite in Holocene sediments, for example, decreases systematically toward the tropics because of an intensification of chemical weathering (Biscaye 1965; Petschick *et al.* 1996). Mechanical weathering of polymictic rocks, which are typical of subduction complexes and collisional orogenic belts, produces clay-mineral assemblages (at mid-latitudes) that are enriched in detrital illite and chlorite, with modest amounts of smectite and kaolinite (Griggs & Hein 1980; Karlin 1980; Naidu & Mowatt 1983; Hathon & Underwood 1991). Minerals of the smectite group are widely regarded as the key tracers for volcanic sources (Parra *et al.* 1986; Petschick *et al.* 1996; Fagel *et al.* 2001). Although some varieties of smectite form through hydrothermal and/or submarine alteration of basalt and volcanic ash, the most widespread origins for expandable clay in Holocene sediments are meteoric weathering and pedogenesis of volcanic-rich substrates (Karlin 1980; Parra *et al.* 1985; Chamley 1989). As a general rule, where deep-marine mud contains more than 50 wt% smectite in the clay-sized fraction, the source probably includes an active volcanic arc. Factors other than parent rock also need to be considered. Fluctuations in the rate and volume of volcanic eruptions (for example, due to changing subduction parameters) can lead to commensurate shifts in the production and delivery of smectite from a unchanging source area. Furthermore, the balances between chemical weathering, mechanical weathering, and source-rock composition can oscillate on both local and regional scales in response to global climate change (glacial–interglacial cycles) and microclimate. Conversely, a gradual, long-term increase of one clay type at the expense of another usually signals a shift in the primary source and transport direction. Taking these general expectations into consideration, we regard the smectite-rich assemblages at ODP Sites 1177 and 1178 as evidence of substantial influx of arc-derived clay during the Miocene. The younger mud deposits at Sites 1174, 1175, and 1176 are comparatively enriched in illite and chlorite, thereby reflecting more input from a recycled-orogen source.

Integrated reconstruction of regional sediment dispersal

Prospects for detrital provenance

Several specific targets around Japan need to be considered as potential sources for volcanic-lithic sand and smectite-rich clay assemblages (Uto & Tatsumi 1996). The island of Shikoku and the Kii Peninsula of central Honshu (Fig. 2) are unusual for an active subduction zone because they are devoid of Holocene volcanic centres. This spatial gap in Quaternary volcanism provides one of the more important constraints on our interpretations of detrital provenance. Quaternary volcanoes in SW Honshu have been restricted to the northern side facing the Sea of Japan (Aramaki & Ui 1977; Uto & Tatsumi 1996). Miocene volcanic rocks within the Outer Zone (Fig. 2) are probably too sparse to produce a smectite-rich clay assemblage. Another local source to consider is the Hohi volcanic zone of central Kyushu, which formed during a late Miocene phase of north–south extension (6 to 5 Ma) (Kamata & Kodama 1999); a more widespread linear chain of active calderas and Pleistocene ignimbrites was emplaced nearby after 1.5 Ma (Kamata & Kodama 1999). The NE Honshu arc is the product of subduction beneath the Japan Trench; those volcanoes, which have been erupting nearly continuously since about 6 Ma (Cambray *et al.* 1995), extend westward beyond the Izu Peninsula (Uto & Tatsumi 1996). Central Honshu also contains older (middle to late Miocene) welded tuffs (14 to 4 Ma) (Kitazato 1997; Otofuji *et al.* 1997) and associated granodiorite bodies (12 to 7 Ma) (Saito *et al.* 1997). Since the middle Miocene, airborne ash layers from the Izu-Bonin island arc (Fig. 1) have accumulated in the Shikoku Basin during four pulses of activity (Cambray *et al.* 1995) (Fig. 8). Voluminous quantities of volcanic turbidites also have been transported into the Izu-Bonin backarc basin (Hiscott & Gill 1992; Marsaglia *et al.* 1995). Farther north, the Izu-Honshu collision zone (Fig. 2) exposes accreted slabs of volcanic and volcaniclastic rock, plus active composite cones such as Mt Fuji (Kitazato 1997; Soh *et al.* 1998).

The Outer Zone of Japan (Fig. 2) has been a widespread source for recycled sedimentary and metasedimentary debris, plus clay-mineral assemblages enriched in illite and chlorite. Located farthest outboard, the Shimanto Belt consists of Cretaceous to Miocene sandstone, shale, chert and basalt (Taira *et al.* 1988), with grades of metamorphism ranging from zeolite to lowermost greenschist facies (Toriumi & Teruya 1988; Nakajima 1997). The Chichibu and Sanbagawa belts represent an older Mesozoic accretionary complex, with the grade of metamorphism increasing to high-pressure

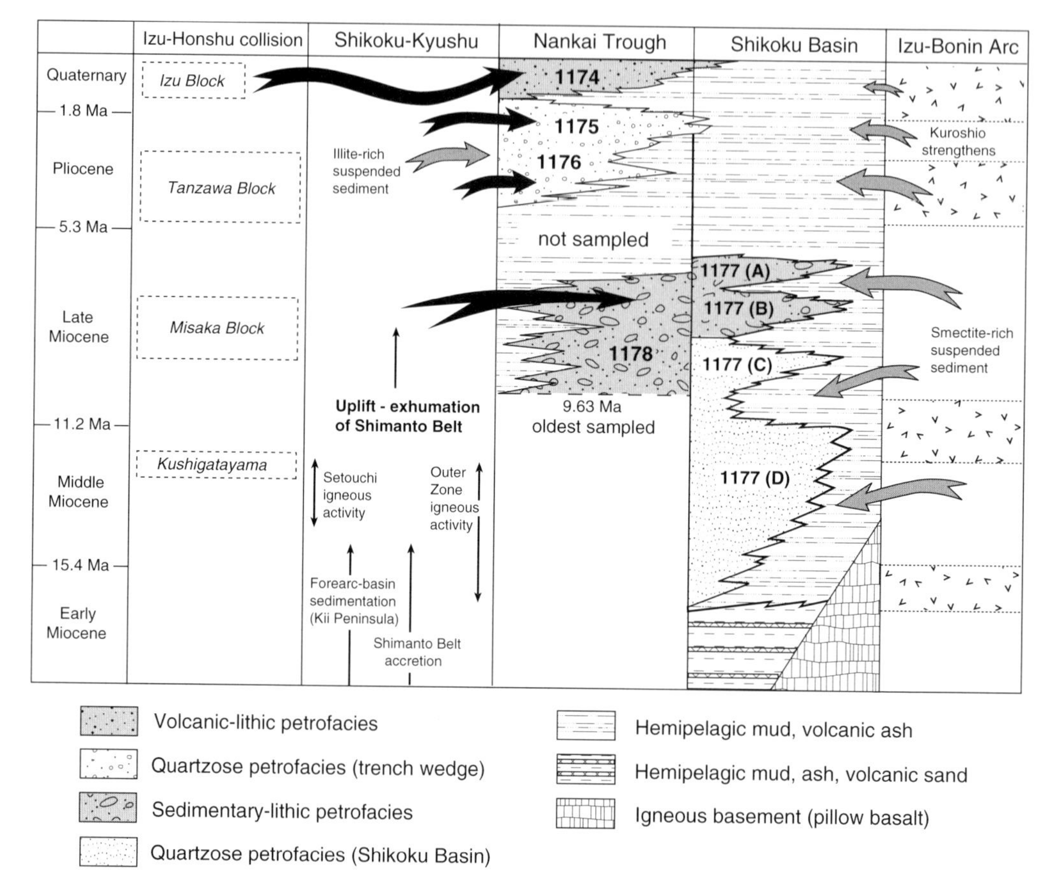

Fig. 8. Time–space correlation for detrital provenance and sedimentation events in Nankai Trough and Shikoku Basin. Black arrows indicate sand influx. Grey arrows indicate clay influx. Also shown are episodes of accretion in the Izu-Honshu collision zone (Amano 1991), phases of explosive volcanism in the Izu-Bonin island arc (Cambray *et al.* 1995), and pertinent stages in the geological evolution of Shikoku Island (Tagami *et al.* 1995; Tatsumi *et al.* 2001). Modified from Fergusson (2003).

towards the Median Tectonic Line (Higashino 1990; Nakajima 1997). Unmetamorphosed forearc-basin assemblages are also preserved locally within the Outer Zone (Chijiwa 1988; Hisatomi 1988; Hibbard *et al.* 1992).

Quaternary dispersal system (<0.46 Ma)

The sand from Site 1174 contains relatively high volcanic-lithic and plagioclase modes, and subordinate sedimentary-lithic and metamorphic-lithic modes. On that basis, we concur with previous workers that the late Pleistocene and Holocene turbidites in the modern Nankai trench wedge were eroded from the collision zone between the Izu-Bonin volcanic arc and Honshu (Fig. 8). The key to this interpretation is the incorporation of fresh neovolcanic debris into the sand supply. The largest through-going conduit for turbidity currents to travel from the collision zone to the trench is the Suruga Trough; this deeply incised canyon heads at the shoreline on the west side of the Izu Peninsula (near Mt Fuji) and continues along the northern flank of Zenisu Ridge into the NE end of the Nankai Trough (Le Pichon *et al.* 1987; Nakamura *et al.* 1987; Soh *et al.* 1995). Beyond the mouth of the Suruga Trough, the Nankai deep-sea channel meanders down the axis of the Nankai Trough to a termination point seaward of the Kii Peninsula (Shimamura 1989). A second important point for turbidity currents to enter the Nankai Trough is the mouth of Tenryu Canyon, which taps the same general source area as the Suruga Trough (Soh *et al.* 1991; Soh & Tokuyama 2002). Several smaller canyons probably reach the trench farther to the SW (Taira & Ashi 1993), but palaeocurrent evidence shows a predominance of axial flow directions in the trench-wedge facies

(Taira & Niitsuma 1986; Pickering *et al.* 1992). The dominance of axial flow in the trench did not materialize until after the watersheds of central Honshu had been redirected by collision and uplift involving the Izu block (Fig. 8).

Suspended sediment with moderate amounts of smectite has been transported along with silt and sand turbidites from the Izu-Honshu collision zone, but that muddy detritus has been mixed with, and diluted by, illite- and chlorite-rich clay from a recycled-orogen source. We can explain this apparent discrepancy by looking at the main elements of present-day ocean-water circulation relative to the control that bathymetry exerts over turbidity currents. The western boundary current of the North Pacific is known as the Kuroshio Current (Taft 1972, 1978; White & McCreary 1976; Taira & Teramoto 1981). This current is swift and deep (equivalent to the Gulf Stream in the North Atlantic), and it acts as the dominant agent for east to NE-directed transport of surface-water plumes from Kyushu and western Shikoku into the Muroto transect area of the subduction margin (Fig. 9). The water depths at the ODP trench-slope sites are between 1740 and 4790 m below sea level; this benthic range is too deep for the Kuroshio Current to have had much effect on bedload transport or drift of bathypelagic or abyssal nepheloid layers. Another mechanism to consider, however, is deep thermohaline circulation. Modern contour currents near the Izu Ridge show two directions of motion (Lee & Ogawa 1998). At depths greater than 2000 m, North Pacific Deep Water (NPDW) flows toward the SSW; flow above 2000 m is northwards. Because of their hadal depths, the Yap and Mariana Trenches block Antarctic Bottom Water (AABW) from entering the Philippine Sea from the southern hemisphere, so the north-directed current in Shikoku Basin probably carries Antarctic Intermediate Water (AAIW). Transfer of deep bottom water is minimal across the Izu-Bonin Ridge because sill depths are typically 1000 to 1500 m below sea level. Instead, AAIW sets up a pattern of anticlockwise rotation once it enters the Shikoku Basin (Lee & Ogawa 1998) (Fig. 9). Even where velocities are sluggish, these deep bottom currents are capable of nepheloid-layer transport.

We suggest that contributions of clay to the Quaternary trench (Site 1174) have come from several sources. Transporting agents have moved in several directions at different levels of the water column: axial flow from the Izu-Honshu collision zone; NE-directed flow of surface water from Kyushu–Shikoku; and anticlockwise flow of bottom water from the Izu-Bonin arc. The net effect has been to homogenize the clay-provenance signatures within near-bottom nepheloid layers before the mud settles permanently from suspension.

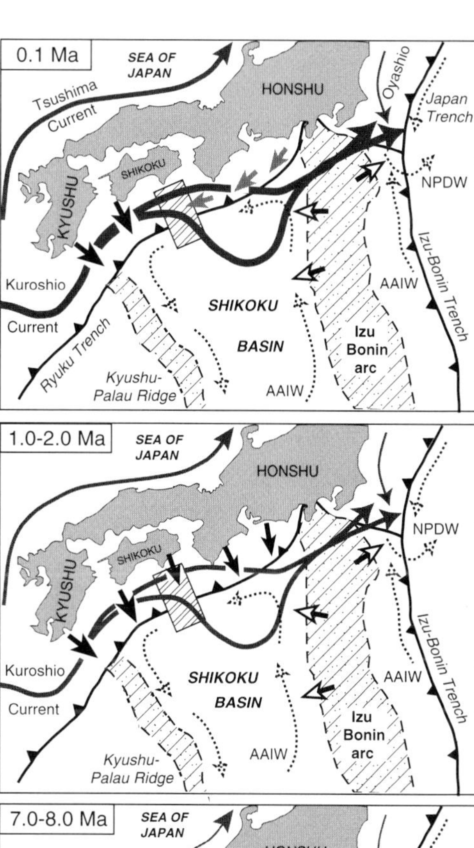

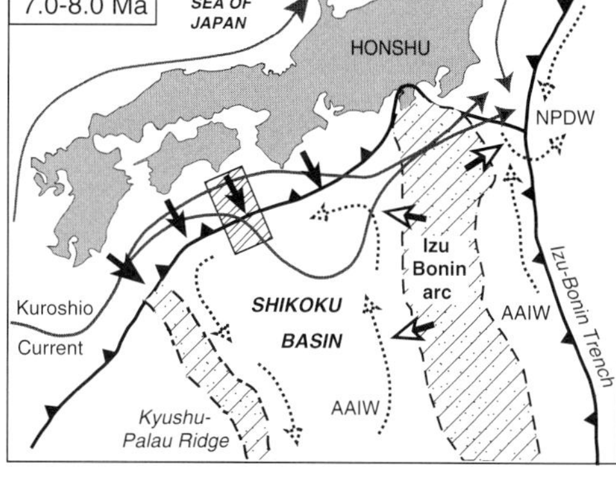

Fig. 9. Schematic illustrations of sources and transport routes for sediments entering the Nankai subduction margin during three intervals of time: late Quaternary (0.1 Ma), late Pliocene to early Pleistocene (1.0 to 2.0 Ma), and late Miocene (7.0 to 8.0 Ma). Box with diagonal lines depicts location of study area. Surface currents are solid lines; meander in Kuroshio Current is generalized from White & McCreary (1976). Bottom currents are dashed lines: AAIW, Antarctic Intermediate Water; NPDW, North Pacific Deep Water. Bold arrows depict transport directions for turbidity currents and other gravity flows: open, Izu-Bonin arc source; grey, Izu-Honshu collision zone source; black, Outer Zone source. From Underwood & Steurer (2003).

Late Pliocene to early Pleistocene dispersal system (2.0 to 0.46 Ma)

The late Pliocene was an important epoch in the geological evolution of SW Japan because it coincided with a shift in convergence direction of the Philippine Sea plate, anticlockwise block rotation of SW Kyushu, and initiation of pyroclastic volcanism along a well-developed linear chain (Kamata & Kodama 1999). This tectonic reorganization evidently had little effect on the composition of suspended sediment within the central Nankai forearc. In fact, data from ODP Sites 1175 and 1176 show no meaningful changes in clay-sized mineral assemblages during the past 2.0 Ma (Fig. 7). Just as we see today, a strong western boundary current probably transported suspended sediment into the central Nankai forearc from recycled-orogen sources on Kyushu and Shikoku (Fig. 9). The existence of a strong palaeo-Kuroshio Current is further supported by high-resolution studies of sandy contourites on the forearc side of the Izu-Honshu collision zone (Ito 1996, 1997). Thus, the clay composition during this phase of sedimentation reflects mixing from multiple sources and transport directions.

Unlike the late Quaternary axial-flow system of Nankai Trough, accreted Pliocene and early Pleistocene sands (Sites 1175 and 1176) are more quartzose with fewer volcanic rock fragments (Fig. 5). Abundant sedimentary rock fragments and chert point to derivation from an uplifted subduction complex (i.e. the Shimanto Belt). Our favoured explanation for this provenance shift is to funnel most of the sand through canyons and channels that headed along the southern margin of Shikoku (Fig. 9). By the end of the early Pleistocene, three factors probably contributed to the dampening, or elimination of, transverse sediment delivery to central Nankai Trough. First, rock units now exposed within the Izu-Honshu collision zone indicate a system of local cannibalism and trapping, in contrast to the late Pleistocene through-going axial conduits (Ogawa *et al.* 1985; Soh *et al.* 1991, 1998; Ito 1994; Kitazato 1997). Second, the Japan Alps, which currently are the highest relief in central Honshu, did not form until around 1.2 Ma, after east–west collision between the Asian and North American plates (Jolivet *et al.* 1994). Rapid and widespread uplift, combined with the tectonically driven incision of the Suruga Trough, redirected the primary source of trench turbidites from transverse to axial sometime between 1.0 Ma and 0.46 Ma. Finally, transverse canyons in the central Nankai forearc may have been blocked, or rerouted by, intense deformation associated with subduction of the Kinan seamounts (Yamazaki & Okamura 1989; Park *et al.* 1999; Kodaira *et al.* 2000). Tenryu Canyon in eastern Nankai Trough shows a similar response to subducting fragments of Zenisu Ridge (Soh & Tokuyama 2002). Reorganization of the Muroto bathymetric architecture probably enhanced sediment trapping higher upslope in the Tosa and Muroto forearc basins (Blum & Okamura 1992; Taira & Ashi 1993). This scenario also helps explain the upward stratigraphic transition at Sites 1175 and 1176 from coarse-grained turbidites to hemipelagic mud (Underwood *et al.* 2003*a*).

Late Miocene to late Pliocene dispersal system (9.6 to 2.0 Ma)

The oldest Miocene turbidites on the abyssal floor of the Shikoku Basin (*c.* 10 to 15 Ma) coincide in age with opening of the Japan Sea (Otofuji 1996; Lee *et al.* 1999) and near-trench magmatism within the Outer Zone (Oba 1977; Terakado *et al.* 1988; Saito *et al.* 1997). Subduction rates at that time may have been inconsistent, as indicated by: (1) discrete phases of collision between the Honshu arc and the Izu-Bonin island arc (Amano 1991); (2) crustal shortening along the north coast of SW Japan in the late Miocene (Itoh & Nagasaki 1996); and (3) resumption of widespread calc-alkaline volcanic activity in Kyushu at around 6 Ma (Kamata & Kodama 1994). The younger turbidites at Site 1177 (intervals A and B) are coeval with the accreted trench-wedge facies at Site 1178 (6.8 to 9.63 Ma), and their compositions are similar to one another. Compared to sands from Sites 1175 and 1176 (1.06 to 1.95 Ma), their quartz modes are lower and sedimentary-lithic fragments are more abundant. The most likely source for this petrofacies is the Outer Zone, where sedimentary and low-grade metasedimentary rocks are widespread. Deep erosion of such forearc-basin deposits as the Kumano Group (Chijiwa 1988; Hisatomi 1988) probably occurred, in addition to exhumation of the underlying Shimanto Belt (Taira *et al.* 1988). The paucity of felsic volcanic detritus points away from the Kii Peninsula and Kyushu as sand sources; 12- to 16-Ma felsic igneous rocks are more limited on Shikoku. Bedload transport from Shikoku to the Miocene trench was largely transverse (Fig. 9). Apatite fission-track cooling ages indicate that the Shimanto Belt on Shikoku experienced widespread uplift through a closure temperature of *c.* 100 °C at approximately 10 Ma (Tagami *et al.* 1995; Hasebe *et al.* 1993, 1997). The progressive adjustment of sand composition from higher quartz contents (interval D) to more sedimentary-lithic fragments (intervals A and B) may be a function of steeper topography and more rapid physical weathering within the growing mountains of the source area (Fig. 8).

The Miocene and early Pliocene clay budget in Nankai Trough and Shikoku Basin included substantial quantities of smectite, much more than was deposited by the Quaternary and late Pliocene systems. Some of the smectite in the slope apron (Site 1178) could have been weathered from the Hohi volcanic zone of Kyushu, which was active between 6 and 5 Ma (Kamata & Kodama 1999). However, a more expansive supply to Shikoku Basin was the Izu-Bonin island arc (Fig. 8). Weathering of the volcanic arc created a smectite-dominated clay assemblage that was transported into both forearc and backarc sites throughout the Miocene and Pliocene (Chamley 1980; Heling *et al.* 1992). Lee & Ogawa (1998) showed that bottom currents in the Izu-Bonin forearc strengthened at about 6 Ma, and that change may have been caused by build up of ice in Antarctica and intensification of AABW flow (Stow & Faugeres 1990). The palaeo-Kuroshio Current and the entire North Pacific subtropical gyre must have been weaker at that time, relative to the Holocene, because the Central America seaway was still open (Molina-Cruz 1997; Tsuchi 1997). A weaker palaeo-Kuroshio Current prior to 3 Ma would have allowed ocean currents and sediment-gravity flows to carry more volcanic sediment into the Shikoku Basin and Nankai Trough. Conversely, intensification of the Kuroshio Current after 3 Ma increased the supply of illite and chlorite to the central Nankai margin, thereby diluting detrital smectite from the Izu-Bonin arc (Fig. 9). During the same time interval, clay mineral assemblages in the Sea of Japan incorporated more illite and chlorite at the expense of detrital smectite (Fagel *et al.* 1992). That change in clay composition has been attributed to strengthening of the Tsushima Current at the end of the Pliocene, which carried more continental sediment from the East China Sea through the Korea Strait into the backarc basin (Fig. 9).

Conclusions

The trench-slope environment of Nankai Trough has evolved during the past 10 Ma in response to both tectonic and sedimentary-oceanographic forcing. The structural architecture of the accretionary prism has adjusted to changes in the rate of plate convergence, the volume, thickness, and composition of sediment inputs at the subduction front, and the arrival of bathymetric highs (seamounts) on the downgoing plate. Agents of subduction–accretion (imbricate thrust faults, out-of-sequence faults, etc.) have created numerous, small 'piggyback' basins on the lower slope, which have served as local depocentres. Conduits for sediment-gravity flow (submarine canyons) have been blocked and redirected by structurally controlled bathymetric highs. These manifestations of tectonism are typical of subduction margins, in general.

Compositional data from ODP Leg 190 drill sites provide important new insights into the behaviour of the sediment delivery system. Sand deposits segregate into three main petrofacies:

1. volcanic-lithic sand in the Quaternary trench wedge (Site 1174) was transported by axial flow from the Izu-Honshu collision zone at the eastern end of the Nankai Trough;
2. quartzose sand in the Pliocene to Lower Pleistocene accretionary prism (Sites 1175 and 1176) was transported through transverse canyons and channels from the largely metasedimentary Shimanto Belt on Shikoku; and
3. sedimentary-lithic sand in the Upper Miocene (Sites 1177 and 1178) was also derived from Shikoku during earlier stages of forearc uplift and erosion.

The principal conduits for turbidity currents shifted in response to the uplift of new source areas (Izu-Honshu collision zone) and rerouting of canyon-channel networks in the Nankai forearc during seamount subduction.

Assemblages of clay-sized minerals in coeval mud deposits show that suspended-sediment transport in Nankai Trough and Shikoku Basin was largely decoupled from bottom-seeking turbidity currents. Clay assemblages in Miocene to Lower Pliocene strata contain substantial amounts of smectite. The expandable clay probably was transported toward the west from the Izu-Bonin volcanic arc when the western boundary current of the North Pacific was relatively weak. Smectite became progressively depleted during the late Pliocene and Quaternary when a recycled-orogen provenance (Shimanto Belt) began to supply more detrital illite and chlorite. This compositional shift signals an intensification of the east to NE-directed Kuroshio Current.

When viewed in its entirety, the system of sediment dispersal in Nankai Trough and Shikoku Basin responded to two sets of allocyclic functions. The turbidite component reorganized in response to regional tectonics, whereas the suspended-sediment budget was modulated by hemispheric changes in ocean-water circulation. The lessons from this well documented example are worth considering during attempts to reconstruct temporal and spatial patterns of sedimentation from older exposures in the subaerial rock record.

This research used samples provided by the Ocean Drilling Program (ODP). ODP is sponsored by the US National Science Foundation (NSF) and participating countries under management of Joint Oceanographic Institutions (JOI), Inc. Funding was provided to C.L. Fergusson by the Australian Office for the Ocean Drilling Program and to M.B. Underwood by the US Science Support Program (F001281). J. Steurer assisted with clay-mineral analyses.

K. Marsaglia, W. Soh, J. Ashi, G. Moore and M. Buatier helped clarify our interpretations of the sediment dispersal system. We thank K. Pickering and R. Worden for their reviews of the manuscript.

References

Amano, K. 1991. Multiple collision tectonics of the South Fossa Magna in central Japan. *Modern Geology*, **15**, 315–329.

Aramaki, S. & Ui, T. 1977. Major element frequency distribution of the Japanese Quaternary volcanic rocks. *Bulletin of Volcanology*, **41**, 390–407.

Ashi, J. & Taira, A. 1992. Structure of the Nankai accretionary prism as revealed from IZANAGI sidescan imagery and multichannel seismic reflection profiling. *Island Arc*, **1**, 104–115.

Biscaye, P.E. 1965. Mineralogy and sedimentation of Recent deep-sea clays in the Atlantic Ocean and adjacent seas and oceans. *Geological Society America Bulletin*, **76**, 803–831.

Blum, P. & Okamura, Y. 1992. Pre-Holocene sediment dispersal systems and effects of structural controls and Holocene sea-level rise from acoustic facies analysis; SW Japan forearc. *Marine Geology*, **108**, 295–322.

Cambray, H., Pubellier, M., Jolivet, L. & Pouclet, A. 1995. Volcanic activity recorded in deep-sea sediments and the geodynamic evolution of western Pacific island arcs. *In*: Taylor, B. & Natland, J. (eds) *Active Margins and Marginal Basins of the Western Pacific*. American Geophysical Union, Geophysical Monograph, **88**, 97–124.

Chamley, H. 1980. Clay sedimentation and paleoenvironment in the Shikoku Basin since the middle Miocene (Deep Sea Drilling Project Leg 58, North Philippine Sea). *In*: Klein, G. Dev., Kobayashi, K., et al. *Initial Reports of the Deep Sea Drilling Project*, **58**, Washington, D.C., U.S. Government Printing Office, 669–678.

Chamley, H. 1989. *Clay Sedimentology*. Springer-Verlag, New York.

Chamley, H., Cadet, J.P. & Charvet, J. 1986. Nankai Trough and Japan Trench late Cenozoic paleoenvironments deduced from clay mineralogic data. *In*: Kagami, H., Karig, D.E., Coulbourn, W.T. (eds) *Initial Reports of the Deep Sea Drilling Project*, **87**, Washington, D.C., U.S. Government Printing Office, 633–642.

Chijiwa, K. 1988. Post-Shimanto sedimentation and organic metamorphism: an example of the Miocene Kumano Group, Kii Peninsula. *Modern Geology*, **12**, 363–388.

De Rosa, R., Zuffa, G.G., Taira, A. & Leggett, J.K. 1986. Petrography of trench sands from the Nankai Trough, southwest Japan: implications for long-distance turbidite transportation. *Geological Magazine*, **123**, 477–486.

Dickinson, W.R. & Suczek, C.A. 1979. Plate tectonics and sandstone compositions. *American Association of Petroleum Geologists Bulletin*, **63**, 2164–2182.

Dickinson, W.R., Beard, I.S., Brakenridge, G.R. et al. 1983. Provenance of North American Phanerozoic sandstones in relation to tectonic setting. *Geological Society of America Bulletin*, **93**, 222–235.

Fagel, N., Andre, L., Chamley, H., Debrabant, P. & Jolivet, L. 1992. Clay sedimentation in the Sea of Japan since the Early Miocene: influence of source-rock and hydrothermal activity. *Sedimentary Geology*, **80**, 27–40.

Fagel, N., Robert, C., Preda, M. & Thorez, J. 2001. Smectite composition as a tracer of deep circulation: the case of the northern North Atlantic. *Marine Geology*, **172**, 309–330.

Fergusson, C.L. 2003. Provenance of Miocene-Pleistocene turbidite sands and sandstones, Nankai Trough, Ocean Drilling Program Leg 190. *In*: Mikada, H., Moore, G.F., Taira, A., Becker, K., Moore, J.C. & Klaus, A. (eds) *Proceedings of the Ocean Drilling Program*, Scientific Results, 190/196. College Station, TX, Ocean Drilling Program. <http://wwwodp.tamu.edu/publications/190196SR/VOLUME/CHAPTERS/205.PDF>

Griggs, G.B. & Hein, J.R. 1980. Sources, dispersal, and clay mineral composition of fine-grained sediment off central and northern California. *Journal of Geology*, **88**, 541–566.

Hasabe, N., Tagami, T. & Nishimura, S. 1993. The evidence of along-arc differential uplift of the Shimanto accretionary complex: fission track thermochronology of the Kumano acidic rocks, southwest Japan. *Tectonophysics*, **224**, 327–335.

Hasabe, N., Tagami, T. & Nishimura, S. 1997. Melange-forming processes in the development of an accretionary prism: evidence from fission track theormochronology. *Journal Geophysical Research*, **102**, 7659–7672.

Hathon, E.G. & Underwood, M.B. 1991. Clay mineralogy and chemistry as indicators of hemipelagic sediment dispersal south of the Aleutian arc. *Marine Geology*, **97**, 145–166.

Heling, D., Schwarz, A. & Garbe-Schonberg, D. 1992. X-ray mineralogy and geochemistry studies of sediments, Leg 125 Sites 781 through 784 and 786. *In*: Fryer, P., Pearce, J.A., Stokking, L.B., et al. *Proceedings of the Ocean Drilling Program*, Scientific Results, 125, College Station, TX, Ocean Drilling Program, 115–130.

Hibbard, J., Karig, D. & Taira, A. 1992. Anomalous structural evolution of the Shimanto accretionary prism at Murotomisaki, Shikoku Island, Japan. *Island Arc*, **1**, 130–144.

Higashino, T. 1990. The higher grade metamorphic zonation of the Sambagawa metamorphic belt in central Shikoku, Japan. *Journal of Metamorphic Geology*, **8**, 413–423.

Hisatomi, K. 1988. The Miocene forearc basin of southwest Japan and the Kumano Group of the Kii Peninsula. *Modern Geology*, **12**, 389–408.

Hiscott, R.N. & Gill, J.B. 1992. Major and trace element geochemistry of Oligocene to Quaternary volcaniclastic sands and sandstones from the Izu-Bonin arc. *In*: Taylor, B., Fujioka, K., et al. *Proceedings of the Ocean Drilling Program*, Scientific Results, 126, College Station, TX, Ocean Drilling Program, 467–485.

INGERSOLL, R.V., BULLARD, T.F., FORD, R.L., GRIMM, J.P., PICKLE, J.D. & SARES, S.W. 1984. The effect of grain size on detrital modes: a test of the Gazzi-Dickinson point-counting method. *Journal of Sedimentary Petrology*, **54**, 103–116.

ISOZAKI, Y. 1996. Anatomy and genesis of a subduction-related orogen: a new view of geotectonic subdivision and evolution of the Japanese Islands. *Island Arc*, **5**, 289–320.

ITO, M. 1994. Compositional variation in depositional sequences of the upper part of the Kazusa Group, a middle Pleistocene forearc basin fill in the Boso Peninsula, Japan. *Sedimentary Geology*, **88**, 219–230.

ITO, M. 1996. Sandy contourites of the lower Kazusa Group in the Boso Peninsula, Japan: Kuroshio-Current-influenced deep-sea sedimentation in a Plio-Pleistocene forearc basin. *Journal of Sedimentary Research*, **66**, 587–598.

ITO, M. 1997. Spatial variation in turbidite-to-contourite continuums of the Kiwada and Otadai Formations in the Boso Peninsula, Japan: an unstable bottom-current system in a Plio-Pleistocene forearc basin. *Journal of Sedimentary Research*, **67**, 571–582.

ITOH, Y. & NAGASAKI, Y. 1996. Crustal shortening of southwest Japan in the late Miocene. *Island Arc*, **5**, 337–353.

JOLIVET, L.K., TAMAKI, K. & FROUNIER, M. 1994. Japan Sea, opening history and mechanism: a synthesis. *Journal of Geophysical Research*, **99**, 22 237–22 259.

KAMATA, H. & KODAMA, K. 1994. Tectonics of an arc–arc junction: an example from Kyushu Island at the junction of the southwest Japan Arc and Ryukyu Arc. *Tectonophysics*, **233**, 69–81.

KAMATA, H. & KODAMA, K. 1999. Volcanic history and tectonics of the southwest Japan arc. *Island Arc*, **8**, 393–403.

KARLIN, R. 1980. Sediment sources and clay mineral distributions off the Oregon coast. *Journal of Sedimentary Petrology*, **50**, 543–560.

KIMURA, G. 1996. Collision orogeny at arc–arc junctions in the Japanese Islands. *Island Arc*, **5**, 262–275.

KITAZATO, H. 1997. Paleogeographic changes in central Honshu, Japan, during the late Cenozoic in relation to the collision of the Izu-Ogasawara arc with the Honshu arc. *Island Arc*, **6**, 144–157.

KOBAYASHI, K., KASUGA, S. & OKINO, K. 1995. Shikoku Basin and its margins. *In*: TAYLOR, B. (ed.) *Backarc Basins: Tectonics and Magmatism*. Plenum, New York, 381–405.

KODAIRA, S., TAKAHASHI, N., PARK, J., MOCHIZUKI, K., SHINOHARA, M. & KIMURA, S. 2000. Western Nankai Trough seismogenic zone: results from a wide-angle ocean bottom seismic survey. *Journal of Geophysical Research*, **105**, 5887–5905.

LALLEMAND, S. & LE PICHON, X. 1987. Coulomb wedge model applied to the subduction of seamounts in the Japan Trench. *Geology*, **15**, 1065–1069.

LEE, I.T. & OGAWA, Y. 1998. Bottom-current deposits in the Miocene–Pliocene Misaki Formation, Izu forearc area, Japan. *Island Arc*, **7**, 315–329.

LEE, Y.S., ISHIKAWA, N. & KIM, W.K. 1999. Paleomagnetism of Tertiary rocks on the Korean Peninsula: tectonic implications for the opening of the East Sea (Sea of Japan). *Tectonophysics*, **304**, 131–149.

LE PICHON, X., IIYAMA, T., CHAMLEY, H., ET AL. 1987. The eastern and western ends of Nankai Trough: results of box 5 and box 7 Kaiko survey. *Earth and Planetary Science Letters*, **83**, 199–213.

MARSAGLIA, K.M., INGERSOLL, R.V. & PACKER B.M. 1992. Tectonic evolution of the Japanese islands as reflected in modal compositions of Cenozoic forearc and backarc sand and sandstone. *Tectonics*, **11**, 1028–1044.

MARSAGLIA, K.M., BOGGS, S., JR., CLIFT, P.D., SEYEDOLALI, A. & SMITH, R. 1995. Sedimentation in western Pacific backarc basins: new insights from recent ODP drilling. *In*: TAYLOR, B. & NATLAND, J. (eds) *Active Margins and Marginal Basins of the Western Pacific*. American Geophysical Union, Geophysical Monograph, **88**, 291–314.

MARUYAMA, S., ISOZAKI, Y., KIMURA, G. & TERABAYASHI, M. 1997. Paleogeographic maps of the Japanese Islands: plate tectonic synthesis from 750 Ma to the present. *Island Arc*, **6**, 121–142.

MAZZOTTI, S., LALLEMANT, S.J., HENRY, P., LE PICHON, X., TOKUYAMA, H. & TAKAHASHI, N. 2002. Intraplate shortening and underthrusting of a large basement ridge in the eastern Nankai subduction zone. *Marine Geology*, **187**, 63–88.

MOLINA-CRUZ, A. 1997. Closing of the Central American Gateway and its effects on the distribution of Late Pliocene radiolarians in the eastern tropical Pacific. *Tectonophysics*, **281**, 105–111.

MOORE, G.F. & KARIG, D.E. 1976. Development of sedimentary basins on the lower trench slope. *Geology*, **4**, 693–697.

MOORE, G.F., TAIRA, A., KLAUS, A. & SHIPBOARD SCIENTIFIC PARTY 2001. New insights into deformation and fluid flow processes in the Nankai Trough accretionary prism; Results of the Ocean Drilling Program Leg 190. *Geochemistry, Geophysics, Geosystems*, **2**, 2001GC000166.

NAIDU, A.S. & MOWATT, T.C. 1983. Sources and dispersal patterns of clay minerals in surface sediments from continental shelf areas off Alaska. *Geological Society of America Bulletin*, **94**, 841–854.

NAKAJIMA, T. 1997. Regional metamorphic belts the Japanese Islands. *Island Arc*, **6**, 69–90.

NAKAMURA, K., RENARD, V., ANGELIER, J., ET AL. 1987. Oblique and near collision subduction, Sagami and Suruga Troughs – preliminary results of the French–Japanese 1984 Kaiko cruise, Leg 2. *Earth and Planetary Science Letters*, **83**, 229–242.

NIITSUMA, N. 1989. Collision tectonics in the southern Fossa Magna, central Japan. *Modern Geology*, **14**, 3–18.

OBA, N. 1977. Emplacement of granitic rocks in the Outer Zone of southwest Japan and geological significance. *Journal of Geology*, **85**, 383–393.

OGAWA, Y., HORIUCHI, K., TANIGUCHI, H. & NAKA, J. 1985. Collision of the Izu arc with Honshu and the effects of oblique subduction in the Miura-Boso Peninsulas. *Tectonophysics*, **119**, 349–379.

OKINO, K. & KATO, Y. 1995. Geomorphological study on a clastic accretionary prism: the Nankai Trough. *Island Arc*, **4**, 182–198.

OTOFUJI, Y. 1996. Large tectonic movement of the Japan Arc in late Cenozoic times inferred from paleomagnetism: review and synthesis. *Island Arc*, **5**, 229–249.

OTOFUJI, Y-I., NISHIZAWA, Y., TAMAI, M. & MATSUDA, T. 1997. Palaeomagnetic and chronological study of Miocene welded tuffs in the northern part of central Japan: tectonic implications for the latest stage of arc formation of Japan. *Tectonophysics*, **283**, 263–278.

PARK, J.-O., TSURU, T., KANEDA, Y., KONO, Y., KODAIRA, S., TAKAHASHI, N. & KINOSHITA, H. 1999. A subducting seamount beneath the Nankai accretionary prism off Shikoku, southwest Japan. *Geophysical Research Letters*, **26**, 931–934.

PARK, J.-O., TSURU, T., KODAIRA, S., CUMMINS, P.R. & KANEDA, Y. 2002. Splay fault branching along the Nankai subduction zone. *Science*, **297**, 1157–1160.

PARRA, M., DELMONT, P., FERRAGNE, A., LATOUCHE, C., PONS, J.C. & PUECHMAILLE, C. 1985. Origin and evolution of smectites in recent marine sediments of the NE Atlantic. *Clay Minerals*, **20**, 335–346.

PARRA, M., PONS, J.C. & FERRAGNE, A. 1986. Two potential sources for Holocene clay sedimentation in the Caribbean Basin: the Lesser Antilles arc and the South American continent. *Marine Geology*, **72**, 287–304.

PETSCHICK, R., KUHN, G. & GINGELE, F. 1996. Clay mineral distribution in surface sediments of the South Atlantic: sources, transport, and relation to oceanography. *Marine Geology*, **130**, 203–229.

PICKERING, K.T., UNDERWOOD, M.B. & TAIRA, A. 1992. Open-ocean to trench turbidity-current flow in the Nankai Trough: Flow collapse and reflection. *Geology*, **20**, 1099–1102.

PLATT, J. 1986. Dynamics of orogenic wedges and the uplift of high-pressure metamorphic rocks. *Geological Society of America Bulletin*, **97**, 1037–1053.

RETTKE, R.C. 1981. Probable burial diagenetic and provenance effects on Dakota Group clay mineralogy, Denver Basin. *Journal Sedimentary Petrology*, **51**, 541–551.

SAITO, K., KATO, K. & SUGI, S. 1997. K–Ar dating studies of Ashigawa and Tokuwa granodiorite bodies and plutonic geochronology in the South Fossa Magna, central Japan. *Island Arc*, **6**, 158–167.

SENO, T., STEIN, S. & GRIPP, A. 1993. A model for the motion of the Philippine Sea plate consistent with NUVEL-1 and geological data. *Journal of Geophysical Research*, **98**, 17941–17948.

SHIMAMURA, K. 1989. Topography and sedimentary facies of the Nankai Deep Sea Channel. *In*: TAIRA, A. & MASUDA, F. (eds) *Sedimentary Facies in the Active Plate Margin*. Terra Science Publishing Company, Tokyo, 529–556.

SHIPBOARD SCIENTIFIC PARTY 1986. Site 582. *In*: KAGAMI, H., KARIG, D.E., COULBOURN, W.T., ET AL. *Initial Reports of the Deep Sea Drilling Project*, 87. Washington, DC, U.S. Government Printing Office, 35–122.

SHIPBOARD SCIENTIFIC PARTY 2001. Leg 190 summary. *In*: MOORE, G.F., TAIRA, A., ET AL. *Proceedings of the Ocean Drilling Program*, Initial Reports, 190. College Station, TX, Ocean Drilling Program, 1–87.

SOH, W. & TOKUYAMA, H. 2002. Rejuvenation of submarine canyon associated with ridge subduction, Tenryu Canyon, off Tokai, central Japan. *Marine Geology*, **187**, 203–220.

SOH, W., PICKERING, K.T., TAIRA, A. & TOKUYAMA, H. 1991. Basin evolution in the arc–arc Izu Collision Zone, Mio-Pliocene Miura Group, central Japan. *Journal Geological Society, London*, **148**, 317–330.

SOH, W., TANAKA, T. & TAIRA, A. 1995. Geomorphology and sedimentary processes of a modern slope-type fan delta (Fujikawa fan delta), Suruga Trough, Japan. *Sedimentary Geology*, **98**, 79–95.

SOH, W., NAKAYAMA, K. & KIMURA, T. 1998. Arc–arc collision in the Izu collision zone, central Japan, deduced from the Ashigara Basin and adjacent Tanzawa Mountains. *Island Arc*, **7**, 330–341.

STEURER, J.F. & UNDERWOOD, M.B. 2003. Clay mineralogy of mudstones from the Nankai Trough reference sites and frontal accretionary prism. *In*: MIKADA, H., MOORE, G.F., TAIRA, A., BECKER, K., MOORE, J.C. & KLAUS, A. (eds) *Proceedings of the Ocean Drilling Program*, Scientific Results, 190: College Station, TX, Ocean Drilling Program. <http://wwwodp.tamu.edu/publications/190196SR/VOLUME/CHAPTERS/211.PDF>

STOW, D.A.V. & FAUGERES, J.C. 1990. Miocene contourites from the proto Izu–Bonin forearc region, southern Japan. Abstr., 13th International Sedimentology Congress, 526.

TAFT, B.A. 1972. Characteristics of the flow of the Kuroshio south of Japan. *In*: STOMMEL, H. & YOSHIDA, K. (eds) *Kuroshio, Physical Aspects of the Japan Current*. Seattle, University of Washington Press, 165–216.

TAFT, B.A. 1978. Structure of the Kuroshio south of Japan. *Journal of Marine Research*, **16**, 77–117.

TAGAMI, T., HASEBE, N. & SHIMADA, C. 1995. Episodic exhumation of accretionary complexes: fission-track thermochronologic evidence from the Shimanto Belt and its vicinities, southwest Japan. *Island Arc*, **4**, 209–230.

TAIRA, A. & ASHI, J. 1993. Sedimentary facies evolution of the Nankai forearc and its implications for the growth of the Shimanto accretionary prism. *In*: HILL, I.A., TAIRA. A., FIRTH, J.V., ET AL. *Proceedings of the Ocean Drilling Program*, Scientific Results, 131. College Station, TX, Ocean Drilling Program, 331–341.

TAIRA, A. & NIITSUMA, N. 1986. Turbidite sedimentation in the Nankai Trough as interpreted from magnetic fabric, grain size, and detrital modal analyses. *In*: KAGAMI, H., KARIG, D.E., COULBOURN, W.T., ET AL. *Initial Reports of the Deep Sea Drilling Project*, **87**. Washington, U.S. Government Printing Office, 611–632.

TAIRA, K. & TERAMOTO, T. 1981. Velocity fluctuations of the Kuroshio near the Izu Ridge and their relationship to current path. *Deep-Sea Research*, **28A**, 1187–1197.

TAIRA, A., KATTO, J., TASHIRO, M., OKAMURA, M. & KODAMA, K. 1988. The Shimanto Belt in Shikoku, Japan–evolution of Cretaceous to Miocene accretionary prism. *Modern Geology*, **12**, 5–46.

TAIRA, A., TOKUYAMA, H. & SOH, W. 1989. Accretion tectonics and evolution of Japan. *In*: BEN-AVRAHAM, Z. (ed.) *The Evolution of the Pacific Ocean Margins*. Oxford, Oxford University Press, 100–123.

TAIRA, A., HILL, I., FIRTH, J., ET AL. 1992. Sediment deformation and hydrogeology of the Nankai Trough accretionary prism: synthesis of shipboard results of

ODP Leg 131. *Earth and Planetary Science Letters*, **109**, 431–450.

TAKAHASHI, M. & SAITO, K. 1997. Miocene intra-arc bending at the arc-arc collision zone, central Japan. *Island Arc*, **6**, 168–182.

TAMAKI, K., SUYEHIRO, K., ALLAN, J., INGLE, J.C. & PISCIOTTO, K.A. 1992. Tectonic synthesis and implications of Japan Sea ODP drilling. *In*: TAMAKI, K., SUYEHIRO, K., ALLAN, J., MCWILLIAMS, M., ET AL. *Proceedings of the Ocean Drilling Program*, Scientific Results, 127/128: College Station, TX, Ocean Drilling Program, 1333–1348.

TATSUMI, Y., ISHIKAWA, N., ANNO, K., ISHIZAKA, K. & ITAYA, T. 2001. Tectonic setting of high-Mg andesite magmatism in the SW Japan arc: K–Ar chronology of the Setouchi volcanic belt. *Geophysical Journal International*, **144**, 625–631.

TERAKADO, Y., SHIMIZU, H. & MASUDA, A. 1988. Nd and Sr isotopic variations in acidic rocks formed under a peculiar tectonic environment in Miocene Southwest Japan. *Contributions in Mineralogy and Petrology*, **99**, 1–10.

TORIUMI, M. & TERUYA, J. 1988. Tectono-metamorphism of the Shimanto Belt. *Modern Geology*, **12**, 303–324.

TORIUMI, M. & ARAI, T. 1989. Metamorphism of the Izu–Tanzawa collision zone. *Tectonophysics*, **160**, 293–303.

TSUCHI, R. 1997. Marine climatic responses to Neogene tectonics of the Pacific Ocean seaways. *Tectonophysics*, **281**, 113–124.

UNDERWOOD, M.B. & KARIG, D.E. 1980. Role of submarine canyons in trench and trench–slope sedimentation. *Geology*, **8**, 432–436.

UNDERWOOD, M.B. & MOORE, G.F. 1995. Trenches and trench–slope basins. *In*: BUSBY, C.J. & INGERSOLL, R.V. (eds) *Tectonics of Sedimentary Basins*. Cambridge, MA, Blackwell Science, 179–219.

UNDERWOOD, M.B. & PICKERING, K.T. 1996. Clay-mineral provenance, sediment dispersal patterns, and mudrock diagenesis in the Nankai accretionary prism, southwest Japan. *Clays and Clay Minerals*, **44**, 339–356.

UNDERWOOD, M.B. & STEURER, J. 2003. Composition and sources of clay from the trench slope and shallow accretionary prism of Nankai Trough. *In*: MIKADA, H., MOORE, G.F., TAIRA, A., BECKER, K., MOORE, J.C. & KLAUS, A. (eds) *Proceedings of the Ocean Drilling Program*, Scientific Results, 190/196. College Station, TX, Ocean Drilling Program. <http://www.odp.tamu.edu/publications/190196SR/VOLUME/CHAPTERS/206.PDF>

UNDERWOOD, M.B., ORR, R., PICKERING, K. & TAIRA, A. 1993. Provenance and dispersal patterns of sediments in the turbidite wedge of Nankai Trough. *In*: HILL, I.A., TAIRA. A., FIRTH, J.V., ET AL., *Proceedings of the Ocean Drilling Program*, Scientific Results, **131.** College Station, TX, Ocean Drilling Program, 15–34.

UNDERWOOD, M.B., MOORE, G.F., TAIRA, A., KLAUS, A., WILSON, M.E.J., FERGUSSON, C.L., HIRANO, S., STEURER, J. & LEG 190 SHIPBOARD SCIENTIFIC PARTY 2003*a*. Sedimentary and tectonic evolution of a trench-slope basin in the Nankai subduction zone of southwest Japan. *Journal of Sedimentary Research*, **73**, 589–602.

UNDERWOOD, M.B., BASU, N., STEURER, J. & UDAS, S. 2003*b*. Data Report: normalization factors for semi-quantitative X-ray diffraction analysis, with application to DSDP Site 297, Shikoku Basin. *In*: MIKADA, H., MOORE, G.F., TAIRA, A., BECKER, K., MOORE, J.C. & KLAUS, A. (eds) *Proceedings of the Ocean Drilling Program*, Scientific Results, 190/196. College Station, TX, Ocean Drilling Program. <http://wwwodp.tamu.edu/publications/190196SR/VOLUME/CHAPTERS/207.PDF>

UTO, K. & TATSUMI, Y. 1996. Quaternary volcanism of the Japanese Islands. *Island Arc*, **5**, 250–261.

WHITE, W.B. & MCCREARY, J.P. 1976. On the formation of the Kuroshio meander and its relationship to the large-scale ocean circulation. *Deep-Sea Research*, **23**, 33–47.

YAMAZAKI, T. & OKAMURA, Y. 1989. Subducting seamounts and deformation of overriding forearc wedges around Japan. *Tectonophysics*, **160**, 207–229.

Erosion of canyons in continental slopes

NEIL C. MITCHELL

School of Earth, Ocean and Planetary Sciences, Cardiff University, Cardiff CF10 3YE, Wales, UK (e-mail: neil@ocean.cardiff.ac.uk)

Abstract: Sonar images of the Atlantic USA continental slope reveal an eroded landscape that appears remarkably similar to subaerial landscapes eroded by surface runoff. Analysis of multi-beam data reveals that they are also similar in a number of quantitative aspects, such as similar scaling between channel gradient and contributing area, they show Hack's law scaling of channel length and contributing area, and tributary channels join trunk channels at the same elevation without an intervening waterfall. In modern geomorphology, the physics of river bed erosion and rules for runoff hydrology are used to model how erosion rate varies spatially and temporally, in order to predict large-scale landscape characteristics. This paper describes attempts to adapt such an approach to submarine canyon systems eroded by sedimentary flows. The mathematical form of the erosion is studied using the vertical relief of the canyons for the net erosion depth and is compared with results deduced from long-profile concavity. The rough correspondence between the two approaches lends support to the model. It is shown how the model can be used to help interpretation of canyon morphology by relating the pattern of erosion to the pattern of hemipelagic sediment supplied to the slope and other properties.

Canyon systems are prominent, common features of continental slopes (Shepard 1981). The erosive processes involved in creating them have been studied with increasing detail for several decades using traditional marine geological and geophysical techniques (e.g. Dillon & Zimmerman 1970; McGregor *et al.* 1979; Valentine *et al.* 1980; Malahoff *et al.* 1982; McGregor *et al.* 1982; Twichell & Roberts 1982; Farre *et al.* 1983; Embley & Jacobi 1986; Pratson *et al.* 1994). On the New Jersey slope, one of the most thoroughly researched slope areas, samples recovered by drilling show facies typical of debris flows, slumps and turbidity currents (McHugh *et al.* 2002), deep-tow sidescan sonar images reveal flow scours and slumps (Farre 1987), and high-resolution seismic data reveal sequences of erosion, infilling and re-excavation (Pratson *et al.* 1994). Working at a larger scale, researchers have characterized the gross forms of continental margins in terms of their steepness, topographic roughness and shapes in profile (Pratson & Haxby 1996; Pirmez *et al.* 1998; Adams & Schlager 2000; O'Grady *et al.* 2000; Goff 2001). These studies, however, still leave a gap in our understanding, as it would be desirable to be able to link the effects of individual sedimentary slope erosive processes to the larger-scale form of the submarine landscape. Many new multibeam echo-sounder datasets are emerging from surveying by oceanographic and government agencies (e.g. Pratson & Haxby 1997), prompting the need for a more complete conceptual understanding of the processes creating and modifying slope morphology.

The studies described here were motivated by the striking similarity of submarine and subaerial erosive systems (e.g. McGregor *et al.* 1982), which suggests that some of the recent work developed for understanding river bed erosion could help in describing how erosion proceeds in submarine slopes. For example, it is commonly observed that mountain rivers show an inverse power-law relationship between the gradient of the channel and its rainfall catchment area (Hack 1957). In rivers this is explained by the effect of increasing discharge down-stream which is balanced by decreasing gradient in order that the channel has spatially equilibrated erosion rate, analogous to the balanced profiles of graded rivers in lowland areas. Measurements of erosion rates by repeat surveying of bedrock channels in an artificially generated badland led Howard & Kerby (1983) to deduce that 'detachment limited' erosion of river beds there occurred at rates that were proportional to the shear stress exerted by the flow on its bed. Detachment-limited bedrock erosion by streams has therefore been predicted (e.g. Howard 1994) to occur at a time-averaged rate $\dot{E}$:

$$\dot{E} = KA^m S^n \tag{1}$$

where A is rainfall catchment area (m^2) and S is the channel gradient (m/m). The parameters K, m and n depend on the dominant bedrock erosion processes (abrasion by suspended particles and plucking (Whipple *et al.* 2000)), type of bedrock, degree of alluvial cover and other factors, which are typically assumed to be constant for the sake of simplifying the analysis. The parameter A is a proxy for water discharge. A similar relation to equation (1) can be derived by assuming that $\dot{E}$ is proportional to the stream's flow power (Seidl *et al.* 1994). In tectonic landscapes where erosion rate is spatially constant

From: HODGSON, D.M. & FLINT, S.S. (eds) 2005. *Submarine Slope Systems: Processes and Products*. Geological Society, London, Special Publications, **244**, 131–140. 0305–8719/$15.00

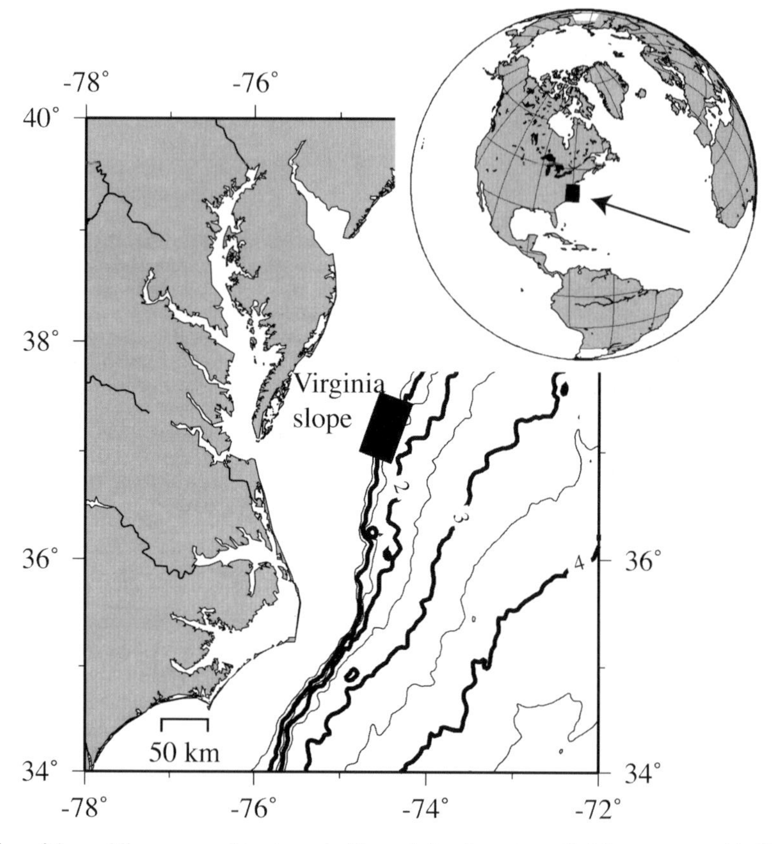

Fig. 1. Location of the multibeam sonar data shown in Figure 2. Depth contours (bold) are annotated in kilometres.

and equal to the rate of tectonic uplift (so-called 'steady state' landscapes), equation (1) is constant, so there arises a relationship $S{\sim}A^{-m/n}$, a result that has been used to explain the inverse power-law gradient–area relationships of some mountain rivers.

Studies of canyons in the USA continental slope (Figs 1 & 2) have found similar relationships though with a diversity of forms and hence power-law scaling between gradient and area (Mitchell 2005). An example of a gradient–area graph for the simple linear slope canyons in Figure 2 is shown in Figure 3. Although most of this group of canyons shows slightly curved graphs, their average power-law relationships obtained by regression is $S{\sim}A^{-\theta}$ with $\theta=0.4$–0.6, which is similar to the scaling of rivers such as the example for Taiwan shown by the dotted line in Figure 2 (from Whipple & Tucker 1999). This gradient-area scaling is interpreted to arise because sedimentary flows in these slope areas originate mostly from *in-situ* landsliding of over-steepened hemipelagic deposits in canyon walls. Failure of such deposits leads to the canyon thalweg experiencing flows at a frequency that increases down-canyon and with increasing contributing area. This has an analogous effect on erosion rate to increasing downstream discharge in river networks and needs to be balanced by decreasing gradient so that erosion rate is equilibrated spatially. Gradient-area scaling can be predicted using similar approaches to those used in river bed erosion (Mitchell 2005). This is achieved by combining the above effect of contributing canyon wall area effect on flow frequency with the Chezy equation for turbidity current velocity and by assuming that the channel floor is eroded by abrasion and plucking of material by sedimentary flows in an analogous manner to that in rivers.

A second important observation is that the channels of side gullies and tributary canyons commonly approach their principal channels at the same elevation, effectively obeying Playfair's (1802) law. If the main canyons were eroded by only a small number of large landslides or sedimentary flows, the tributary canyons would be left as hanging valleys with an intervening waterfall to the main canyon floor, which is not commonly observed. This implies that the systems have evolved by many small erosive events that have kept each pair of branches of a confluence eroding at the same time-averaged rate,

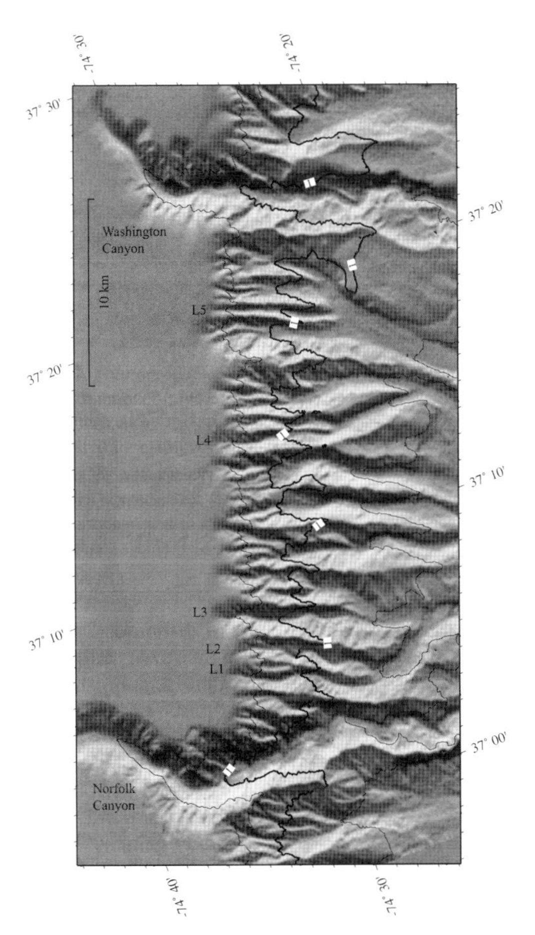

Fig. 2. Bathymetry of the USA Atlantic continental slope off Virginia collected with multibeam sonars of National Ocean Service survey ships *Whiting* and *Mt Mitchell* and made available by the National Geophysical Data Center (Coastal Relief Model). The canyons marked include the major shelf-incising canyons Norfolk and Washington and linear continental slope canyons L1 to L5. Depths are contoured every 500 m, with 1000 m in bold and annotated in kilometres. Light source: upper-right.

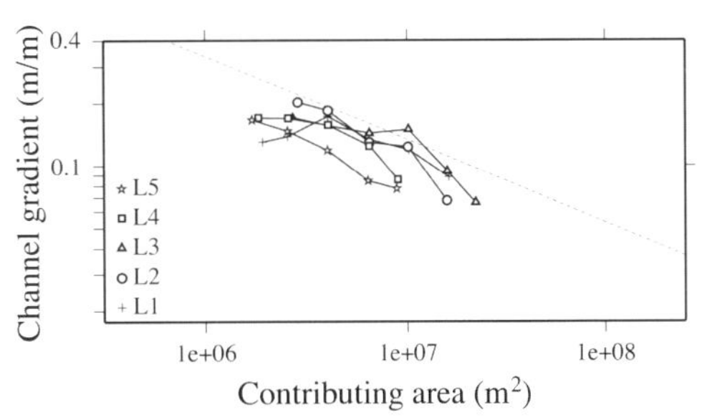

Fig. 3. Logarithmic graph of channel gradient S versus contributing area A for the linear slope canyons shown in Figure 2. The values adjacent to the canyon names show the power-law exponent θ (channel 'concavity') derived by regressing $\log_{10}S$ on $\log_{10}A$. The oblique dotted line is a similar relationship derived for rivers in Taiwan (Whipple & Tucker 1999).

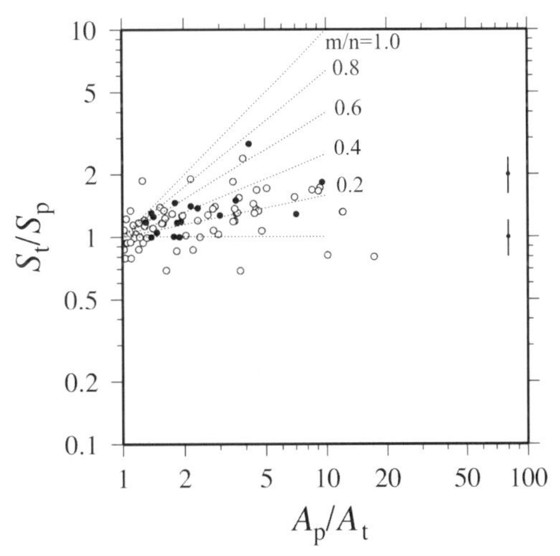

Fig. 4. Logarithmic graph of the ratio of channel gradients and contributing areas for principal and tributary channels measured at confluences. Open symbols represent canyons which head at the shelf edge whereas solid symbols represent canyons which head within the slope.

much like in river networks. Seidl & Dietrich (1992) used this observation to test the detachment-limited erosion law for rivers (equation (1)). They reasoned that, as the two branches of rivers have equal erosion rate, they should have balanced contributing areas and channel gradients such that, from equation (1), $A_p^m S_p^n = A_t^m S_t^n$, where the subscripts 'p' and 't' represent the principal and tributary channels, respectively. Thus, plotting the ratio of S_t/S_p against A_p/A_t should produce a straight line graph with power-law slope m/n if the erosion law equation (1) were correct.

Figure 4 shows such a graph for the continental slope canyons from the Norfolk area shown in Figure 2 and including data further south of the map shown (Mitchell 2004). The oblique lines give the trends expected if the submarine canyons obeyed equation (1) with the m/n ratios shown. The data clearly do not follow a simple trend and erosion seems to have produced a more varied pattern of channel gradients. Closer examination of the data revealed that the canyons have fairly common 'knickpoints' (reaches of anomalously steep gradient). In fluvial systems, knickpoints can be produced by variations in bedrock erodibility (Miller 1991) or from transients propagating through the system (Seidl *et al.* 1994). For whatever their origins, the presence of knickpoints means that the variability in Figure 4 does not rule out erosion controlled by equations of the type (1). Although the canyons share a great deal of common properties with fluvial systems, the analogy may be imperfect. The model nevertheless provides a useful means with which to compare different canyon systems and discuss the origins of differences as will be discussed below.

A further interesting result of the studies by Mitchell (2004) was that canyons that head at the shelf edge have the same inverse power-law scaling between channel gradient and catchment area as those that head within the slope and that are isolated from sources of shelf sediment. If there were significant direct supply of sediment to the slope during sea-level lowstands as is implied by the classical sequence stratigraphic model (Vail *et al.* 1977), we would expect to observe canyon channels with a different gradient (for a given area) than those isolated from such a sediment supply, but instead no difference is observed. This does not rule out the possibility of enhanced supply of hemipelagic sediment originating from the shelf but in this area appears to rule out direct supply such as by turbidity currents produced by storm agitation of shelf sediment (e.g. Scully *et al.* 2002; Wright *et al.* 2002).

This paper uses the vertical relief of the canyons as a measure of how time-averaged erosion rate varies down-canyon. Based on a similar erosion model to that described above, the data suggest that erosion has occurred with a different set of exponents (m, n) to those inferred from channel concavity, i.e. from gradients and contributing areas (Mitchell 2004, 2005). This discrepancy is interesting as it could in part reflect erosion of unconsolidated sediment as well as bedrock along canyon floors, so this forms a basis for the discussion.

Observations

The middle Atlantic USA continental slope (Fig. 2) is an erosional surface (Uchiupi 1970; Schlee *et al.* 1979). Seismic data show that the canyons have incised a simple layered stratigraphy, probably during the Pleistocene (McGregor 1979; Forde 1981). Uchiupi (1970) shows earlier Tertiary rocks exposed in the lower slope here, including one Upper Cretaceous sample. However, high resolution seismic data from the New Jersey slope (Farre 1987; Pratson *et al.* 1994), near Wilmington Canyon (McGregor & Bennett 1977) and from the slope 50 km NE of Washington Canyon (McGregor *et al.* 1979) show that stratigraphy within canyon walls typically dips towards the canyon floors (i.e. it tends towards subparallel to walls). This implies that some of the canyon topography has grown by aggradation of the interfluves (inter-canyon divides) as well as by canyon floor erosion revealed by truncation of deeper reflectors. Therefore, the erosion is considered in this paper as having both removed buried, consolidated stratigraphy and less indurated material that would otherwise build the slope, i.e. the hemipelagic fallout occurring between erosive events. Topographic sections drawn parallel to the shelf break (Mitchell 2005) along this upper part of the continental slope are V- or U-shaped in cross-section but canyons analysed are rarely sharply flat-floored, which might otherwise indicate aggradation along channels.

The age and timing over which the canyons developed is not well constrained. Although the classical sequence stratigraphy model (Vail *et al.* 1977) predicts that most sediment supply and erosion of slopes occurs during sea level lowstands, some recent attempts at testing these predictions have been contradictory (McHugh & Olson 2002; McHugh *et al.* 2002; Sommerfield & Lee 2004). In the following model, therefore, erosion is considered to be an episodic process in the sense that erosion of river beds also occurs mainly during sporadic floods (Snyder *et al.* 2003).

Figure 5a shows a longitudinal (thalweg) profile for canyon L3, a relatively simple linear canyon of the continental slope (Figure 2) with typical characteristics. The channel profile is concave-upwards, with undulations so that the channel slope does not vary systematically. Such undulations may be produced by varied strength of the incised strata or, in places, reflect knickpoints created by blocks slumped into the channel from the adjacent walls of the canyon. Whereas the channel is convex-upwards, the inter-canyon divides (interfluves) are typically either linear or convex-downwards in long-profile. The net relief H of the canyon increases away from the shelf break but then steadies or decreases beyond the mid-slope. The canyons' contributing area A is shown, calculated as though the canyon were a rainfall catchment. Such contributing areas are typically linear with distance for these linear canyons.

Channel bed erosion model

Apart from the possibility of bed shear failure in weakly consolidated sediments by over-flowing turbidity currents (Mulder *et al.* 1998), the substrate erosion by a turbidity current probably involves similar processes of plucking and abrasion by particles carried by the flow as those in rivers (Whipple *et al.* 2000). Thus, using the flow-power model (Seidl *et al.* 1994), the instantaneous bed erosion rate is related to the specific flow power P of the tur-

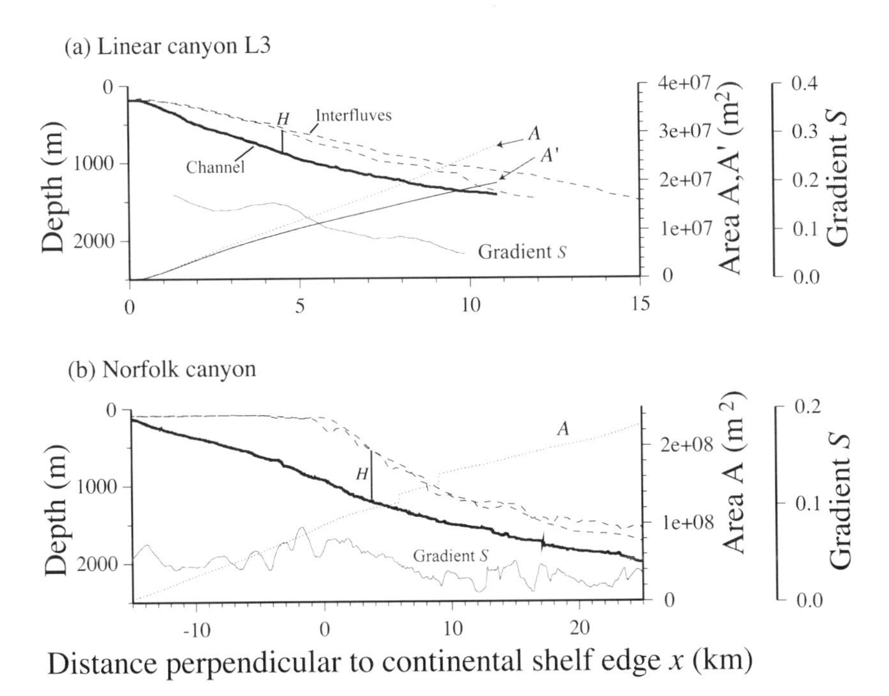

Fig. 5. Topographic profiles showing the canyon channel (bold line) and adjacent interfluves (dashed lines) for (**a**) the slope canyon 'L3' and (**b**) the shelf-incising Norfolk Canyon located in Figure 2. The contributing areas of the canyons (scale to right) are shown by the dotted lines. The adjacent fine continuous line in (**a**) represents $A'(x)$ or area weighted by the hemipelagic supply $U(x)$. Also shown is the channel gradient (fine continuous line and second scale to right) calculated over a 2 km sliding window along the channel.

bidity current, $\dot{E} \sim P^a$. where 'a' is an unknown exponent. P is defined by $\rho u h S$, where ρ is the flow's density (kg m^{-3}), u is the flow velocity (m s^{-1}), h is the flow depth (m) and S is the channel gradient (dimensionless). The values ρ and u are averaged over the depth of the flow. The velocity u is predictable from the balance of gravitational body force and flow resistance based on the classical Chezy formula since, given the large flow distances here, the currents should have reached steady flow conditions.

$$u = \left(\frac{8g\Delta\rho h S}{(f_0 + f_i)\rho} \right)^{1/2} \quad (2)$$

where g is the acceleration due to gravity (m s^{-2}) and f_0 and f_i are the Darcy-Weisbach friction factors of the flow's base and overlying water column, respectively. The erosion rate during flow can then be written as:

$$\dot{E} = K_{tc} F^{a/3} S^a \quad (3)$$

where

$$F = \frac{\rho^2 g' h^3}{(f_0 + f_i)} \quad (4),$$

and $n = 3a/2$ and $g' = g\Delta\rho/\rho$. The parameter F groups the more poorly known variables of the flow, whereas S is readily measured from bathymetry data. K_{tc} is a constant of proportionality representing the erodibility of the bed and the type of abrading load in the flow, analogous to K used in the river bed erosion models (equation (1)). Clearly the type of bed and the tools carried by the flow will have strong influences on erosion rate, but they are first treated as spatially constant here to reduce the complexity of the problem.

The following analysis relies on down-canyon variations in $F^{1/3}$ being smaller than those in S in order for us to detect the principal effect of slope on the erosion. This is difficult to verify given the lack of observations of turbidity currents in steep slope settings. However, many of the processes that occur during flow evolution that affect F could be at least partially compensating. For example, if a flow inflates by incorporating ambient water, it will increase h at the expense of $\Delta\rho$. Thus, in the absence of other effects, the product $\Delta\rho h$ would be constant with flow inflation alone. A further justification is that, if F increases or decreases down the canyons strongly, it should lead to non-linearity in the following graphs; the fact that we do not detect non-linearity is indirect justification of smaller variations in $F^{1/3}$ than those in S. Nevertheless, the possibility of flows incorporating bed material and thus altering their flow properties (i.e. F) is a significant uncertainty.

The net erosion H at any point along a channel will depend on the total number of flows that have passed that point during the canyon's history and their sizes. (Seidl & Dietrich (1992) used a similar idea to explain progressive scour with area in debris flow erosion of colluvial channels.) If the flows originate primarily by disintegration of landslides initiated around the canyon head and walls (Pratson & Coakley 1996), the frequency of flows experienced by the channel is expected to relate to the cumulative area of the canyon above that point. If the slope failures are not of equal size, the net erosion should still relate to area in some way as this dictates the mass of potentially unstable material in the up-canyon walls available for erosion. In this model, the chance of a turbidity current passing a point along a channel at a given time is given by the canyon contributing area weighted by the hemipelagic supply. This probability is represented by:

$$A'(x) = \int_{x_0}^{x} U(x)W(x)\mathrm{d}x \qquad (5)$$

where $W(x)$ is the along-margin width of the canyon, $U(x)$ represents the hemipelagic sediment supply and x is down-stream distance from the shelf break. The following linear function was used for $U(x)$, which is similar to that used by Pratson & Coakley (1996): $U(x)=(1-x/x_b)$ for $0<x<x_b$, $U(x)=1$ for $x<0$ and $U(x)=0$ for $x>x_b$, where x_b is the distance to the base of the continental slope. This variation in $U(x)$ represents the high sedimentation rates observed in the upper part of the continental slope, tailing off to smaller values seaward (Pirmez *et al.* 1998), the pattern of seaward-tapering surficial strata observed in seismic reflection images (Pratson *et al.* 1994) and enhanced deposition rates in the upper slope measured with ^{210}Pb (Sanford *et al.* 1990). Incorporating A' in equation (4), the net erosion expected from passage of a large number of turbidity currents is therefore:

$$\dot{E} \sim K_{tc} A'^{m} F^{n/3} S^{n} \qquad (6)$$

An exponent m is applied to A' because the above-mentioned effect of contributing area is unlikely to be perfect (because sedimentary flows do not all run-out to the continental rise, as evidenced by their deposits remaining in the slope (McHugh *et al.* 2002)) and there could be effects of flow widening as seen in rivers (Montgomery & Gran 2001). The model's effect of area needs to be generalized in any further development to consider the effect of up-canyon eroded volume. If an up-canyon region has a large area but small vertical relief, this implies a smaller cumulative mass of solid material has transported down-canyon than if the region had large vertical relief (Dade & Mitchell 2005). Hence erosion depth is also a function of erosion depth higher up the canyon. Erosive sediment mass flows transported directly from above the shelf break are probably not important today as the topography is remarkably smooth in depths <400 m (Figure 2) with no evidence for gullies, and surface sediments consist of hemipelagic muds with little evidence for sand in the continental slope that would be produced by shelf over-spill (Doyle *et al.* 1979), so erosion is considered to originate from sources entirely within the slope in this model.

Results

It is assumed that all parts of an individual canyon have been exposed to erosion for the same period T, so that their relief $H \sim \dot{E}T$, where $\dot{E}$ is the time-averaged erosion rate. The variation in H down-canyon can then represent variations in $\dot{E}$. Figure 6 shows the data of the linear canyons such as Figure 5a combined by calculating the average gradients as a function of the ratio H/A'. According to equation (6), the data plotted in this form should show a linear trend with slope n if the variation in $F^{1/3}$ is small relative to S and if $m=1$. Although individual canyons show

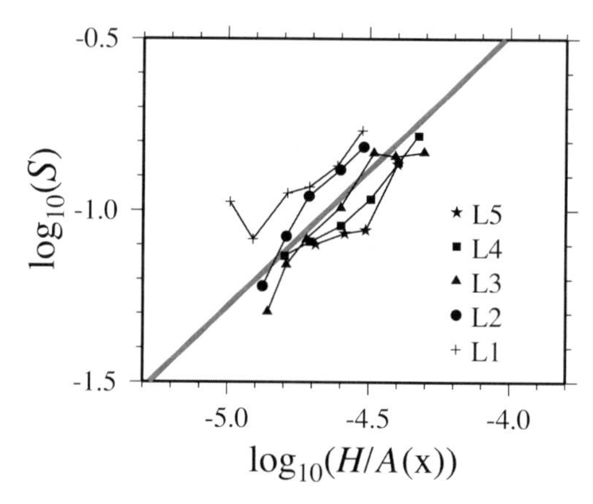

Fig. 6. Logarithmic graphs of the channel slope $S(x)$ versus the ratio of erosive relief $H(x)$ to hemipelagic catchment area $A'(x)$ derived from the linear slope canyons shown in Figure 2. The data coordinate values $\log_{10}(S)$ are averaged within bins of $\log_{10}(H/A')=0.1$. Since the amphitheatre-shaped upper reaches of the canyons are caused by slope failures (Pratson & Coakley 1996) rather than carved by turbidity currents, data from depths shallower than 500 m were excluded. The grey line was calculated by regressing the data shown for each canyon separately and then averaging the regression coefficients.

non-linear graphs, there is no systematic sense of non-linearity (graphs can be concave or convex upwards). The non-linearity of individual canyons can be ascribed to complicating factors, such as canyon wall landslides affecting S or reducing the heights of interfluves and hence limiting H or varied substrate erodibility. Overall, the data form a roughly linear array, consistent with the proposed erosion law. The graph has an average slope of $n=0.80\pm0.14$ (1σ standard error calculated from the precision of the regressions). This slope value suggests $a=5/6$, i.e. erosion rate slightly less than proportional to flow power. The spread of data in Figure 6a is interpreted to reflect varied canyon initial slope, ages or substrate resistance to erosion.

Slope failures probably occurred in these canyon walls to produce the sharp inter-canyon divides shown in Figure 2. This will have modified the pattern of canyon relief down-slope, by limiting the height of the divides. However, the effect is probably less important near the shelf break where the inter-canyon areas are smooth (hence in Figure 6 for large H/A'). Also considering that there is no evidence for systematic curvature in Figure 6, wall failures probably have not dramatically affected these results.

Discussion

Comparison with gradient-area approach

The above results which suggest $n=0.8$ ($m=1$) indicate a larger value of m/n than the values inferred from the scaling between gradient and area ($m/n=0.3$–0.6 (Mitchell 2004, 2005)). This is potentially interesting as the vertical relief of the canyon only partly represents erosion of indurated sediment and bedrock along the channel. Enhanced currents in canyons are known to retard deposition of sediments and can lead to non-deposition (Shepard 1981; Cacchione *et al.* 2002). Furthermore, the unconsolidated sediments deposited in canyon floors are expected to be eroded easily by turbidity currents (Parker *et al.* 1986), so the vertical relief of the canyon represents this removal of unconsolidated material as well as bedrock erosion. Interestingly, the inferred value for the exponent 'a' (5/6) implies that erosion rate is nearly proportional to shear stress, as has been assumed in modelling how currents incorporate unconsolidated sediments (Kampf *et al.* 1999).

Implications for interpreting canyon morphology

Although simplified, equation (6) provides a useful basis for understanding the controls on continental slope canyon morphology. (It applies to detachment-limited erosion but a similar equation can be derived for transport-limited erosion as for rivers (Whipple & Tucker 2002)). For example equation (6) predicts how the pattern of erosion relates to the pattern of sediment supply to the slope. If the whole slope receives hemipelagic sediment at the same rate, all canyon walls will over-steepen at equal rates so canyon wall slope failures initiating erosive sediment-laden flows will occur with equal frequency over the whole slope. Canyon floor erosion rates then increase steadily downslope and with increasing A'. Once erosion has proceeded to a state of equilibrium as observed in river systems, the canyon will become upward-concave so that the effect of increasing A' downslope is balanced by decreasing gradient S (Mitchell 2005). If deposition from hemipelagic fallout is more concentrated near the upper slope, as shown for the USA Atlantic slope from sediment traps (Biscaye *et al.* 1988; Biscaye & Anderson 1994) and sedimentation rates derived from ^{210}Pb measurements in cores (Sanford *et al.* 1990), $U(x)$ will be sharply decreasing with x (downslope) so that, at equilibrium, S will also be sharply decreasing. The canyon would therefore have a more sharply concave longitudinal profile towards the upper slope.

Thus, different concavities of well-developed slope canyons are predictable from variations in the long-term pattern of hemipelagic sediment supply to the slope. Where the pattern of sediment supply is known, anomalies compared with the expected effect on the canyon long-profile concavity can be interpreted in terms of varied bedrock erodibility (i.e. varied K), texture of sediment in flows and importance of plucking and abrasion (which produce erosion with different gradient exponent 'n'; Whipple *et al.* 2000) and detachment- versus transport-limited erosion. Where the pattern of sediment supply is not known, but suspected not to vary along-strike, variations in the concavity of canyons can also potentially be interpreted in terms of these properties.

Where the canyon breaches the shelf edge to intersect shelf sands (Farre *et al.* 1983), the effect of hemipelagic sediment depositing in canyon walls becomes less important compared with erosive flows of shelf material bypassing the slope down the canyon. Equation (6) then predicts that, for a given F and S, erosion rate along the canyon floor will be uniform because $U(x)$ would be a point source at the canyon head. As slope canyons are typically concave (S increases landward, Figure 5a), erosion rate would be greatest towards the canyon head. The upper canyon would erode back more quickly than the lower canyon and the canyon's gradient-area curve would progressively flatten. Norfolk Canyon provides an example of this (Fig. 5b), where the upper canyon floor now has little systematic variation in gradient landward of the shelf edge. Toms,

Lindenkohl, Washington and Norfolk canyons form an evolutionary sequence (Mitchell 2005) with the latter two representing fully mature and the former two are canyons that have some remaining concavity ($\theta \sim 0.3$). Norfolk Canyon now has a small gradient compared with the slope canyons, which probably represents a graded system in which bedrock is rarely exposed and channel floor sands move down-canyon with a constant and uniform time-averaged flux controlled by the uniform gradient and by the frequency and size of flow events originating from the canyon head.

Conclusions

The turbidity current erosion model is based on a number of assumptions on the origin of the erosion and on how turbidity currents vary in erosive potential down canyons. Furthermore, it does not account for variation in flow properties that could result from assimilation of more abrasive bed material into the flow or deposition. Nevertheless, it provides a viable explanation for the observed trends in canyon relief, gradient and canyon area. The model result ($\dot{E} \sim S^{1.25}$) implies that erosion rate is slightly less than proportional to flow power and slightly higher than proportional to bed shear stress. Although differences in flow properties are to be expected between turbidity currents and fluvial systems, the slope exponent is similar to that found in mountain fluvial systems.

The predicted value of the gradient exponent ($n=1.25$) implies a ratio m/n of 0.8 which is greater than that inferred from the inverse power-law variation of the gradient-area graphs for these canyons assuming equilibrated erosion ($m/n=0.4$–0.6; Mitchell 2005). The discrepancy could have arisen because the canyon channels have not yet reached equilibrium (the concavities inferred from the gradient-area graphs do not represent m/n) or because the canyon relief also represents aggradation of inter-canyon divides and effects of canyon wall slope failures limiting relief of the divides. Nevertheless, the values derived from the two methods do not differ greatly, lending support to the model.

Equation (6) provides a potentially useful conceptual basis for interpreting variations in canyon morphology as it relates the down-stream pattern of erosion rate to the pattern of hemipelagic sediment supply ($U(x)$) and channel gradient (S). Where the sediment is supplied to the slope dictates where the canyon wall slope failures will be most frequent and hence the pattern of erosion experienced by the channel below these locations. Thus, how sharply varied the sediment supply is can determine channel concavity, as channel gradient adjusts over time to compensate for this pattern of erosion to produce more spatially balanced erosion. Anomalies compared with the model predictions can then be interpreted in terms of varied sediment properties (tools carried by the flows), substrate erodibility and nature of substrate erosion. Where the canyon intersects shelf sands, the potential erosion rate becomes uniform for a given gradient and over time the channel evolves to a graded profile with uniform gradient.

Brian Dade is thanked for thought provoking discussion and guidance at an earlier stage of this work. Helpful comments by reviewers Michael Underwood and Bill Austin prompted a significant revision of this paper. The multi-beam sonar data used in this study were supplied by the National Geophysical Data Center, Boulder, Colorado. Figures in this paper were produced with the GMT software system (Wessel & Smith 1991). This work was supported by a research fellowship from the Royal Society.

References

ADAMS, E.W. & SCHLAGER, W. 2000. Basic types of submarine slope curvature. *Journal of Sedimentary Research*, **70**, 814–828.

BISCAYE, P.E. & ANDERSON, R.F. 1994. Fluxes of particulate matter on the slope of the southern Middle Atlantic Bight: SEEP-II. *Deep-Sea Research*, **41**, 459–509.

BISCAYE, P.E., ANDERSON, R.F. & DECK, B.L. 1988. Fluxes of particles and constituents to the eastern United States continental slope and rise: SEEP-I. *Continental Shelf Research*, **8**, 855–904.

CACCHIONE, D.A., PRATSON, L.F. & OGSTON, A.S. 2002. The shaping of continental slopes by internal tides. *Science*, **296**, 724–727.

DADE, W.B. & MITCHELL, N.C. 2005. Regional morphology of submarine canyons in the mid-Atlantic continental slope, USA. *Journal of Geophysical Research*, in press.

DILLON, W.P. & ZIMMERMAN, H.B. 1970. Erosion by biological activity in two New England submarine canyons. *Journal of Sedimentary Petrology*, **40**, 542–547.

DOYLE, L.J., PILKEY, O.H. & WOO, C.C. 1979. Sedimentation on the eastern United States continental slope. *In*: DOYLE, L.J. & PILKEY, O.H. (eds) *Geology of continental slopes*, Society Economic Palaeontologists Mineralogists, Special Publications **27**, Tulsa, Oklahoma, 119–129.

EMBLEY, R.M. & JACOBI, R. 1986. Mass wasting in the western North Atlantic. *In*: VOGT, P.R. & TUCHOLKE, B.E. (eds) *The Geology of North America, Volume M, The Western North Atlantic Region*. Geological Society of America, Boulder, Colorado, 479–490.

FARRE, J.A. 1987. Surficial geology of the continental margin offshore New Jersey in the vicinity of Deep Sea Drilling Project Sites 612 and 613. *In:* POAG, C.W. & WATTS, A.B. (eds) Initial Report of the Deep Sea Drilling Project Volume 95. US Government Print. Offices: Washington, D.C., 725–759.

FARRE, J.A., MCGREGOR, B.A., RYAN, W.B.F. & ROBB,

J.M. 1983. Breaching the shelfbreak: passage from youthful to mature phase in submarine canyon evolution. *In*: STANLEY, D.J. & MOORE, G.T. (eds) *The shelfbreak: critical interface on continental margins*. Society of Economic Paleontologists and Mineralogists Special Publications, **33**, 25–39.

FORDE, E.B. 1981. Evolution of Veatch, Washington and Norfolk submarine canyons: inferences from strata and morphology. *Marine Geology*, **39**, 197–214.

GOFF, J.A. 2001. Quantitative classification of canyon systems on continental slopes and a possible relationship to slope curvature: *Geophysics Research Letters*, **28**, 4359–4362.

HACK, J.T. 1957. *Studies of longitudinal stream profiles in Virginia and Maryland*. US Government Printing Office, Washington, 42–97.

HOWARD, A.D. 1994. A detachment-limited model of drainage basin evolution. *Water Resource Research*, **30**, 2261–2285.

HOWARD, A.D. & KERBY, G. 1983. Channel changes in badlands. *Geological Society America Bulletin*, **94**, 739–752.

KAMPF, J., BACHAUS, J.O. & FOHRMANN, H. 1999. Sediment-induced slope convection: two-dimensional numerical case studies. *Journal of Geophysical Research*, **104**, 20509–20522.

MALAHOFF, A., EMBLEY, R.W. & FORNARI, D.J. 1982. Geomorphology of Norfolk and Washington Canyons and the surrounding continental slope and upper rise as observed with DSRV Alvin. *In*: SCRUTTON, R.A. & TALWANI, M. (eds) *The Ocean Floor*. John Wiley and Sons, New York, 97–111.

MCGREGOR, B.A. 1979. Variations in bottom processes along the US Atlantic continental margin. *In*: WATKINS, J.S., MONTADERT, L. & DICKERSON, P.W. (eds) *Geological and geophysical investigations of continental margins*, AAPG Memoir **29**. American Association of Petroleum Geologists, Tulsa, Oklahoma, 139–149.

MCGREGOR, B.A. & BENNETT, R.H. 1977. Continental slope sediment instability northeast of Wilmington Canyon. *American Association of Petroleum Geologists Bulletin*, **61**, 918–928.

MCGREGOR, B.A., BENNETT, R.H. & LAMBERT, D.N. 1979. Bottom processes, morphology and geotechnical properties of the continental slope south of Baltimore Canyon. *Applied Ocean Research*, **1**, 177–187.

MCGREGOR, B.A., STUBBLEFIELD, W.L., RYAN, W.B.F. & TWICHELL, D.C. 1982. Wilmington submarine canyon: a marine fluvial-like system. *Geology*, **10**, 27–30.

MCHUGH, C.M.G. & OLSON, H.C. 2002. Pleistocene chronology of continental margin sedimentation: new insights into traditional models, New Jersey. *Marine Geology*, **186**, 389–411.

MCHUGH, C.M.G., DAMUTH, J.E. & MOUNTAIN, G.S. 2002. Cenozoic mass-transport facies and their correlation with relative sea-level change, New Jersey continental margin. *Marine Geology*, **184**, 295–334.

MILLER, J.R. 1991. The influence of bedrock geology on knickpoint development and channel-bed degradation along downcutting streams in south-central Indiana. *Journal of Geology*, **99**, 591–605.

MITCHELL, N.C. 2004. Form of submarine erosion from confluences in Atlantic USA continental slope canyons. *American Journal of Science*, **304**, 590–611.

MITCHELL, N.C. 2005. Interpreting long-profiles of canyons in the USA Atlantic continental slope. *Marine Geology*, **214**, 75–99.

MONTGOMERY, D.R. & GRAN, K.B. 2001. Downstream variations in the width of bedrock channels. *Water Resource Research*, **37**, 1841–1846.

MULDER, T., SYVITSKI, J. & SKENE, K. 1998. Modeling of erosion and deposition by turbidity currents generated at river mouths. *Journal of Sedimentary Research*, **68**, 124–137.

O'GRADY, D.B., SYVITSKI, J.P.M., PRATSON, L.F. & SARG, J.F. 2000. Categorizing the morphologic variability of siliclastic passive continental margins. *Geology*, **28**, 207–210.

PARKER, G., FUKUSHIMA, Y. & PANTIN, H.M. 1986. Self-accelerating turbidity currents. *Journal of Fluid Mechanics*, **171**, 145–181.

PIRMEZ, C., PRATSON, L.F. & STECKLER, M.S. 1998. Clinoform development by advection-diffusion of suspended sediment: modeling and comparison to natural systems. *Journal of Geophysical Research*, **103**, 24141–24157.

PLAYFAIR, J. 1802. *Illustrations of the Huttonian Theory of the Earth*. Dover, London.

PRATSON, L.F. & COAKLEY, B.J. 1996. A model for the headward erosion of submarine canyons induced by downslope-eroding sediment flows. *Geological Society of America Bulletin*, **108**, 225–234.

PRATSON, L.F. & HAXBY, W.F. 1996. What is the slope of the U. S. continental slope? *Geology*, **24**, 3–6.

PRATSON, L.F. & HAXBY, W.F. 1997. Panoramas of the seafloor. *Scientific American*, **276**, 66–71.

PRATSON, L.F., RYAN, W.B.F., MOUNTAIN, G.S. & TWICHELL, D.C. 1994. Submarine canyon initiation by downslope-eroding sediment flows: evidence in late Cenozoic strata on the New Jersey continental slope. *Geological Society of America Bulletin*, **106**, 395–412.

SANFORD, M.W., KUEHL, S.A. & NITTROUER, C.A. 1990. Modern sedimentary processes in the Wilmington Canyon area, United States east coast. *Marine Geology*, **92**, 205–226.

SCHLEE, J.S., DILLON, W.P. & GROW, J.A. 1979. Structure of the continental slope off the Eastern United States. *In*: DOYLE, L.J. & PILKEY, O.H. (eds) *Geology of continental slopes*. Society of Economic Paleontologists Mineralogists, Tulsa, Oklahoma, Special Publications **27**, 95–117.

SCULLY, M.E., FRIEDRICHS, C.T. & WRIGHT, L.D. 2002. Application of an analytical model of critically stratified gravity-driven sediment transport and deposition to observations from the Eel River continental shelf, Northern California. *Continental Shelf Research*, **22**, 1951–1974.

SEIDL, M. & DIETRICH, W.E. 1992. The problem of channel erosion into bedrock. *In*: SCHMIDT, K.H. & DE PLOEY, J. (eds) *Functional geomorphology: landform analysis and models. Catena Supplement*, **23**, 101–124.

SEIDL, M.A., DIETRICH, W.E. & KIRCHNER, J.W. 1994. Longitudinal profile development into bedrock: an analysis of Hawaiian channels. *Journal of Geology*, **102**, 457–474.

SHEPARD, F.P. 1981. Submarine canyons: multiple causes

and long-time persistence. *American Association of Petroleum Geologists Bulletin*, **65**, 1062–1077.

SNYDER, N.P., WHIPPLE, K.X., TUCKER, G.E., & MERRITTS, D.J. 2003. Importance of stochastic distribution of floods and erosion thresholds in the bedrock river incision problem. *Journal of Geophysical Research*, **108**, DOI: 10.1029/2001JB001655.

SOMMERFIELD, C.K. & LEE, H.J. 2004. Across-shelf sediment transport since the Last Glacial Maximum, southern California margin. *Geology*, **32**, 345–348.

TWICHELL, D.C. & Roberts, D.G. 1982. Morphology, distribution, and development of submarine canyons on the United States Atlantic continental slope between Hudson and Baltimore Canyons. *Geology*, **10**, 408–412.

UCHIUPI, E. 1970. *Atlantic continental shelf and slope of the United States – shallow structure*. Geological Survey Professional Paper 529-I, U.S. Geological Survey.

VAIL, P.R., MITCHUM, R.M. & THOMPSON, S. 1977. Seismic stratigraphy and global changes of sea level; Part 4, Global cycles of relative changes of sea level. *In*: PAYTON, C.E. (ed.). *Seismic stratigraphy – applications to hydrocarbon exploration*. American Association of Petroleum Geologists, Memoir **26**, 83–97.

VALENTINE, P.C., UZMANN, J.R. & COOPER, R.A., 1980. Geologic and biologic observations in Oceanographer submarine canyon: descriptions of dives aboard the research submarsibles Alvin (1967, 1978) and Nekton Gamma (1974): U.S. Geological Survey Open File Report, 80–76, p. 40.

WESSEL, P. & SMITH, W.H.F. 1991. Free software helps map and display data. *EOS Transactions*. AGU, **72**, 441.

WHIPPLE, K.X. & TUCKER, G.E. 1999. Dynamics of the stream-power river incision model: implications of height limits of mountain ranges, landscape response timescales, and research needs. *Journal of Geophysical Research*, **104**, 17661–17674.

WHIPPLE, K.X. & TUCKER, G.E. 2002. Implications of sediment-flux-dependent river incision models for landscape evolution. *Journal of Geophysical Research*, **107**, DOI: 10.1029/2000JB000044.

WHIPPLE, K.X., HANCOCK, G.S. & ANDERSON, R.S. 2000. River incision into bedrock: mechanics and relative efficacy of plucking, abrasion, and cavitation. *Geological Society of America Bulletin*, **112**, 490–503.

WRIGHT, L.D., FRIEDRICHS, C.T. & SCULLY, M.E. 2002. Pulsational gravity-driven sediment transport on two energetic shelves. *Continental Shelf Research*, **22**, 2443–2460.

Quantitative textural analyses of TOBI sonar imagery along the Almería Canyon, Almería Margin, Alborán Sea, SE Spain

OLGA GÓMEZ SICHI[1], PHILIPPE BLONDEL[1], EULÀLIA GRÀCIA[2], JUAN JOSÉ DAÑOBEITIA[2] & THE HITS-2001 SCIENCE PARTY[3]

[1] *Department of Physics, University of Bath, Bath BA2 7AY, UK (e-mail: O.Gomez@bath.ac.uk)*
[2] *UTM-CSIC; Centre Mediterrani d'Investigacions Marines i Ambientals (CMIMA); 08003 Barcelona, Spain*
[3] *HITS-2001 Science Party comrpises R. Bartolomé, L. Bullock, E. Costa, M. Farrán, M. Fernández, J. García, M. Gómez, J. Gonçalves, C. Jacobs, G. Lastras, H. Perea, M.J. Román, C. Roque, M. Ruiz, A. Sánchez, P. Terrinha, V. Willmott*

Abstract: Hydrocarbon exploration and the ongoing assessment of potential seismic risks are the main drivers behind the high-resolution mapping of continental margins. The large volume of literature devoted to turbidite systems in particular shows the importance of detailed descriptions of their characteristics and overall geomorphological variability, primarily through the distribution of sediment facies. These descriptions rely mainly on acoustic measurements, which are notoriously difficult to interpret. Textural analyses quantify the second-order statistics of sonar imagery, detecting and quantifying details invisible to the human eye. We show the potential (and limitations) of this approach using high-resolution (6 m) towed ocean bottom instrument (TOBI) sidescan sonar imagery acquired in the Alborán Sea, south of Almería, Spain, during the high resolution imaging of Tsunamigenic structures (HITS) 2001 programme. The imagery is co-registered with EM-12 multibeam bathymetry, topographic parametric sonar (TOPAS) sub-bottom profiles, and localized ground truthing. Our study focuses on the Almería Canyon, a meandering channel system more than 57 km long and transporting large amounts of sediments from the coast down to the Alborán Trough, *c.* 1700 m deep. Textural analyses quantify the variations of sediment processes along the slope of the Almería Canyon. They agree with the results of previous studies, and they can be used to provide new insights into the dynamics and evolution of the canyon.

In recent decades, seafloor exploration has revealed the sheer size and variety of continental margins. The investigation of deep-water systems and their architectural organization has shown their importance for understanding global ocean circulation and climate. They have also been highlighted by many scientists (e.g. Stow & Mayall 2000) as a key research theme for frontier hydrocarbon exploration in future decades. This economic impetus is helping to develop the detailed mapping of continental margins and associated turbidite systems around the world (e.g. McCave 2002). Extensive lists of submarine slope instabilities (e.g. Hampton *et al.* 1996), demonstrate that submarine mass movements can exert their influence over very large areas. This is of particular concern for the installation of offshore and coastal structures, seafloor resources, and the protection of coastal communities.

More specifically, submarine canyons are well recognized as important to the study of continental margins and sediment. McCave (2002) stressed that most aspects of present day turbidity currents in canyons (magnitude/frequency, integrated sediment flux out of canyons, etc.) are not well known. Thomsen *et al.* (2002) identified several key 'enabling technologies' of benefit to continental margin researchers, including the combination of high-frequency sonar and image processing. Following on these recommendations, this paper aims to bring together developments in the mapping of continental margins and turbidite systems (i.e. the TOBI survey of the Almería Canyon; Gràcia *et al.* 2001), and developments in image processing applied to sonar imagery (Blondel 1996).

This paper describes the wealth of multidisciplinary data collected in the Alborán Sea, south of Almería, Spain, during the first part of the HITS-2001 survey (Gràcia *et al.* 2001) that focused on TOBI sidescan sonar imagery. We shall then present textural analysis techniques (*TexAn* software), and their application to images along the Almería Canyon. The textural parameters of entropy and homogeneity quantify the acoustic variations along and across the canyon. The acoustic backscatter is directly related to local geological processes, and by quantifying its variations it complements traditional qualitative interpretations. Acoustic textures are analysed in conjunction with high-resolution bathymetry. Our textural analyses agree with the results of previous studies (e.g. Cronin *et al.* 1995;

From: HODGSON, D.M. & FLINT, S.S. (eds) 2005. *Submarine Slope Systems: Processes and Products.* Geological Society, London, Special Publications, **244**, 141–154. 0305–8719/$15.00

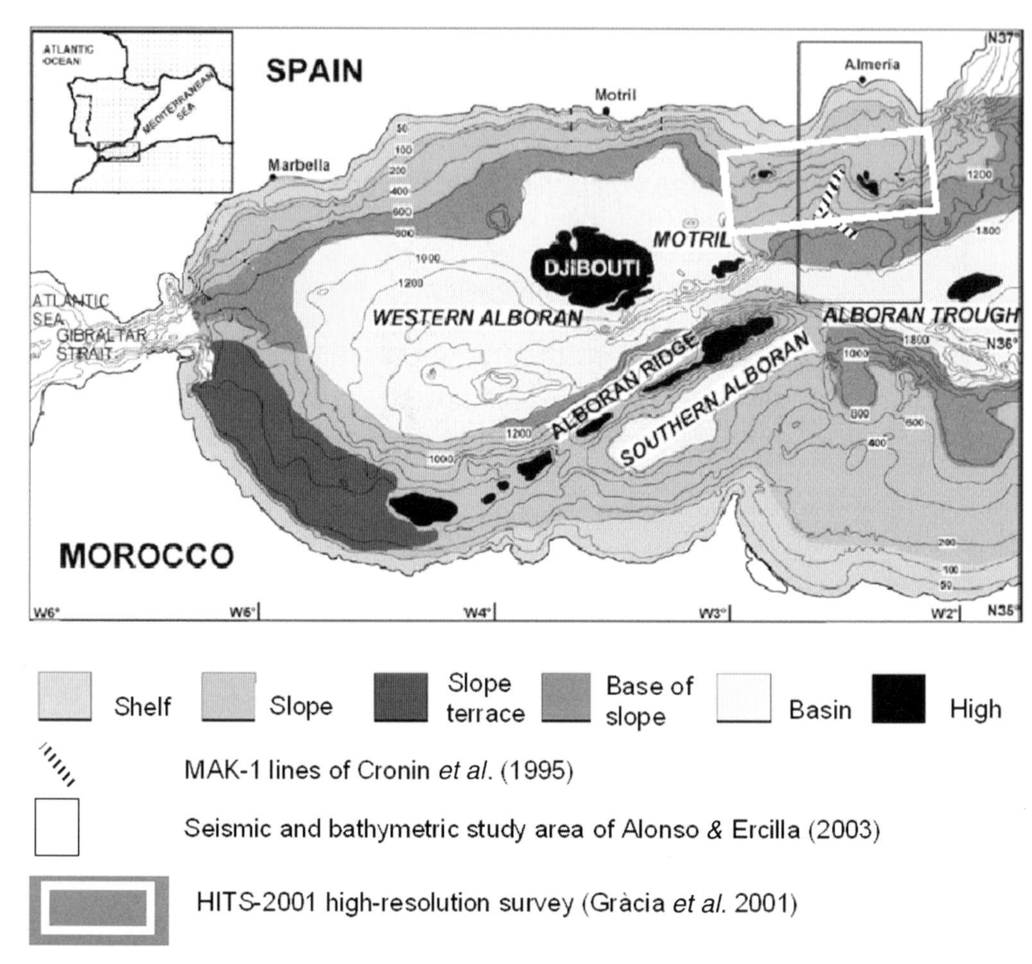

Fig. 1. Location map of the Almería Margin and Alborán Sea, southern Spain (adapted from Alonso & Ercilla 2003). This area was surveyed with multibeam bathymetry, high-resolution TOBI sidescan sonar imagery (see Fig. 2), high-resolution sub-bottom profiles obtained with the TOPAS parametric array, and seismic lines. Ground-truth and heat flow measurements are also available in some areas.

Alonso & Ercilla 2003). The usefulness of the analyses is limited in a few areas because of the geometry of insonification (e.g. sonar beam parallel to the canyon axis), or because of localized high levels of acoustic noise. This technique can be adapted to other areas on continental margins, and can be enhanced further to improve the accuracy of textural analyses and the interpretation of sonar images.

Geodynamic setting and previous studies

The Alborán Sea (SW Mediterranean) is a 150 km wide and 350 km long basin, less than 2000 m deep, located in the zone of collision between the Eurasian and African plates (Fig. 1). It has been characterized by active tectonics ever since its opening in the late Aquitanian or early Burdigalian (Argus *et al.* 1989; Platt & Vissers 1989; Sanz de Galdeano 1990; Campillo *et al.* 1992; Comas *et al.* 1992; Morel & Meghraoui 1996). Consequently, the Alborán Sea presents a highly complex inherited seafloor, including faults with highly variable trends and old relict volcanism from the Miocene (Langhian to Messinian, *c.* 16 to 5 Ma ago; Comas *et al.* 1992). In particular, the shallow continental margin south of Almería (Spain) is geodynamically complex and seismically active, as shown by recent swarms of shallow earthquakes with magnitudes ranging from M_w 4.7 to 5.1 (Gràcia *et al.* 2001). A sediment cover of variable thickness has been deposited since the early Miocene over the entire Alborán Sea, although presently there is a low terrigenous influx into the Almería Sea (Maldonado & Zamarreño 1983). The

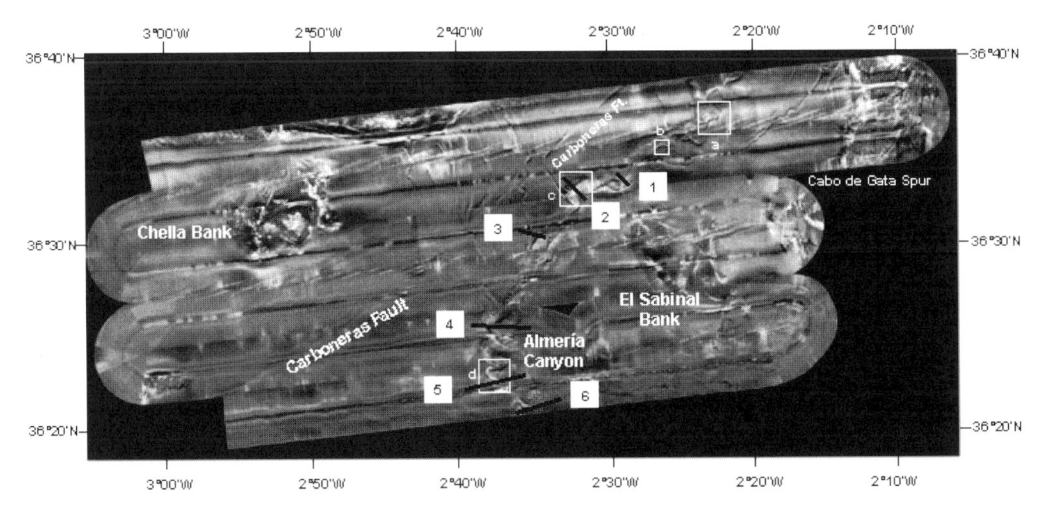

Fig. 2. TOBI side-scan sonar mosaic of the HITS region south of Almería. The entire area (approx. 33.3 × 100 km) has been processed to 6 m resolution, and 3 m resolution in some areas. The white open squares show the location of the smaller images in Figure 4. Note the surface expression of the Carboneras fault that clearly offsets some of the tributaries to the Almería Canyon. The thick black lines (and solid white boxes) show the location of the bathymetric cross-sections of Figure 5. Cross-section 6 is immediately south of the TOBI mosaic, and unfortunately not imaged (but it was surveyed by Cronin *et al.* 1995, with the MAK-1 sonar).

Neogene to Quaternary sediment cover is disrupted by active strike–slip faults (Comas *et al.* 1992) and by submarine canyons.

The longest of those canyons, and the one showing most variations in morphology, is the Andarax Canyon system, starting in Almería Bay, in the NE Alborán Sea. This canyon, also known as Almería Channel or Canyon (e.g. Zamarreño *et al.* 1983; Cronin 1995; Cronin *et al.* 1995; Alonso & Ercilla 2003), shows a highly developed system of tributaries. It is one of the three turbidite systems thoroughly studied by Alonso & Ercilla (2003), and despite the tributaries, was classified by these authors as a single-point source turbidite system. Both the tributaries and the main channel are affected by active tectonics, mostly from the nearby NE–SW sinistral strike–slip Carboneras Fault. It is not clear whether the system is still active, fed during short but intense flood events from the Andarax River (e.g. Maldonado & Zamarreño 1983; Cronin *et al.* 1995), or if it is a relict canyon of the last ice age, when the sea level was lower.

The HITS-2001 survey

The recent HITS cruise ('*High resolution imaging of tsunamigenic structures in SW Iberia*') was carried out on board *BIO Hespérides* in September–October 2001. Its main objectives were: (1) to determine the geometry of the active seismogenic structures in the SW Iberian Margin and their sediment-instability associated processes; (2) to investigate the possible seepage of fluids along these faults; and (3) to calculate their recurrence rate by dating of the turbiditic units generated by seismic events (Gràcia *et al.* 2001).

The present study uses primarily TOBI sidescan sonar imagery acquired during HITS-2001, as most of the survey was devoted to its use, and it has provided the most extensive coverage of the area to date (Fig. 1). TOBI (*towed ocean bottom instrument*) is the high-resolution sidescan sonar developed and operated by the Southampton Oceanography Centre (UK). It is a deep-towed vehicle operating 200–400 m above the seafloor, down to depths of 5000 m. It includes 30 kHz sidescan sonar, a 6–7 kHz sub-bottom profiler and a 3-component magnetometer (Flewellen *et al.* 1993). Simultaneously, hull-mounted Simrad EM-12S swath bathymetry and imagery, and TOPAS sub-bottom profiler data were acquired (Gràcia *et al.* 2001). Our interpretation of the TOBI imagery has therefore benefited fully from the synergy between the different survey methods and instrument resolutions selected. This integration is fundamental in allowing a detailed characterization of the superficial and sub-seafloor structures. This multidisciplinary dataset covers an area of 33.3 × 100 km (Fig. 2), extending from 36°40′N to 36°18′N and from 3°05′W to 2°05′W.

Six adjacent TOBI lines were recorded (Fig. 2), giving nearly full coverage of the continental margin south of Almería, in water depths ranging from 80 m (the shallowest TOBI deployment to date) to

1700 m. The resulting lines and mosaics (6 m resolution and 6 km swath) allow us to identify and map structures not visible with conventional acoustic methods. The survey revealed for the first time the surface expression of the submarine portion of the NE–SW trending Carboneras fault. Known volcanic heights (Chella and El Sabinal Banks), covered by carbonate platforms (extinct corals), were also surveyed and recognized with the HITS-2001 imagery and bathymetry. The survey is the most comprehensive mapping of the Almería Canyon and its depositional system. Parts of the canyon had already been surveyed in the past decade (e.g. the bathymetry and seismic database compiled by Alonso & Ercilla 2003; Fig. 1) and in particular, some portions were imaged in 1992 using the MAK-1 deep-tow sonar, with a resolution similar to TOBI but a 1 km wide swath only (Cronin *et al.* 1995; Fig. 1). As both systems operate at 30 kHz, their images are comparable and the two surveys are complementary.

The position and attitude of TOBI were known from the length of cable out and sensors on the platform (e.g. pitch, depth). The navigation and attitude files were filtered and reprocessed to remove outliers and spikes, and the raw acoustic data were processed, using processing of remotely-sensed imagery for seafloor mapping (PRISM) (LeBas & Hühnerbach 1998). This thorough processing followed the steps outlined in Blondel & Murton (1997): radiometric corrections (speckle removal, time-varying gain corrections), geometric corrections (e.g. slant-range to ground range, anamorphosis), as well as stencilling and mosaicking. To preserve details while reducing the amount of noise in the data, the original resolution was reduced to 6 m across- and along-track. Some portions of the TOBI dataset are also available at 3 m resolution. The final dataset is fully geo-referenced and thorough comparison with EM-12 bathymetry did not reveal any discrepancies.

Quantitative textural analyses

Most of the acoustic energy emitted by sidescan sonar is scattered forward in the specular direction. Only a small portion will be scattered back to the sonar and recorded. Each pixel in a sonar image will have a value corresponding to the local backscatter. Its value is affected, in decreasing order of importance, by three factors (e.g. Blondel & Murton 1997): (1) the geometry of insonification (local angle of incidence of the sonar beam, local slope); (2) the physical characteristics of the interface (micro-scale roughness, at different wavelengths); (3) the volume processes in the sediment (penetration, re-scattering, etc.). The relative contributions of these factors will also depend on the frequency used.

Visual interpretations are not based on the values of the pixels alone. Instead, they focus on local groups of pixels, their organization and their relationships. This corresponds to their textures, as defined in traditional remote sensing (e.g. Haralick 1979). The local textures can be qualified as rough or smooth, local or regional, repetitive or random. Quantitative textural measurements can be extracted from the image with various techniques, the most efficient ones being stochastic (e.g. Haralick 1979). Grey-level co-occurrence matrices (GLCMs) have proved particularly successful for sidescan sonar imagery (Reed & Hussong 1989; Blondel *et al.* 1993) and have already been used profitably on TOBI imagery in several contexts (Blondel 1996, 2000; Cochrane & Lafferty 2002; Huvenne *et al.* 2002).

To use GLCMs, three computation parameters are crucial: the number of grey levels used (256 grey levels mean that 256 × 256 matrices need to be computed for each pixel; fewer grey levels will reduce the computation time but decrease the amount of information used), the window size (too large and it will incorporate unneeded data, too small and it will mainly measure acoustic noise), and the inter-pixel displacement. GLCMs bring information that first-order statistics (simple parameters like contrast, intensity variance etc.) cannot bring (Fig. 3). But GLCMs are not easy to interpret directly. They are described more effectively by statistical measures called indices. More than 25 textural indices are available from the current literature (from Haralick 1979 to Blondel 1996; a complete list of the indices most relevant to sonar imagery analyses is given in the latter). Two of them, entropy and homogeneity, have proved enough to resolve most if not all textures visible in sonar imagery (e.g. Blondel *et al.* 1993; Blondel 1996, 2000; Cochrane & Lafferty 2002; Huvenne *et al.* 2002).

Entropy measures the lack of spatial organization inside the computation window. Entropy is high with rough textures (e.g. rocks), and low when the texture is more homogeneous or smoother (like a sedimentary facies). All geological features encountered in sonar images are characterized by specific entropy levels. For ease of interpretation, entropy is quantized on a dimensionless 0–255 range valid for all sonar images.

Homogeneity quantifies the amount of local similarities inside the computation window. This parameter should distinguish homogeneous regions (e.g. smooth sediments) from faulted or deformed areas (including ripples and slumps). For ease of interpretation, local homogeneity is quantized on a negative logarithmic scale, i.e. lower homogeneities correspond to higher degrees of organization, and *vice versa*.

Once entropy and homogeneity have been calculated at each pixel, texture measurements are

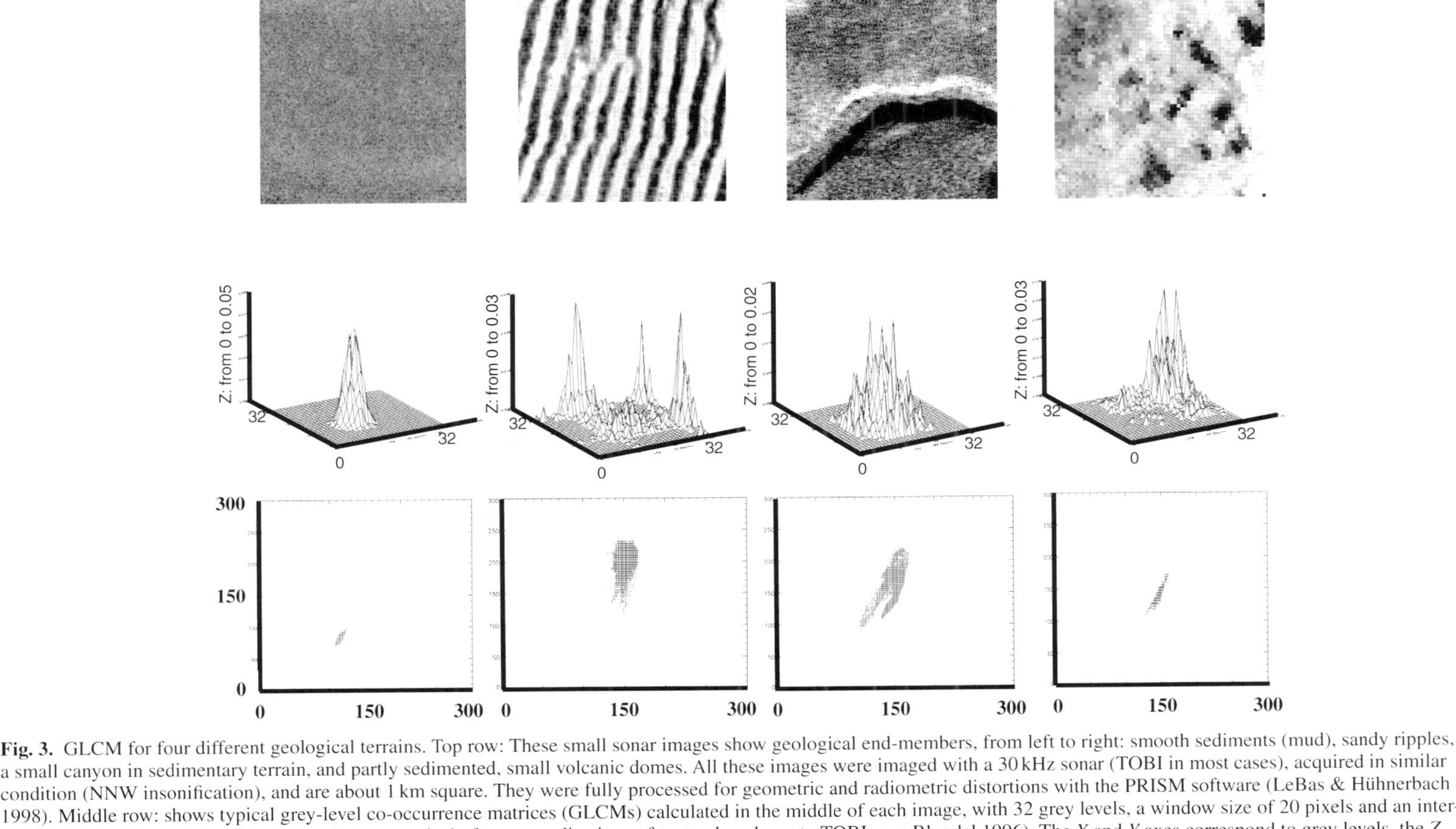

Fig. 3. GLCM for four different geological terrains. Top row: These small sonar images show geological end-members, from left to right: smooth sediments (mud), sandy ripples, a small canyon in sedimentary terrain, and partly sedimented, small volcanic domes. All these images were imaged with a 30 kHz sonar (TOBI in most cases), acquired in similar condition (NNW insonification), and are about 1 km square. They were fully processed for geometric and radiometric distortions with the PRISM software (LeBas & Hühnerbach 1998). Middle row: shows typical grey-level co-occurrence matrices (GLCMs) calculated in the middle of each image, with 32 grey levels, a window size of 20 pixels and an inter-pixel displacement of 10 pixels (these values are typical of many applications of textural analyses to TOBI, e.g. Blondel 1996). The *X* and *Y* axes correspond to grey levels, the *Z* axis to the normalized frequency of co-occurrence for each grey level couple. These matrices show the combined occurrences of grey levels in the surrounding pixels. The number of peaks, their relative sizes, and their positions inside the matrix depend on the proportion of distinct grey levels in the image as well as on their distribution. Each terrain thus corresponds to a distinct GLCM. Bottom row: shows the compilation of 32 400 TexAn measurements of entropy (*X*-axis) and homogeneity (*Y*-axis, expressed as dimensionless indices) for each of the example images, representing different degrees of complexity and/or organization. Note how well defined most regions are: for example, low entropies (i.e. low roughness) and low homogeneities (i.e. high degrees of organization) for smooth sediments, higher entropies (more roughness) for the ripples.

interpreted as characteristic of a specific geological process using measurement-space guided clustering. Comparison with other classification algorithms proved it was the most robust and adapted to sonar images (Blondel 1996). A particular advantage of this algorithm is that it is not biased by the statistical predominance of some regions. The calculation of GLCMs, the derivation of entropy and homogeneity values, and their clustering have been incorporated into the proprietary TexAn software (Blondel 2000).

Along-slope analyses of the Almería Canyon

Methodology

TOBI sonar imagery of the Almería Canyon system was analysed using the *TexAn* software. 27 images of the same size and resolution were selected along the slope of the entire canyon, covering its surface and the surrounding terraces and levees, the end of the tributary channels and some abandoned meanders. Entropy and homogeneity were calculated for each pixel in the image, using a moving window of 20 pixels (commensurate with the scale of the features to be observed) and an inter-pixel displacement of 10 pixels.

Figure 4a shows the method of analysis, as carried out on each of the 27 images. The textural intervals of entropy/homogeneity were inspected in turn and clustered by geological regions (Fig. 4). The valley sediments show the higher homogeneities (low degrees of organization), and can be separated into two regions based on their entropies or degrees of roughness. This separation is also quite clear geographically, although its exact geological meaning cannot be ascertained without ground-truthing. The backscatter levels from slopes facing toward the sonar can become nearly saturated, and this is reflected in the textures: lower entropies (i.e. lower roughness) and lower homogeneities (i.e. higher degree of organization as saturation increases). Background sediments, i.e. those occupying the rest of the continental slope, correspond to most of the image. However, they are restricted to a very small interval of entropy/homogeneity values. Their minute textural variations probably correspond to similar geological processes. Finally, there is a clear textural distinction between the different areas of the canyon.

Textures and local processes

To understand the meaning of textures and how they can be used to complement the interpretation of geological processes, one needs to consider the position of the images along the canyon, and the role played by topography. Although the Almería Canyon has been catalogued as a single point-source turbidite system, based on observations made in the Alborán Sea by Alonso & Ercilla (2003), several tributaries feed it (if active) along its course (Fig. 2). Most of the northern bank tributaries are clearly offset by the Carboneras Fault and may no longer play an active part in the system, but their topography still influences the geometry of insonification of the sonar, and thus the textures.

In order to analyse the importance of topography, we extracted EM-12 bathymetry across representative sections (Fig. 5 and thick black lines in Figs 2 and 4). Cross-sections 1 and 2 show a highly asymmetric channel with differences of several hundred metres between the walls. The canyon wall-to-floor height is 300 to 400 m at the west/north bank and 100 to 200 m in height at the south/east bank (Fig. 5). This corresponds to the section described by Alonso & Ercilla (2003), where erosive flows contribute to the excavation of the canyon system.

Cross-section 3 corresponds to the break of slope, and the transition to a predominantly erosive depositional environment (Alonso & Ercilla 2003). The canyon is slightly shallower (100 m) but wider and more symmetrical. Bathymetric cross-section 4 is from the beginning of the meandering portion of the Almería Canyon. The canyon becomes asymmetrical again (but to a lesser degree) and a 20-m high levee is clearly visible. Cross-section 5 is taken at the end of the meandering system, in the area affected by channel and overbank deposits (according to Alonso & Ercilla 2003). The bathymetric profile shows a very flat area, with a shallow asymmetric canyon (30 and 50 m deeper than each bank) and extensive deposits on each side. Finally the bathymetric cross-section 6 is taken near the end of the Almería Canyon, at the southern edge of the HITS-2001 survey. The low-gradient, topographically smooth area is typical of such systems, as analysed by Richards *et al.* (1998) and Alonso & Ercilla (2003).

Tempered by the local bathymetry, and therefore the actual angle of insonification, the acoustic backscatter is directly influenced by the type of seabed (surface and volume properties; e.g. Blondel *et al.* 2001). The many small-scale acoustic returns combine to form the value recorded in each pixel, following complex mathematical distributions (e.g. Lyons & Abraham 1999). These pixels, and groups/regions of pixels, are those used by the interpreter to delineate areas of geological significance, on the basis of level and textural variations. The textural variations are not a direct representation of specific geological/sedimentary processes. However, they are a 'proxy' by which local geomorphological processes can be perceived, and, more importantly, quantified. Used in conjunction with other data (when available), the entropy and homogeneity variations can provide information about the processes that might be involved.

Along-slope textural variations

We also analysed the variations of entropy (i.e. roughness) and homogeneity (i.e. local similarities) along the slope of the Almería Canyon. They correspond only to the valley of the canyon, although the geographical boundaries between units were not always easy to distinguish on the sonar imagery alone. The textures of sediments in the background of the continental slope do not vary much, and were not deemed relevant for this study, which focuses on the canyon itself.

Figures 4b, c and d are representative examples taken along the slope. As in Figure 4a, they show variations in the canyon textures (represented by different colours). In a southward direction, the textures of the valley change from predominantly 'valley II' to 'valley I' when the canyon becomes narrower (Fig. 4a–c). Then, as the canyon becomes shallower, they nearly disappear, whereas the 'mottled sediments' texture becomes predominant (Fig. 4c, d). The 'slopes' textures follow a similar pattern: their extent decreases as the canyon walls become steeper (which is the case between Fig. 4a & c) and also as the canyon's depth lessens (compare Fig. 4b & d).

Entropy

Globally, the entropy variations are in line with the tests performed earlier on geological end-members (Fig. 3). The entropy varies around the relatively high value of 150. We also found that entropies are higher when the asymmetry of the canyon is higher, showing more roughness. Conversely, entropies decrease when the across-strike profile of the canyon becomes more symmetrical. Small variations around the mean entropy correspond to areas where the canyon and its valley are very well defined. Despite the high noise in some of these images, coming from interference with the TOPAS profiler or from passing ships, TexAn can distinguish between the acoustic noise (high entropies, low homogeneities) and the canyon textures (higher entropies, very high homogeneities).

Homogeneity

Homogeneity (local similarities) varies much more along the slope of the Almería Canyon than the entropy. Typical values are centred on 200, but there are significant deviations, increasing to 240 (before cross-section 1; see Fig. 2 for location) or decreasing to 100 or less (most visibly between cross-sections 4 and 5; Fig. 2). Homogeneities decrease from one bathymetric cross-section to the next, and increase sharply immediately after each cross-section. These cross-sections were chosen to correspond to geomorphological discontinuities (Alonso & Ercilla 2003), and the regular decrease in homogeneity can be explained by the movement of sediments, increasing their organization down slope (e.g. their flow directions). This hypothesis would also account for the important drop of homogeneity between bathymetric cross-sections 4 and 5, corresponding to a brusque change in canyon direction (Figs 2 & 5).

Entropy and homogeneity

An important dip in entropy and homogeneity is seen between bathymetric cross-sections 4 and 5 (Fig. 2). The only time there are similarly small homogeneity values is between cross-sections 2 and 3 (Fig. 2), but in this case the entropies are close to average. We saw for the former that the decrease in homogeneity was most likely related to the reworking of sediments and their organization along the directions of increased flow. The corresponding image indeed shows an abrupt change in the direction of the canyon. This will affect the geometry of insonification (from sub-parallel to sub-perpendicular to the canyon axis), and changes in backscatter contrast. Some areas will be in shadows, others will be on slopes facing toward the sonar and therefore much brighter and closer to saturation. This would explain the consistently low entropies (around 100 or lower). The TOBI image showing a similar entropy/homogeneity decrease between cross-sections 2 and 3 also corresponds to a rapid change in the canyon direction (Fig. 2). But the backscatter is generally much lower, preventing saturation; the resulting entropies are thus closer to those for the rest of the canyon. The large decrease in homogeneity and the interpretation of the entropy differences show the potential of TexAn to relate two regions far apart but geologically similar and affected by the same sedimentary processes.

Inner valley sediments will usually have significantly lower entropies and homogeneities, meaning they are acoustically smoother and texturally more organized. This is consistent with the small micro-scale roughness and with the alignment along the flow directions typical of canyon floors. The edges of the valleys will show higher entropies and homogeneities, consistent with larger deposits, or small (rough) rubble at the base of the canyon walls. In some cases, there are two textural intervals inside the valley for the same image. For example, the inner valley sediments and the edges of the canyon valley

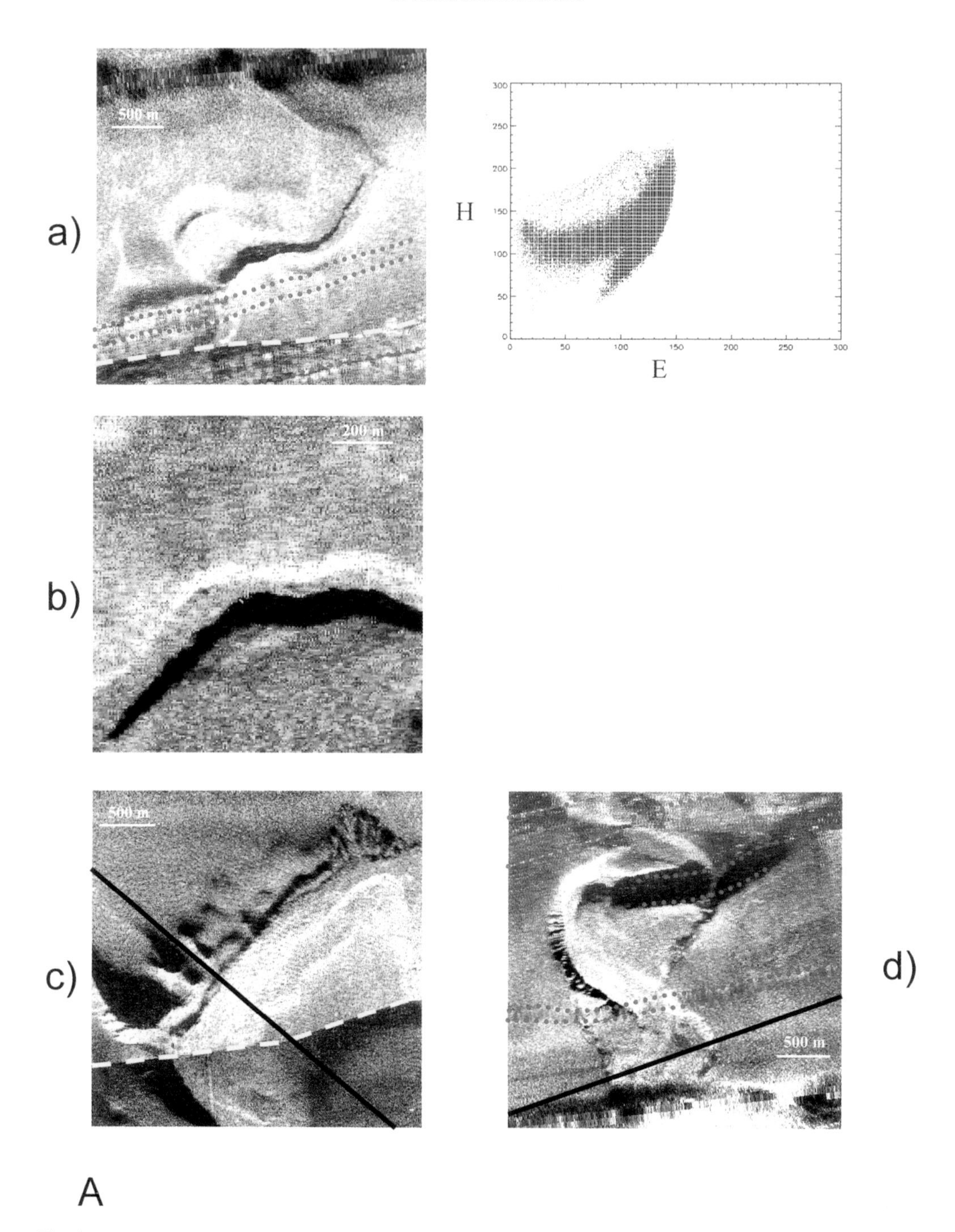

Fig. 4. Example of TexAn textural analysis, on four of the 27 images used in this study. (**A**) Original sonar images. All these images are representative sections of the canyon, processed at 6 m resolution per pixel (see Fig. 2 for exact location). (**a**) is 512 pixels square (3×3 km on the ground). It is located around 36°38′N, 2°22′W (Fig. 2) and corresponds to a change in direction of the canyon, in the upper part of the Almería system. The canyon is already well developed, very narrow (around 100 m at the bottom) and with steep walls. It is therefore clearly visible. The nadir (region directly under the sonar) is visible at the top of the image. It shows the path of the sonar and the origins of the insonifying beams. Most of the image is imaged from the NNW. The dashed line corresponds to the junction between two TOBI runs. The dotted lines correspond to systematic noise (most likely from the TOPAS system). Expressed in

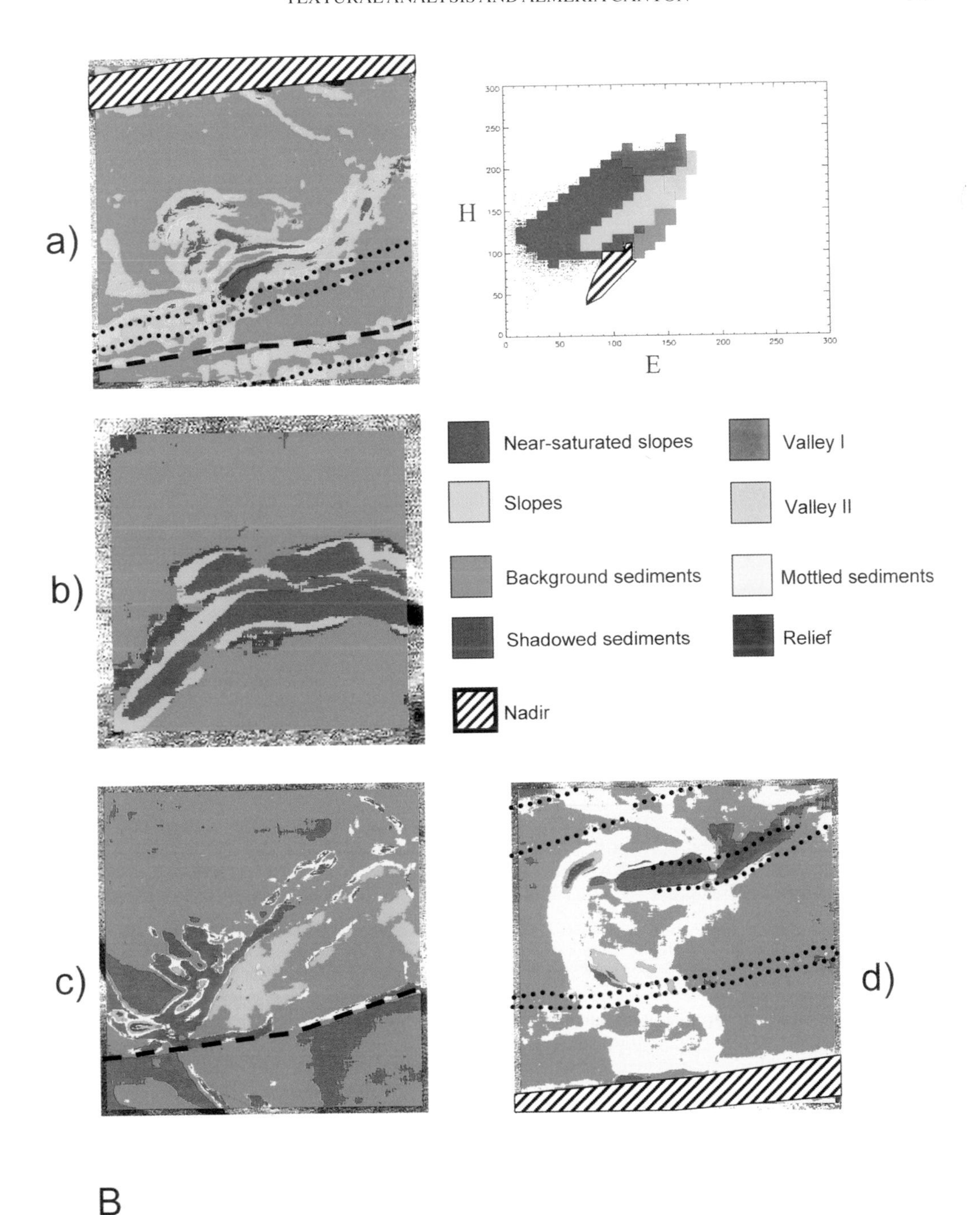

dimensionless indices ranging from 0 to 255 in the following plots, the entropy (*E*)/homogeneity (*H*) plot is at top right. (**b**) is 1 km square, whereas (**c**) and (**d**) are 3 km square each. The thick black line shows the track of a bathymetric profile. (**B**) Corresponding textural interpretations for the same images. The interpretation of the entropy (*E*)/homogeneity (*H*) plot is top right. Note the clear distinction between the different areas of the canyon, and the fact that background sediments, although more numerous, correspond to only a small interval of entropy/homogeneity values. Regions recognized from entropy and homogeneity values are colour-coded. Note the variations in texture (colours) and the changes in relative areas as one moves down the slope of the canyon.

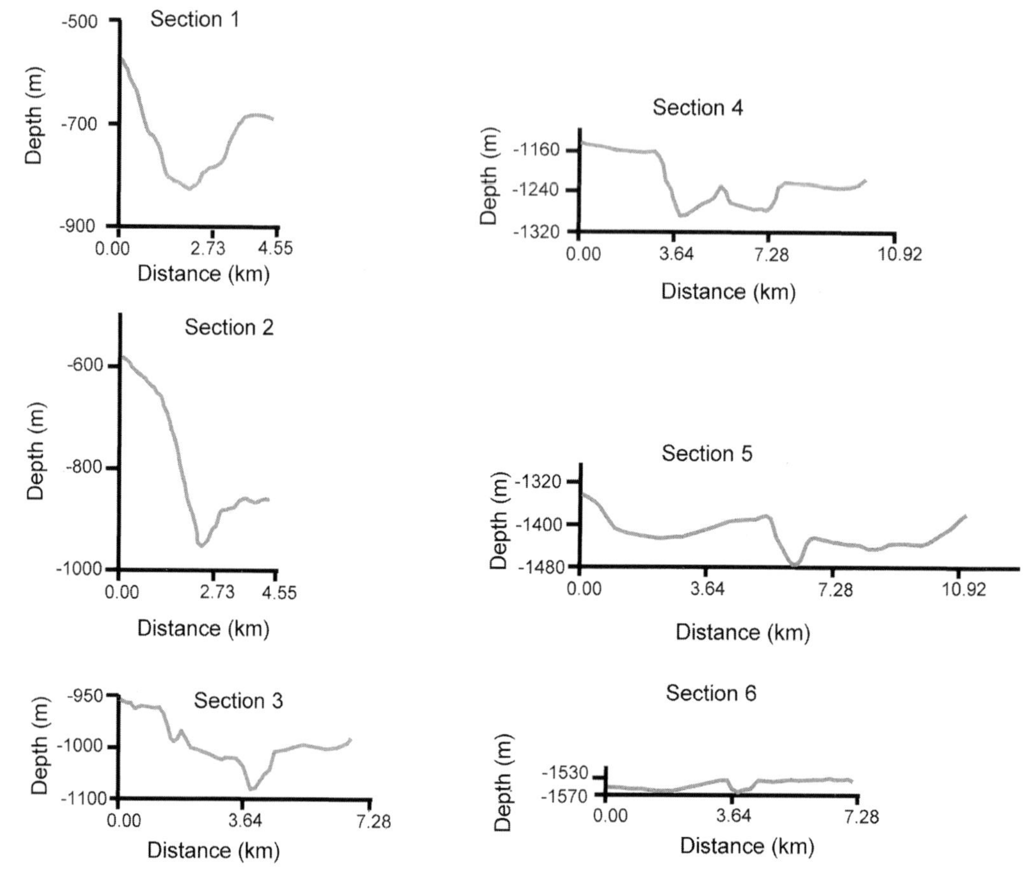

Fig. 5. EM-12 bathymetric cross-sections from the HITS-2001 survey, numbered 1–6, and measured along the canyon (see Fig. 2 for their locations). The topographical asymmetry between the northern/western banks and their counterparts is strongest in the upper portion of the canyon, where erosive flows contribute to the excavation of the system, and progressively decrease downslope, when depositional processes become more important (Alonso & Ercilla 2003).

will have clearly distinct textural signatures (two distinct entropy intervals, two distinct homogeneity intervals). These variations can be explained by changes in the angle of insonification, but as these changes are small between inner valley and valley edge, they are probably due to variations in the sediment cover.

Not all images will be as clear but in most of them, the valley is recognizable enough that its entropy/homogeneity signatures can be extracted. In a few cases, it was not possible to distinguish between the valley of the canyon and the background sediments, either through visual interpretation or with textural signatures. This stemmed from unfavourable imaging geometries (e.g. parallel to the local canyon axis or excessive acoustic shadows), or because the exact border of the canyon could not be distinguished from the background continental slope sediments. In one occurrence (section immediately west of Fig. 4a), two meanders were superposed and affected by important interference from TOPAS. It was not possible to identify which meander was currently active, and which was abandoned; the textural signatures for this particular image were therefore discarded. It is possible that TOBI penetrated the local loose sediments to some depth, thereby imaging the present and ancient meanders at the same time, but knowledge of the actual penetration depth of TOBI is anecdotal (e.g. Akhmetzanov, pers. comm. 2003) and further analyses would be required.

Discussion

Morphologically, the Almería Canyon system is very close to the mixed sand-mud point-source submarine fans described in Richards *et al.* (1998) and Stow & Mayall (2000). This fits the detailed analysis of bathymetry and seismic profiles carried out by

Alonso & Ercilla (2003). Geomorphologically, the Almería Canyon system is very close to the fine-grained submarine fan system described in the synthesis of Bouma (2000). Entropy and homogeneity exhibit consistent, large-scale variations, which can be divided into four zones.

The first zone corresponds to the upper reaches of the channel and ranges approximately from the beginning of the visible part of the canyon to bathymetric cross-section 1 (see Fig. 2 for locations). The entropies are centred on 150, albeit with large variations, and the homogeneities are the highest along the entire canyon (*c*. 210), with very small variations. The homogeneities correspond to more disorganized textures, in part because the canyon is still shallow and possibly because the sediments are less well sorted. Richards *et al*. (1998) say that such a system will typically have an upper fan dominated by a single feeder channel (which is the case here), flanked by mud-dominated levees. In the absence of ground-truthing in this area, it is tempting to attribute the changes in homogeneity to the differences between mud and sand, on spatial scales that are short compared to the *TexAn* computation window (tests were conducted with smaller windows, but were hampered by the small-scale noise of the TOBI images). This was compounded by the fact that, owing to operational considerations, part of the canyon was imaged along-strike by TOBI, making it even more difficult to see the variations across the slopes.

The second zone corresponds to the near-linear part of the canyon (a distance roughly between bathymetric cross-section 1 and half-way between cross-sections 3 and 4; Fig. 2). This section shows the largest variation in depth along the canyon, from 400 m to 50 m (down the continental slope), and the gradual decrease of the high asymmetry between the canyon walls (from 300 m to nearly zero). This section shows few variations in entropy (*c*. 170 in the asymmetric sections, *c*. 130 in the more symmetrical sections), partly explained by changes in the angles of insonification but also likely to correspond to changes in the roughness of the sediments. Conversely, the homogeneities vary between approximately 160 and 220. This is explained by varying degrees of organization of the acoustic textures. The degree of organization decreases as the canyon's profile becomes symmetrical. A detailed analysis of across-track textural variations, in conjunction with the 3 TOPAS sub-bottom profiles available, could help to assess whether this corresponds to different types of sediment loading on the canyon walls.

Entropy/homogeneity plots reveal the existence of a third zone, made of two regions well apart in the Almería Canyon (18 km away, southern part of Fig. 4c and northern part of Fig. 4d). The entropies (with two peaks around 50 and 140) and the homogeneities (always lower than 100, compared to typical values in the 150–230 range) are significantly lower than for the rest of the canyon. Close examination shows that they correspond to abrupt changes in the canyon direction (*c*. 90°), and to high bathymetry differences between one wall of the canyon and the other (300 m in the northern region — the highest asymmetry encountered — and 30 m in the southern region, where typical asymmetry is 20 m). According to Richards *et al*. (1998), the bifurcations into highly sinuous or meandering tributary channels form conduits for the transport of coarse-grained clastics to the middle and lower fan. However, because of the geometry of insonification, significant portions of the canyon are in shadows, or poorly contrasted. This results in lower entropies (i.e. lower roughness) and lower homogeneities (i.e. higher degree of organization). The potential of *TexAn* is therefore slightly limited here (as would any visual interpretation).

The fourth zone is visible when correlating the position along the canyon with the entropy/homogeneity distribution. It corresponds to the region south of bathymetric cross-section 5 (Fig. 2). At this point, the canyon is very shallow again, and bounded by large deposits on each side. The Almería Canyon is close to its end and the distal lobes discussed by Cronin *et al*. (1995). But in the absence of TOBI or MAK-1 sidescan sonar imagery, we cannot observe the discharge zone. The entropies are centred on 160–170, the homogeneities on 180–200, with somewhat larger variations. They are close to the entropies and homogeneities associated to some sections of the second zone. Consistently lower entropies are associated with the sediment cover of the abandoned meanders, at 36.43°N and 36.35°N. This could tally with the evolution of the lower parts of the channels by intermittent and repeated avulsion and abandonment of distributary channels, and the lateral stacking of depositional lobes demonstrated by Richards *et al*. (1998). But again, more ground-truthing would be necessary to match the textural evolutions with a general process.

Noise is a constant problem, as in many sidescan sonar datasets. The most common form of noise corresponds to the nadir, directly below the path of the sonar. Nadir points never yield much useful information, because they are not directly imaged by the main sonar beam (Blondel & Murton 1997). They are made of dark and bright groups of pixels, which may be wrongly interpreted by automatic image processing systems. Fortunately, *TexAn* always shows the nadir with low entropies and low homogeneities. Another systematic source of noise in shallow water is the reflection from the sea surface; this can be removed using the PRISM software (LeBas & Hühnerbach 1998). The HITS-2001 dataset was also

affected by two types of systematic noise. The TOPAS sub-bottom profiler is a parametric array; as such it transmits two frequencies. The difference between the primary and secondary frequencies is very close to the TOBI frequency (30 kHz) and the resulting interferences are visible as regularly spaced bright stripes at an angle to the sonar's track, usually at the edges of the images. They could not always be separated from the seabed backscatter, even on the base of their textural signatures. The second source of noise came from passing ships, as the HITS-2001 survey area was very close to the shipping lanes to and from the Strait of Gibraltar. This type of noise is less common, and manifests itself as saturated white triangles, perpendicular to the track of the sonar and at the edges of images. This type of noise was also easily recognized with *TexAn*.

Conclusion

As applied here, textural entropy and homogeneity are good descriptors of along-slope sediment variations. We were able to follow the general results of Richards *et al.* (1998) and Bouma (2000). Our dataset extended the results of Cronin *et al.* (1995), mostly because of the larger swath width of TOBI, and the extensive east-west coverage of the HITS-2001 survey. Although we did not insonify the end of the channel imaged by Cronin *et al.* (1995) and the discharge zone, the HITS-2001 survey mapped the early onset of the channel, further up the slope, and covered (entirely) all the meanders as well as the across-slope variations. We were also able to extend the results of Alonso & Ercilla (2003), as the TOBI imagery covers more ground in the north, in particular the earlier development stages of the canyon. In general, entropy and homogeneity variations, associated to the high resolution of TOBI, were able to give us insights into the local sediment dynamics, for example in regions of increased flow, and to distinguish between coarse-grained and fine-grained areas.

The analyses of entropy and homogeneity distributions across the Almería Canyon, in conjunction with EM-12 bathymetry and the few high-resolution TOPAS sub-bottom profiles available, should help to assess the across-strike variations in sediments. In particular, this should help us to investigate the likelihood of slides on the relatively steep-walled and fine-grained levees of the valley (cf. Hampton *et al.* 1996). The exact influence of fine-grained versus coarse-grained sediment deposits on acoustic textures needs to be ascertained in more detail. We are currently modelling the theoretical acoustic backscatter expected from different types of sediments, imaged with different geometries. Using state-of-the-art high-frequency scattering models (e.g. Williams & Jackson 1996), this study will also investigate how far TOBI can penetrate different sediments.

One problem that must be addressed is the lack of absolute calibration, typical of most marine geophysical sonars. The backscatter recorded by a sonar is quantized along a certain number of levels (e.g. 0–255), but the dynamic range is related to the electronic gains used during the survey, and to the power transmitted by the sonar itself. In most cases these parameters are not accessible to the average sonar user, and it is impossible to relate these backscatter levels to an exact acoustic reflectivity (e.g. in dB), making impractical the quantitative comparison between different surveys of the same area. Absolute calibration has proved its worth, in particular with multibeam sonars (e.g. Urgeles *et al.* 2002). It should therefore be adapted to sidescan sonars.

The present study, and in particular the use of *TexAn*, are a first step towards the geotechnical characterization of mass movements. Merged with *in-situ* data, and even better, with calibrated sonar imagery, this can be integrated into a risk assessment methodology similar to the one advocated by Locat (2001) and used in major international programmes such as COSTA (continental slope stability). The link with geotechnical parameters (e.g. grain size, micro-scale roughness) is another important step toward understanding the present dynamics and the evolution of Almería Canyon. Once fully developed, this methodology will be readily applicable to high-resolution sidescan sonar imagery of other turbidite systems throughout the world.

The authors are grateful to the officers and crew of BIO *Hespérides* for their assistance throughout the HITS-2001 survey. The high quality of the sonar data is a result of the hard work of the TOBI team from the Southampton Oceanography Centre (UK). The entire TOBI dataset was processed in 2002 at SOC by O. Gómez Sichi and J. Gonçalves, under the expert guidance of T. LeBas (SOC) and with funding from the programme EASSS-III (European Access to Seafloor Survey Systems: grant HPRI-CT99-0047). The HITS survey also benefited from MCYT Acción Especial HITS REN2000-2150-E. O.G.S. is a European Marie Curie Fellow (grant HPMF-CT-2002-01970). This paper benefited from reviews by B.T. Cronin and D. Hodgson. We are very grateful to G. Ercilla (CSIC-Barcelona) for sending us a preprint of her 2003 article on the Alborán Sea turbidite systems.

References

ALONSO, B. & ERCILLA, G. 2003. Small turbidite systems in a complex tectonic setting (SW Mediterranean Sea): morphology and growth patterns. *Marine and Petroleum Geology*, **19**, 1225–1240.

ARGUS, D.F., GORDON, R.G., DE METS, C. & STEIN, S. 1989. Closure of the Africa-Eurasia-North America

plate motion circuit and tectonics of the Gloria fault. *Journal of Geophysical Research*, **94**, 5585–5602.
BLONDEL, P. 1996. Segmentation of the Mid-Atlantic Ridge south of the Azores, based on acoustic classification of TOBI data. *In*: MACLEOD, C.J., TYLER, P. & WALKER, C.L. (eds) *Tectonic, Magmatic and Biological Segmentation of Mid-Ocean Ridges*. Geological Society, London, Special Publications, **118**, 17–28.
BLONDEL, P. 2000. Automatic mine detection by textural analysis of COTS sidescan sonar imagery. *International Journal of Remote Sensing*, **21**, 3115–3128.
BLONDEL, P. & MURTON, B.J. 1997. *Handbook of Seafloor Sonar Imagery*. PRAXIS-Wiley & Sons, 314 p.
BLONDEL, P., SEMPÉRÉ, J.-C. & ROBIGOU, V. 1993. Textural Analysis and Structure-Tracking for geological mapping: applications to sonar data from Endeavour Segment, Juan de Fuca Ridge, *Proceedings of OCEANS'93. IEEE-OES*, 209–213.
BLONDEL, P., PACE, N.G., HEALD, G.J. & BROTHERS, R. 2001. High-frequency bistatic scattering: comparison of tank and sea experiments. *In*: Leighton, T.G., HEALD, G.J., GRIFFITHS, H.D. & GRIFFITHS, G. (eds) *Acoustical Oceanography*. Proceedings of the Institute of Acoustics, **23**, 276–282.
BOUMA, A.H. 2000. Coarse-grained and fine-grained turbidite systems as end member models: applicability and dangers. *Marine and Petroleum Geology*, **17**, 137–143.
CAMPILLO, A.C., MALDONADO, A. & MAUFFRET, A. 1992. Stratigraphic and tectonic evolution of the Western Alborán Sea: late Miocene to present. *Geo-Marine Letters*, **12**, 165–172.
COCHRANE, G.R. & LAFFERTY, K.D. 2002. Use of acoustic classification of sidescan sonar data for mapping benthic habitat in the Northern Channel Islands, California. *Continental Shelf Research*, **22**, 683–690.
COMAS M.C., GARCÍA-DUEÑAS, V. & JURADO, M.J. 1992. Neogene tectonic evolution of the Alborán Sea from MCS data. *Geo-Marine Letters*, **12**, 157–164.
CRONIN, B.T. 1995. Structurally-controlled deep-sea channel courses: examples from the Miocene of South-east Spain and the Alborán Sea, South-west Mediterranean. *In*: HARTLEY, A.J. & PROSSER, D.J. (eds) *Characterization of Deep Marine Clastic Systems*. Geological Society, London, Special Publication, **94**, 113–133.
CRONIN, B.T., KENYON, N.H., WOODSIDE, J., ET AL. 1995. The Almeria Canyon: a meandering channel system on an active margin, Alborán Sea, Western Mediterranean. *In:* PICKERING, K.T. HISCOTT, R.N. KENYON, N.H., RICCI LUCCHI, F. & SMITH, R.D.A. (eds) *Atlas of deep-water environments: Architectural style in turbidite systems*. Chapman & Hall, London, 84–88.
FLEWELLEN, C., MILLARD, N. & ROUSE, I. 1993. TOBI - A vehicle for deep ocean survey. *Electronics and Communication Engineering Journal*, 85–93.
GRÀCIA, E., DAÑOBEITIA, J.J. & HITS cruise party. 2001. High-resolution imaging of tsunamigenic structures in the SW Iberian Margin (Eurasia-Africa convergence): implications for seismic hazard assessment. *EOS Transactions AGU*, **82**, 47, S51B–0610.
HAMPTON, M.A., LEE, H.J. & LOCAT, J. 1996. Submarine landslides. *Reviews of Geophysics*, **34**, 33–59.
HARALICK, R.M. 1979. Statistical and structural approaches to texture. *Proceedings of the IEEE*, **67**, 5.
HUVENNE, V., BLONDEL, P. & HENRIET, J.-P. 2002. Sidescan sonar imagery from the Porcupine Seabight and implications from geostatistical analyses. *Marine Geology*, **189**, 323–341.
LEBAS T.P. & HÜHNERBACH, V. 1998. PRISM: processing of remotely-sensed imagery for seafloor mapping. A collection of software for the processing, analysis and enhancement of sidescan sonar imagery. *SOC Technical Report*, Southampton, UK, 76 p.
LOCAT, J. 2001. Instabilities along ocean margins: a geomorphological and geotechnical perspective. *Marine and Petroleum Geology*, **18**, 503–512.
LYONS, A.P. & ABRAHAM, D.A. 1999. Statistical characterization of high-frequency shallow-water seafloor backscatter. *Journal of the Acoustical Society of America*, **106**, 1307–1315.
MALDONADO, A. & ZAMARREÑO, I. 1983. Modelos sedimentarios en las plataformas continentals del Mediterráneo español: factores de control, facies y procesos que rigen su desarrollo. *In*: PIULACHS, J.C. (ed.) *Estudio Oceanográfico de la Plataforma Continental*, Comité conjunto Hispano-Norteamericano, Barcelona, 15–52.
MCCAVE, I.N. 2002. Sedimentary settings on continental margins – An overview. *In*: WEFER, G. BILLETT, D., HEBBELN, D., JØRGENSEN, B.B., VAN WEERING, T. (eds) *Ocean Margin Systems*. Springer Verlag, Berlin, 1–14.
MOREL, J.-L. & MEGHRAOUI, M. 1996. Goringe-Alborán-Tell tectonic zone: a transpression system along the Africa-Eurasia plate boundary. *Geology*, **24**, 755–758.
PLATT, J.P. & VISSERS, R.L.M. 1989. Extensional collapse of thickened continental lithosphere: a working hypothesis for the Alboran Sea and the Gibraltar arc. *Geology*, **17**, 540–543.
REED, T.B. & HUSSONG, D. 1989. Digital image processing techniques for enhancement and classification of SeaMARC II Side Scan Sonar Imagery. *Journal of Geophysical Research*, **94**, 7469–7490.
RICHARDS, M., BOWMAN, M. & READING, H. 1998. Submarine-fan systems I: characterization and stratigraphic prediction. *Marine and Petroleum Geology*, **15**, 689–717.
SANZ DE GALDEANO, C. 1990. Geologic evolution of the Betic Cordilleras in the Western Mediterranean, Miocene to present. *Tectonophysics*, **172**, 107–119.
STOW, D.A.V. & MAYALL, M. 2000. Deep-water sedimentary systems: new models for the 21st century. *Marine and Petroleum Geology*, **17**, 125–135.
THOMSEN, L., VAN WEERING, T., BLONDEL, P., ET AL. 2002. Margin building – regulating processes. *In:* WEFER, G., BILLETT, D., HEBBELN, D., JØRGENSEN, B.B., VAN WEERING, T. (eds) *Ocean Margin Systems*. Springer Verlag, Berlin, 195–203.
URGELES, R., LOCAT, J., SCHMITT, T. & HUGHES CLARKE, J.E. 2002. The July 1996 flood deposit in the Saguenay Fjord, Quebec, Canada: implications for sources of spatial and temporal backscatter variations. *Marine Geology*, **184**, 41–60.
WILLIAMS, K.L. & JACKSON, D.R. 1996. A model for bistatic

scattering into ocean sediments for frequencies from 10–100 kHz (APL-UW Technical Report TR-9505), University of Washington, APL-UW.

ZAMARREÑO, I., VÁZQUEZ, A. & MALDONADO, A. 1983. Sedimentación en la plataforma de Almería: un ejemplo de la sedimentación mixta silícico-carbonatada en clima templado. *In*: *Estudio oceanográfico de la plataforma continental*. Proyecto n. 793020, ed. Comité conjunto Hispano-Norteamericano, Cádiz, Spain, 97–120.

Mud prone entrenched deep-water slope channel complexes from the Eocene of eastern Turkey

BRYAN T. CRONIN[1], HASAN ÇELIK[2], ANDREW HURST[1] & IBRAHIM TURKMEN[2]

[1] *Department of Geology and Petroleum Geology, University of Aberdeen, Meston Building, King's College, Aberdeen AB24 3UE, Scotland, UK (e-mail: cronin@abdn.ac.uk)*

[2] *Department of Geological Engineering, Engineering Faculty, Firat University, Elaziğ 23119, Turkey*

Abstract: A series of deep-water channel deposits are exposed near Baskil, 50 km west of Elaziğ in eastern Turkey. The use of correlation panels, sedimentary logs, biostratigraphy and mapping revealed that all of the channel elements are found within much larger features. One series of channels from the southern margin of the basin lie, within an entrenched deep-water slope channel complex, over 3 km wide, called the Nohut Channel Complex. This channel complex has three main fill packages. The lower package is a highly disturbed, slumped interval that directly overlies the erosional base of the main channel complex. The slumped interval is interpreted as a series of mass transport complexes, derived from shallow marine or upper slope facies. The second package comprises a mixed carbonate-siliciclastic series, principally of interbedded calcarenites, marls and mudstones. Locally, outer shelf/upper slope offset-stacked channels with calcarenite fills occur. The upper package comprises isolated conglomerate and sandstone filled deep-water channels that are incised into laterally extensive depositional lobes. The coarse-grained fills are dominated by tabular beds. The lobes are comprised of fine–medium grained sandstones. Some of these channels have low aspect ratios (25:1), and are asymmetric in cross-section, suggesting sinuosity. The upper part of this fill package is either incised into by pro-fan delta conglomerate filled channels, or downlapped onto by shelfal calcarenites. A separate series of channels come from the northern margin of the basin, but are interpreted to have developed on an open, deep-water slope or ramp, rather than as an entrenched channel complex. These channels occur in two main sets, collectively referred to as the Aydinlar Channel Complexes. The lower set is characterized by syn-sedimentary foundering of the sand-filled channels within slumped enveloping finer-grained slope sediments. The upper set of channels, dominated by one large sand and gravel-filled fairway, is characterized by large bedforms at the base, passing upwards into stacked conglomerates, mud chip breccias and sandstones. The conglomerate facies is locally injected upwards into the fill or laterally into finer-grained marginal facies. The channel is capped by finer-grained facies, including graded sandstones and siltstones with complete Bouma sequences.

In the Gulf of Guinea in recent years, a new type of deep-water slope architectural element has been recognized in subsurface seismic and well datasets that had not previously been documented from ancient, modern or subsurface datasets. Called slope (or confined) channel complexes (e.g. Sprague *et al.* 2002), these features have proven highly prolific as oil reservoirs (Mayall & Stewart 2001). Seen in late Tertiary subsurface sections in particular, these features are now found in the offshore stratigraphy of most West African countries, from Mauritania to Namibia.

On seismic sections, these channel complexes are spectacular, particularly when displayed on time slices. Typically the upper parts of the complexes are characterized by highly sinuous channel elements. The lower parts of these complexes vary enormously. According to Mayall & Stewart (2001), the fills are four-fold, usually with a gravelly, bypass package at the base, passing upwards into a slumped muddy interval, and then a third package of high net:gross, well connected sandstones, with locally residual elements of heterolithic, finer-grained facies. The fourth division consists of localized, smaller, sinuous channel elements. Here the reservoir elements usually consist of well-connected lateral accretion packages (LAPs; Abreu *et al.* 2003). The Mayall & Stewart (2000) model for confined slope channel fills was developed largely from a suite of Lower Miocene reservoirs offshore Angola and Congo. Elsewhere in West Africa the same channel complexes are also seen and act as reservoirs, but the net:gross variations are more marked. The edges of the complexes are not as welldefined as originally thought, with a large confining erosional 'master' surface not always being as discrete as originally modelled. Secondly, and more critically in terms of hydrocarbon exploration, the interpretation of high-amplitude bundles of seismic reflectors as being well connected oil charged sands, has not always been correct.

There is a huge knowledge gap that frustrates the

From: HODGSON, D.M. & FLINT, S.S. (eds) 2005. *Submarine Slope Systems: Processes and Products*. Geological Society, London, Special Publications, **244**, 155–180. 0305–8719/$15.00

prediction of sedimentary facies distribution and quality, and general heterogeneity, in this type of architectural element that is common offshore West Africa, and for which there appear to be few exposed outcrop analogues in the literature. These channel complexes may be several hundred kilometres in length, extending from the inner shelf (often from the river mouth) down to the lower slope and upper rise, and have coarse sedimentary fill elements down to those depths (Barrufini *et al.* 2000; Abreu *et al.* 2003; Deptuck *et al.* 2003; Fonnesu 2003). They clearly have a multiphase history of occupancy, overall in a confined fairway, or as previously described, an 'erosionally confined' channel complex.

A series of such erosionally confined channel complexes in the Eocene of eastern Turkey, include mud prone, and more sand or gravel prone examples. This paper documents a mud-prone example from the southern margin of the Elaziğ Basin, the Nohut Channel Complex, which we call an entrenched deep-water slope channel complex. The paper also documents a series of isolated deep-water channel elements found on what is interpreted to be an open slope, or ramp, environment on the northern margin of the basin. The two complexes are considered to be broadly time equivalent, according to current biostratigraphic and mapping data. We document the Nohut and Aydinlar channel complexes to illustrate the heterogeneity and distribution of architectural elements, specifically the different styles and fills of deep-water channel elements, within a mud prone setting for use as an analogue for mud prone channel complexes in the Gulf of Guinea and elsewhere in the offshore West Africa subsurface.

Mud prone entrenched deep-water slope channel complexes in eastern Turkey

Geological setting of the Elaziğ Basin

A geological map of the area is shown in Figure 1a. During the Middle Eocene deep-water sedimentation was widespread in the region, within narrow, back arc basins that opened rapidly in the Upper Paleocene–Lower Eocene. These basins varied in water depth and there was significant topography on both northern and southern margins. Most of this topography is interpreted as block-faulted topography (Cronin *et al.* 2000*b*). A general geomorphological map for the late Middle Eocene is shown in Figure 1b. The areal extent of the Kirkgeçit Formation, within which the deep-water slope sediments are contained, is enormous. The northern margin of the basin is exposed almost continuously for 70 km from the study area west of Baskil to Hasret Mountain, east of Elaziğ (Cronin *et al.* 2000*a*, *b*). The southern margin of the basin is only exposed to the south of the study area. Allowing for recent estimates of later tectonic shortening in the area in the order of 40% (Çelik 2003), we can estimate the basin to have had a width of approximately 40 km.

The stratigraphy and geological evolution of the Elaziğ area has recently been summarized by Turan & Bingöl (1991), Bingöl & Beyarslan (1996) (Figs 2 & 3a, b), and Aksoy *et al.* (1996). The continental Lower Paleocene Kuşçular Formation is overlain by carbonate build-ups of the Middle Paleocene–Lower Eocene Seske Formation (Özkul 1988). These two formations immediately underlie the Kirkgeçit Formation in the Aydinlar area. In the Middle Eocene the area subsided rapidly by block faulting in a back-arc setting, forming the deep-water volcanic-floored Elaziğ and Maden Basins (Fig. 4), in an extensional, or strike-slip-dominated, setting (Robertson 2000). After these major tectonic phases, the Elaziğ Basin filled passively during the late Middle Eocene, predominantly with deep-water slope sediments.

Previous work on the Elaziğ Basin fill

The Kirkgeçit Formation (Middle Eocene to Lower Oligocene: Avsar 1989*a*, *b*) filled the Elaziğ Basin, and was sourced primarily from the north (Fig. 3). The formation consists of deep-water and shelf sediments (Özkul & Kerey 1996), which drape or onlap against older rocks. In the earliest stages of filling, the basin floor had a highly irregular morphology. The Kirkgeçit Formation is now exposed over a large area between Kovancilar in the east and Baskil in the west (Fig. 1a, b). In the Aydinlar area, it is characterized by shelf facies (calcarenites and gravelly sandstones) in the north and by slope and basin plain facies in the south (Özkul & Kerey 1996). Facies associations such as inner, middle and outer fan, slope, basin plain, carbonate shelf and shelf-front carbonate were identified in the Aydinlar area (Özkul 1993). A recent study was undertaken to correlate the deeper-water facies of the Kirkgeçit Formation (Kerey *et al.* pers. comm.), from the conglomerate-filled deep-water channels of Hasret Mountain, 13 km east of Elaziğ (Özkul & Usenmez 1986; Cronin *et al.* 2000*a*, *b*), to the slope and fan facies around Aydinlar and Baskil 65 km west of Elaziğ (Fig. 4). This figure shows the major thickness changes across the northern basin margin from west to east. It was shown that the palaeoslope of the Elaziğ Basin was oriented NE–SW, faced SSE and prograded in that direction. The upper slope facies are downlapped onto by prograding shelf sands of Late Eocene–Lower Oligocene age, after a period of slope regrading (Cronin *et al.* 2000*b*).

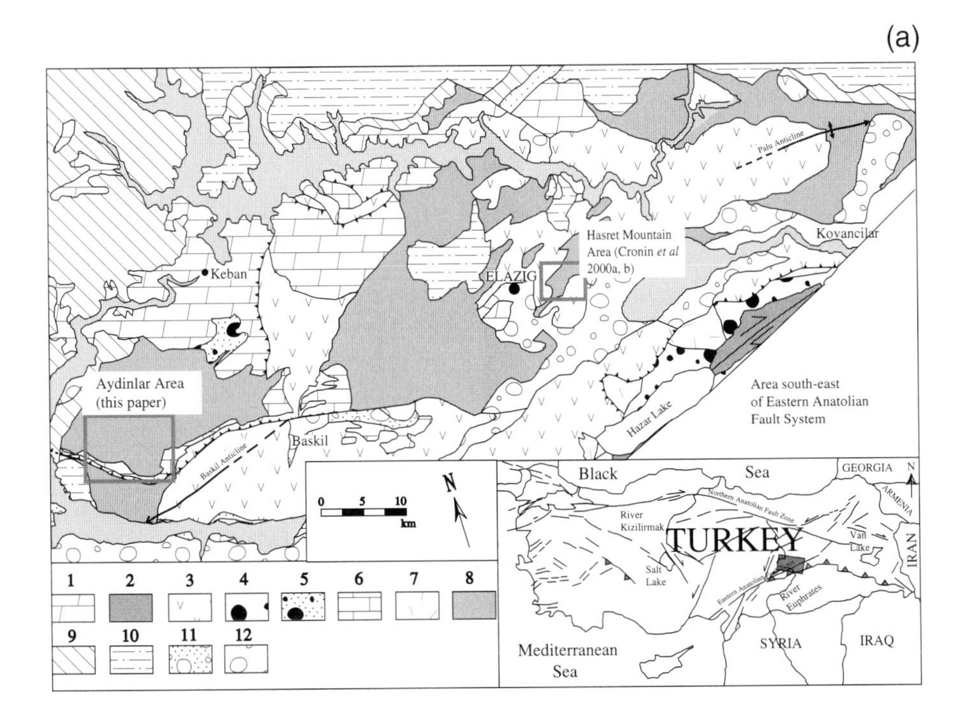

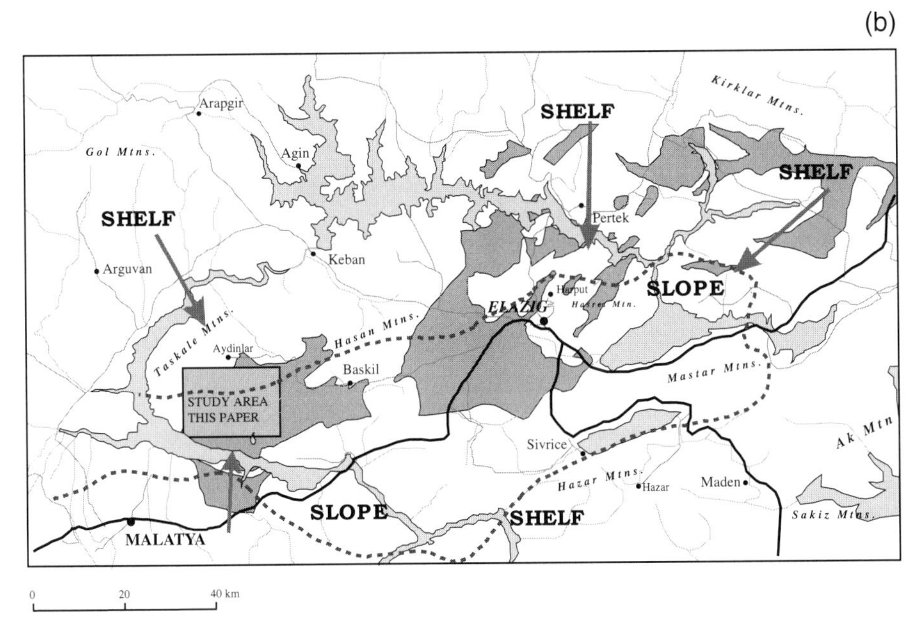

Fig. 1. (**a**) Geological map of the Elaziğ Basin in eastern Turkey, after Bingöl (1984). 1, Keban metamorphics (Permo-Triassic); 2, Jurassic–Cretaceous ophiolite; 3, Upper Cretaceous magmatics; 4, Hazar Group (Upp. Cretaceous–Paleocene); 5, Kuşçular Formation (Lower Paleocene); 6, Seske Formation (Upper Paleocene–Lower Eocene); 7, Maden Complex (Middle Eocene); 8, Kirkgeçit Formation (Middle Eocene–Lower Oligocene); 9, Albonica Formation (Lower Miocene); 10, Karabakir Formation (Upper Miocene–Pliocene); 11, Pliocene–Quaternary deposits; 12, Alluvium. Formations from Permian to Oligocene shown in stratigraphic column in Figure 2; (**b**) general geomorphology of the study area during the late Middle Eocene. Dashed line shows the position of the shelf break. The arrows show the main directions of sediment input from the north, and locally from the SW. Note that the map has not been palinspastically restored for the compression that occurred post-basin fill (shortening between 30 and 60%).

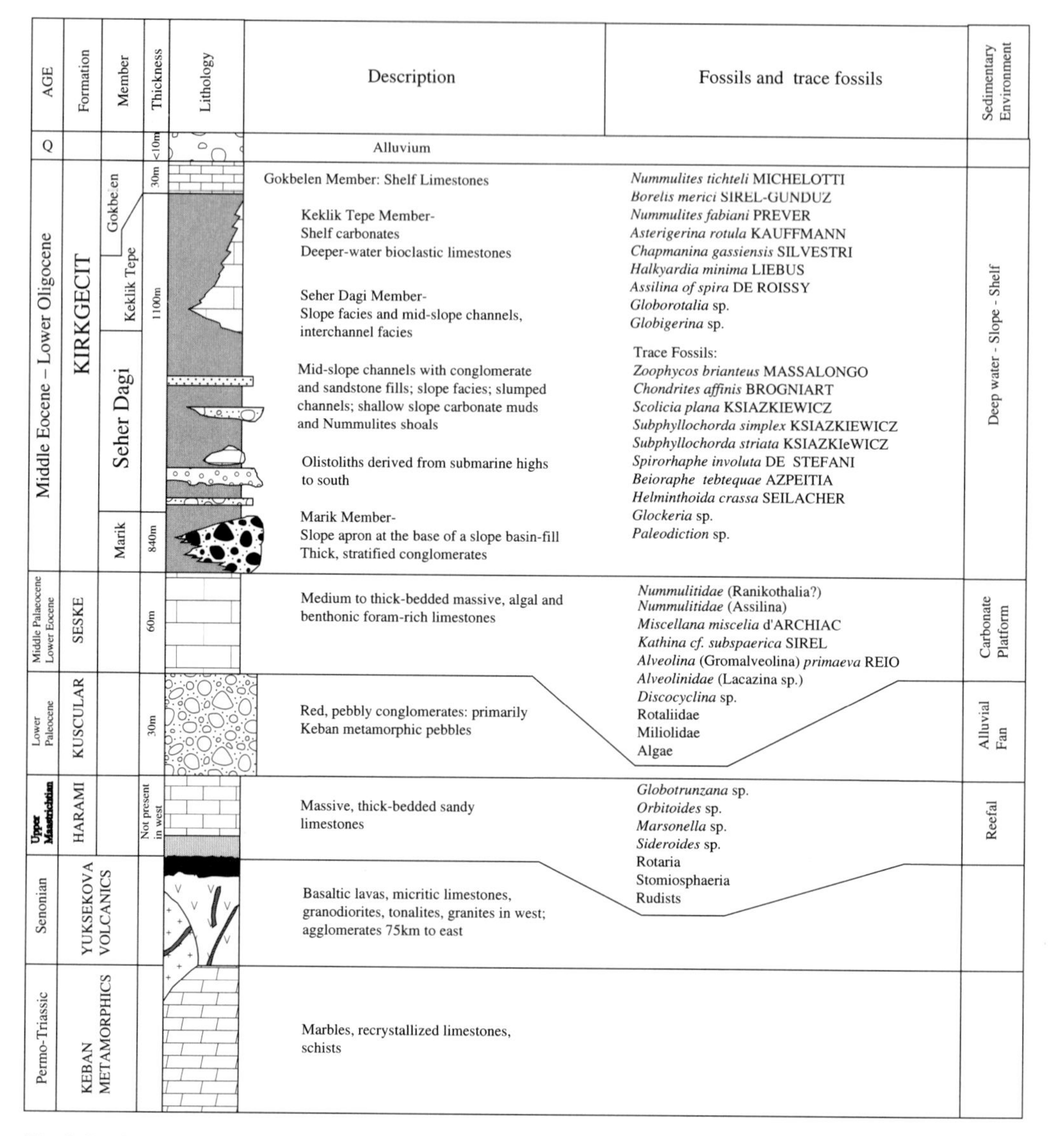

Fig. 2. Stratigraphy of the western Elaziğ Basin (Baskil and Aydinlar) areas, eastern Turkey (after Ozkul 1988).

The basin margin physiography in the vicinity of Aydinlar (Fig. 3b) is made up of:

1 A NE–SW striking shelf-slope break that is exposed continuously for at least 6 km across strike (Figs 3c & 5), with the main northern basin margin slope facing SE.
2 An opposing shelf break is inferred south of the Hor Thrust, where sediments are sourced from the south at Nohut Tepe (Fig. 5), with a north-facing slope. The area has been subjected to at least 40% shortening (Çelik 2003).
3 A coarse grained fan delta, called the Marik Member, extended from the shelf to the base of slope, east of the study area and prograded westwards into the study area due to topographic confinement to the south (see palaeocurrent directions in Fig. 5).
4 The period of compression preceding the block faulting that opened the Elaziğ Basin led to the formation of a series of low amplitude folds (in Kuşçular and Seske Limestone Formations), and the fold axes plunged SW. Extension in the Lower Eocene saw block faulting predominantly on the limbs of these folds.

(a)

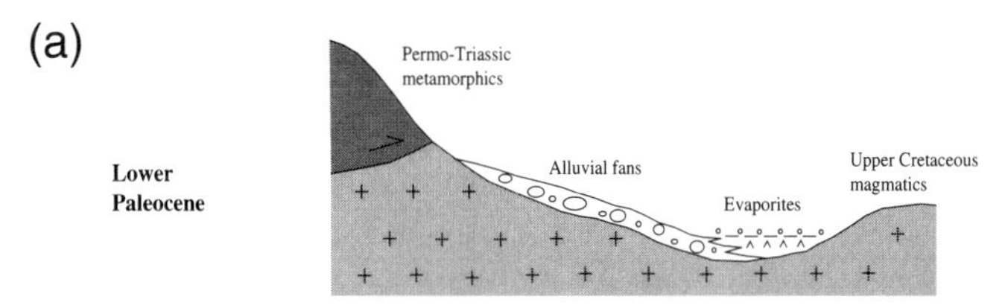

End of thrusting sees emergent hinterland to the north. Alluvial fans shed towards the south and interdigitate with evaporites (Kuscular Formation)

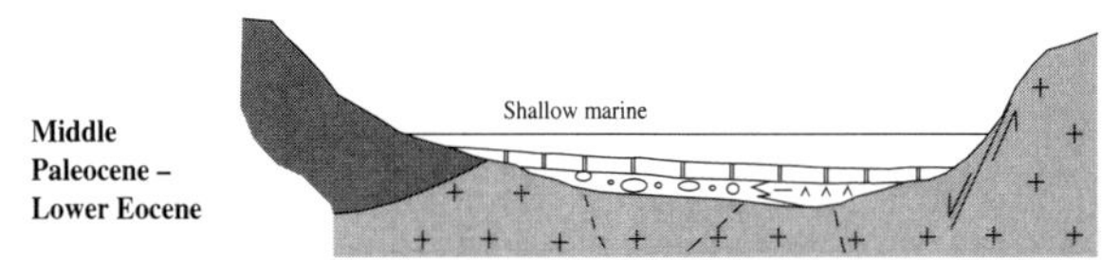

Elazig Basin is transgressed, with reefal and platform limestones growing on elevated sea floor topography. Extensional faults open at basin margins, usually on the steep limbs of earlier broad folds (Seske Formation)

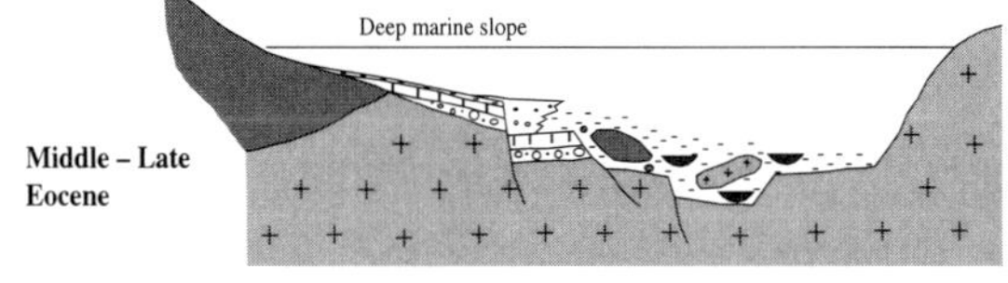

Rapid block faulting was marked by deepening of the Elazig Basin, with deep-water clastic sediments shedding over the fault-block generated sea floor topography from north, and locally from the south (Kirkgecit Formation)

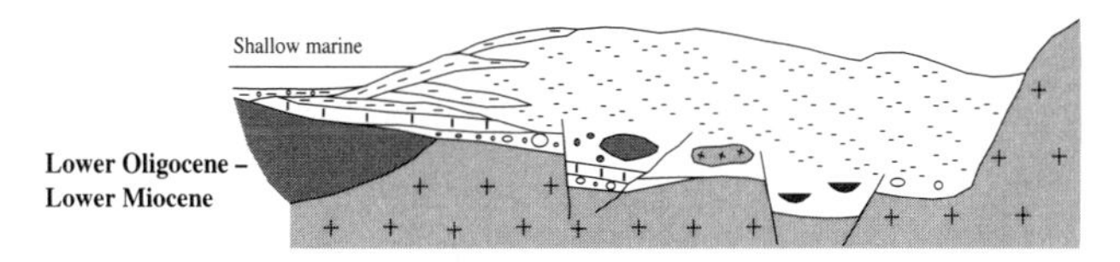

The Elazig Basin is shallow marine from Late Eocene – Lower Oligocene as the tectonic regime switches from extensional to compressional with the onset of thrusting from the north Kirkegcit Formation [Gokbelen Member] – Alibonca Formation

(b)

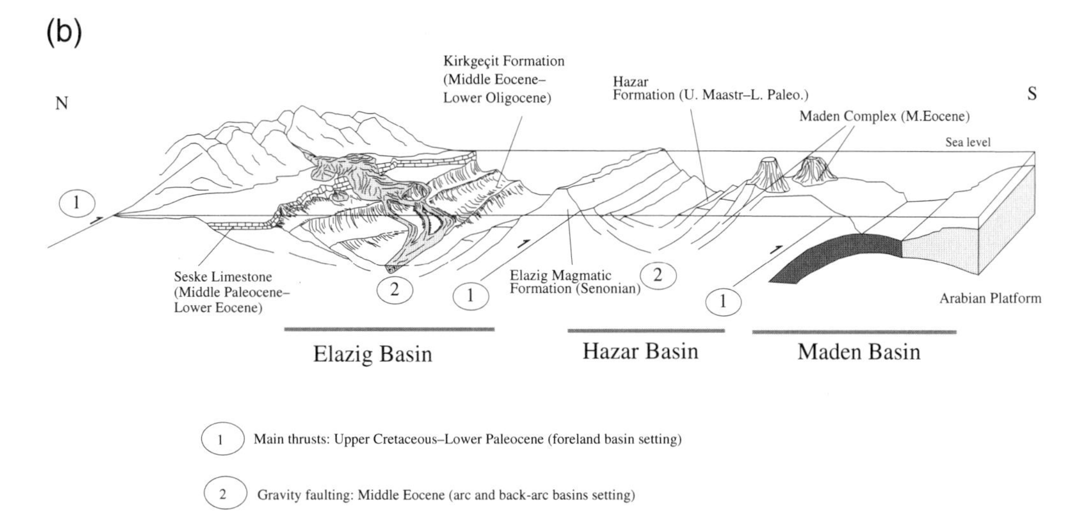

Fig. 3. (**a**) Evolution of the Baskil area, Lower Paleocene–Lower Miocene; (**b**) block diagram showing the palaeogeography of the Elaziğ Basin during the late Middle Eocene.

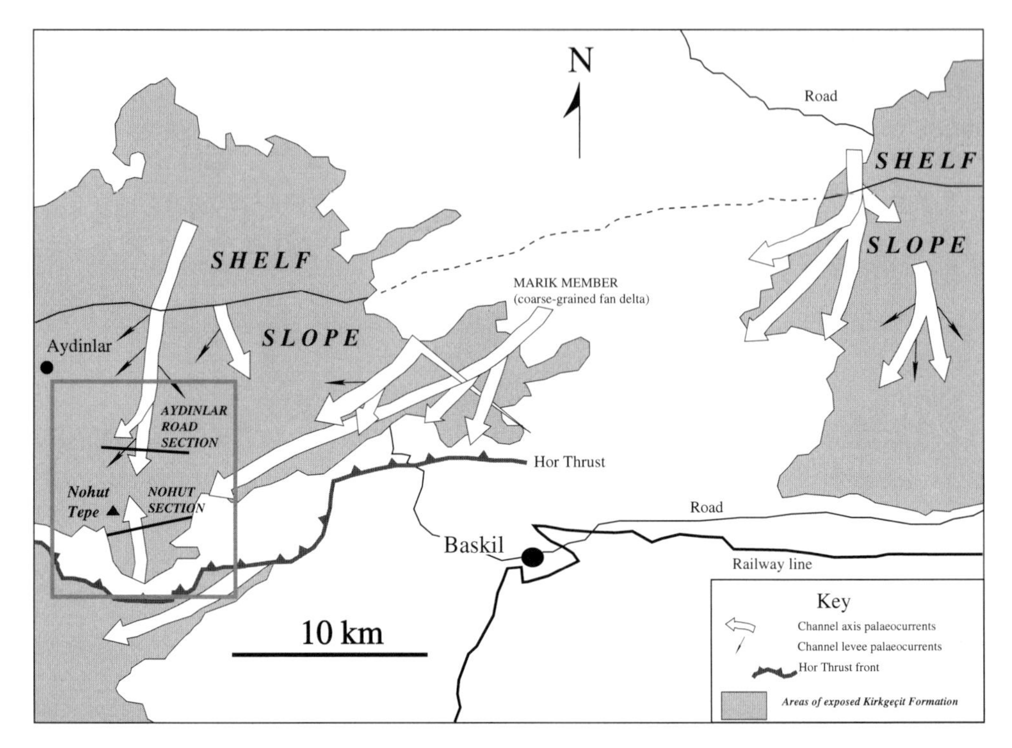

Fig. 4. Kirkgeçit Formation exposed in the Baskil region, Elaziğ, eastern Turkey (showing main palaeocurrent directions and section localities). The shelf and slope areas are defined by a very sharp shelf break which can be mapped across the area. Boxed outline markes the Aydinlar study area.

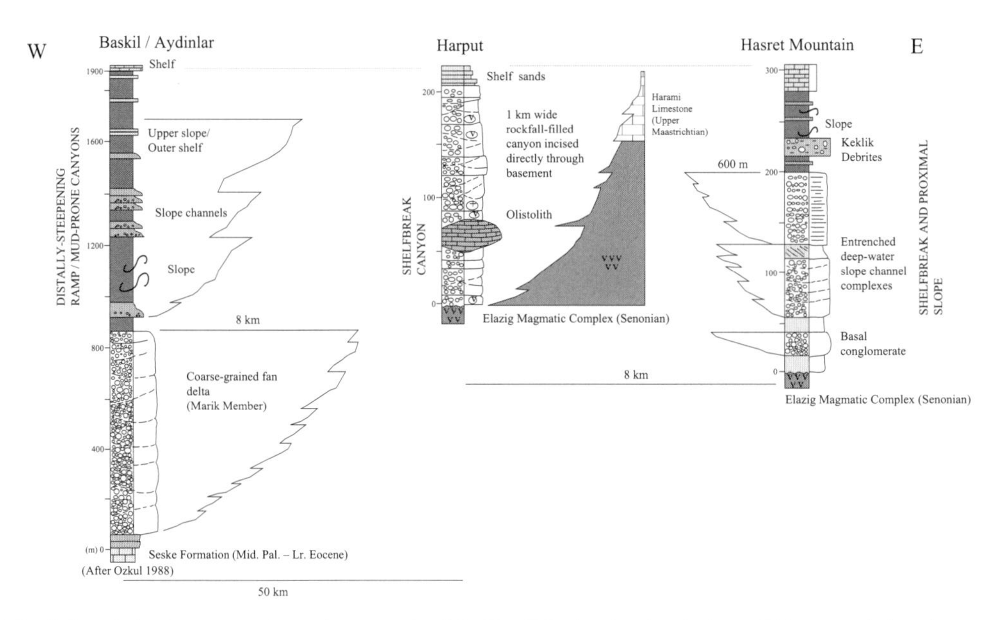

Fig. 5. Correlation logs across the northern margin of the Elaziğ Basin, showing the large thickness variations in Kirkgeçit Formation sediments. This is due to the highly irregular sea floor topography on the margin. In the study area in this paper (Aydinlar/ Baskil) the slope is interpreted to be a low-angle ramp, whereas in the Elaziğ area to the east it has a much steeper slope profile.

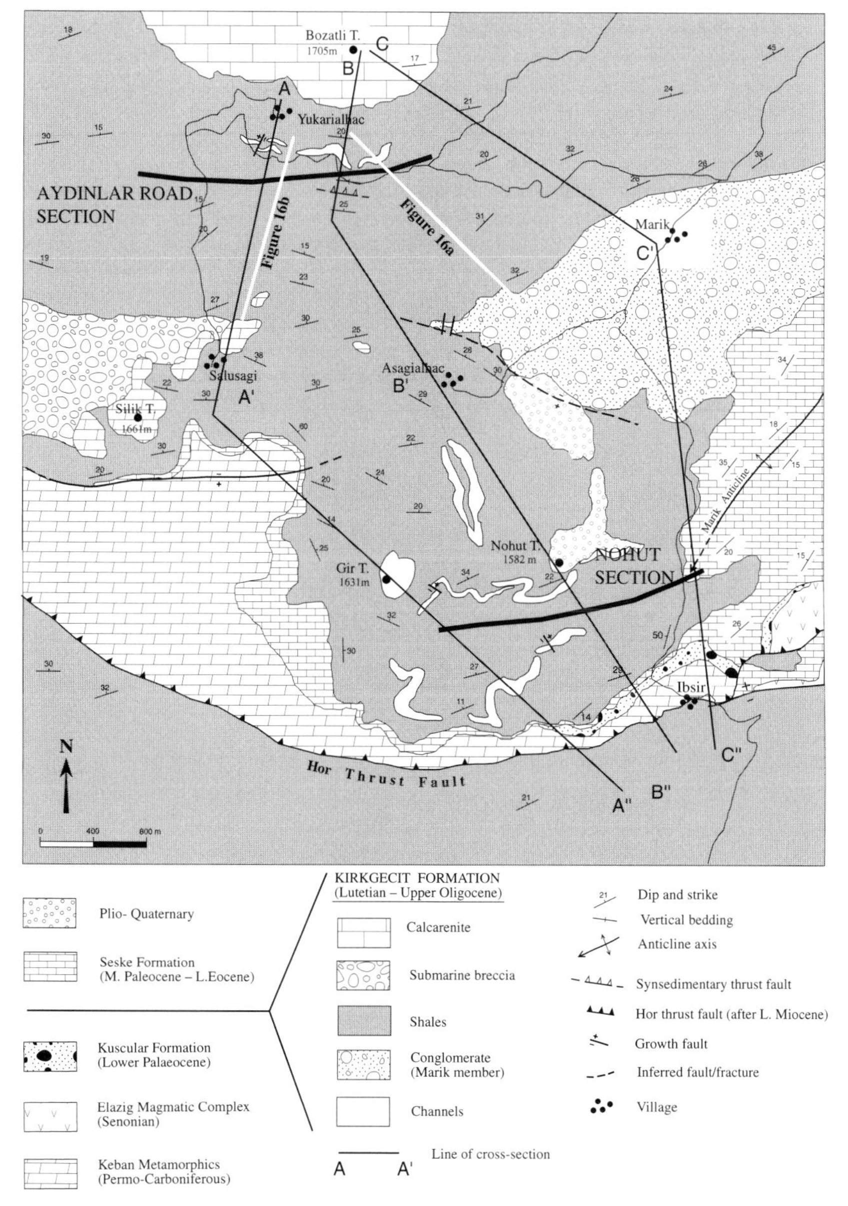

Fig. 6. Geological map of the Aydinlar study area, showing locations of the Aydinlar Road and Nohut study sections, and the locations of structural cross-sections shown in Figure 7.

The geology of the area was mapped in detail (Figs 6 & 7), using GPS mapping (resolution +/−1 m). Several kilometres of vertical sedimentary logs were recorded to produce fence diagrams of the succession in dip and strike section. Biostratigraphic sampling was undertaken as part of a Ph.D. thesis (Dellamonica 2004). The datasets were collected over long field seasons undertaken twice a year over an eight-year period.

Nohut section

The Nohut section is a 2.5 km long cliff section perpendicular to palaeocurrent through the Kirkgeçit Formation at Nohut Hill (Figs 6 & 7). Here the Kirkgeçit Formation is confined to the east, where it onlaps an erosional surface through the older Seske Limestone Formation (Eocene) and Kuşçular Formation red beds (Paleocene) (Fig. 6). The

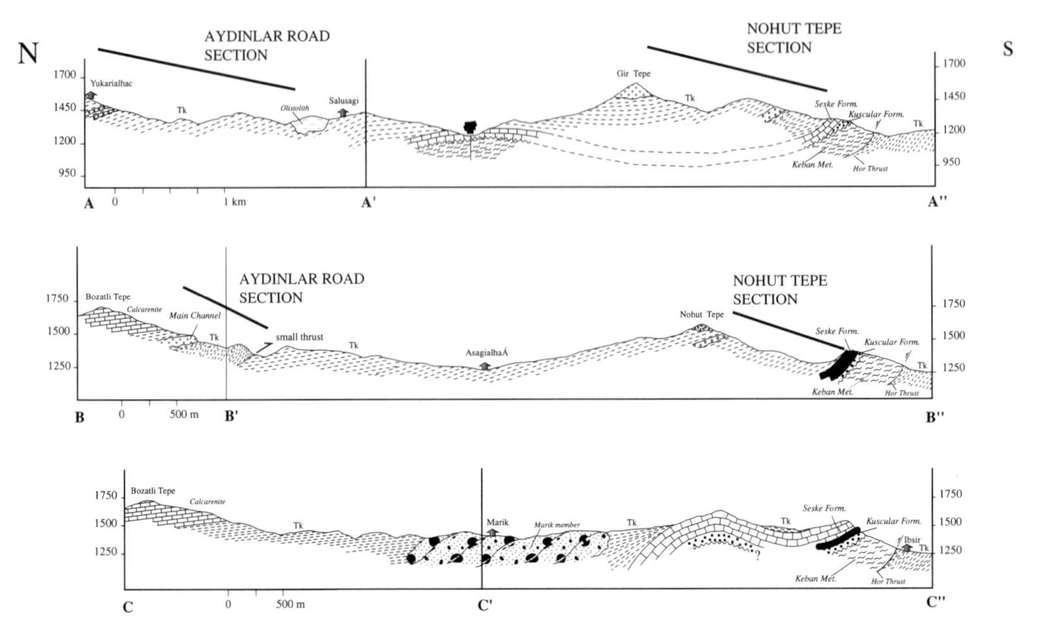

Fig. 7. Cross-sections A–C through the study area, showing the relative stratigraphic positions of the low net:gross channel fill elements at Aydinlar Road and Nohut.

Kirkgeçit Formation also onlaps these formations to the west, though this is not shown on the Nohut section photo mosaic (Fig. 8). The erosional contact with older formations is cut through the Seske Anticline, which is a SW-plunging anticline formed during the compression that preceded Middle Eocene block faulting on this basin margin. A close-up of the eastern margin of the Nohut Complex is shown in Figure 9a. The Nohut section is interpreted as an entrenched deep-water slope channel complex, and is called the Nohut Channel Complex. A series of vertical sedimentary logs were collected from the Nohut section, and those referred to in this paper are marked on Figure 8. The fill of the Nohut Complex is three fold (Figs 8 & 9a).

The basal surface of the channel complex cuts deeply into older bedrock. The geometry of the incision is seen on Figure 6. Beginning on the centre-right of Figure 6, the Kirkgeçit Formation shales (grey pattern) are seen to be abruptly unconformable with the bedding orientations within the Seske Formation (M. Paleocene–L. Eocene) limestones, which form the Marik Anticline immediately to the east of the Nohut Complex. The contact, also seen in Figure 9a, is very steep (almost vertical at that locality) and is onlapped by Kirkgeçit Formation shales. The corresponding western margin of the Nohut Channel Complex is seen west of Gir Mountain to the left of the Nohut Section on Figure 6. The base of the channel complex is poorly exposed but crops out NW of Ibsir in the lower part of Figure 6, where it never erodes through the older Seske Limestone. The Kirkgeçit Formation above this contact at that locality is composed of slumped marls. The geometry of the incision is thus a vertical to sub-vertical walled canyon, less than 3 km wide and at least 250 m deep, incised into older bedrock of Seske Limestone and overlain or onlapped by slumped or coherent Kirkgeçit Formation marls.

Phase 1: Slumped carbonates

The lower part of the Nohut Complex fill is characterized by a thick succession of slumped limestones and marls (Fig. 9a). This lower package thickens dramatically towards the axis of the Nohut section. The facies within Phase 1 are seen in log N2 (Fig. 10a). The limestones are characterized by common gastropods, *Nummulites*, echinoid shells and bryozoans, some of which have been strongly reworked. Section N3 (Fig. 10b) shows the upper part of Phase 1. Phase 1 sediments are more than 190 m thick, though much of the sedimentary thickness has been increased due to the effects of slumping. Thin interbedded limestones at the base, pass upwards over 8 m into thin interbedded limestones, marls and rare medium-grained sandstones. These beds have abundant benthic and planktonic foraminifera, which yield dates of lower Middle Eocene and indicate sedimentary environments below the shelf break. The section passes up into thick micrite and

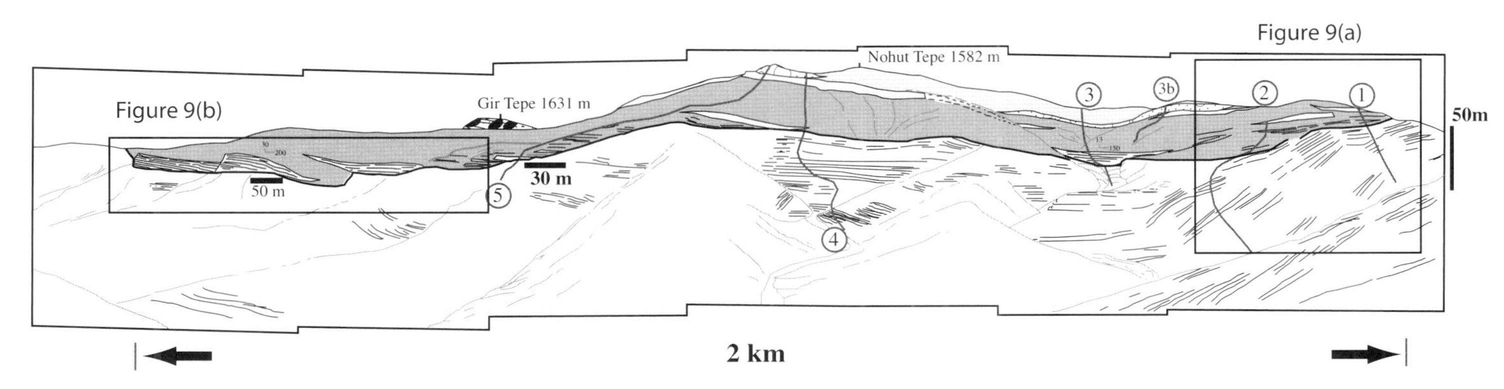

Fig. 8. Photomosaic and line drawing interpretation of the Nohut section. The three main entrenched channel complex fill packages are observed. The mosaic shows the axis and margin of the complex, the western margin is also exposed but out of the plane of view (see Fig. 6). Palaeocurrents are towards the north (into the section). Numbered sections refer to sedimentary logs collected.

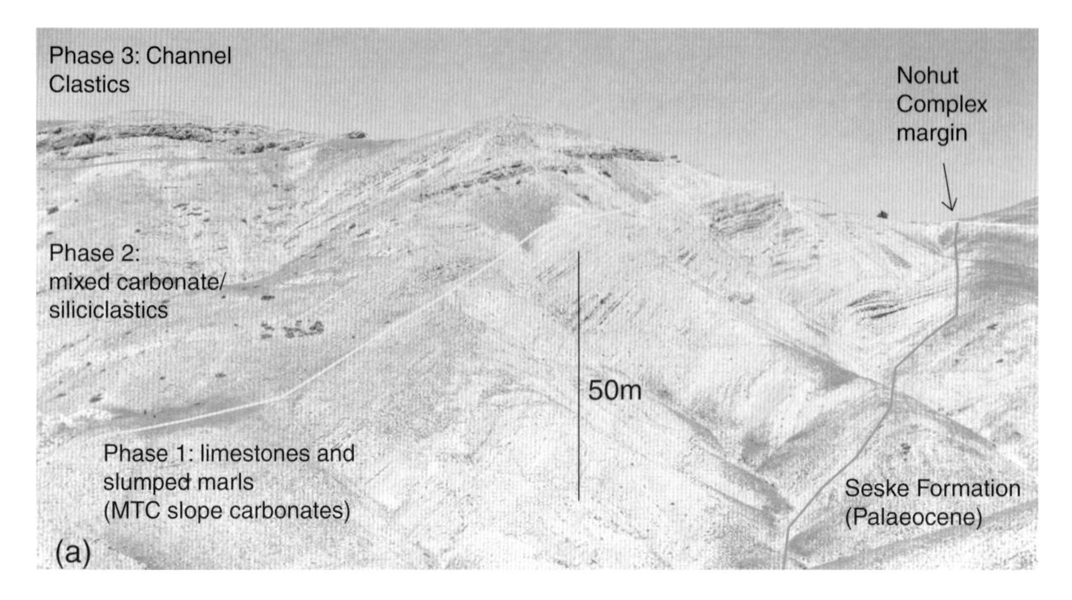

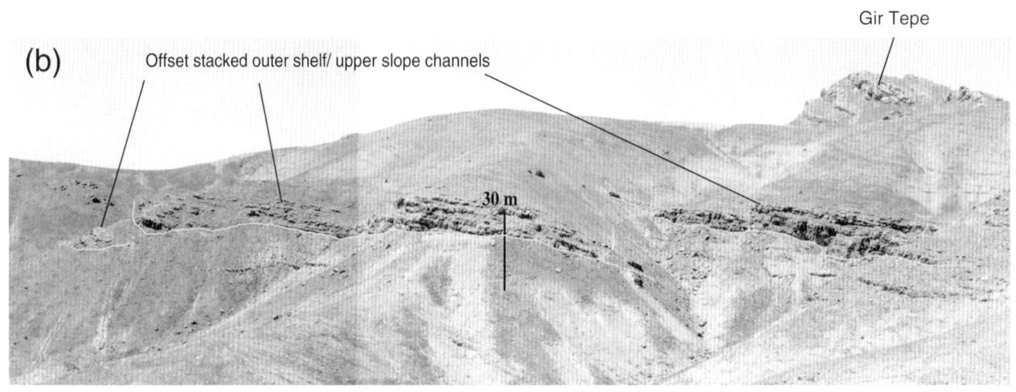

Fig. 9. (**a**) Margin of the Nohut channel complex, showing the incised margin into Eocene Seske Limestone, and the subdivision of the fill into a lower MTC (mass transport complex) limestones and slumped marls, a middle mixed carbonate-siliciclastic subdivision, and an upper clastic subdivision. Palaeocurrent direction is in the direction of view (towards the north); (**b**) Offset stacked mixed carbonate-siliciclastic slope channel elements from Phase 2 of the Nohut Complex. The view is towards the west (see Fig. 8 for location). Note Gir Tepe over the brow of the hill (see text for details).

calcarenite intervals, with local slumping. Some of the very thin-bedded calcarenites form very prominent and continuous beds of *Nummulites* detritus. The transition from Phase 1 to Phase 2 is seen clearly on Figure 10b.

Phase 2: Mixed carbonate-siliciclastic sediments

Phase 2 of the Nohut Complex comprises interbedded marls, calcarenites and sandstones, with a maximum thickness of 160 m, though this is again subject to thickness variations due to slumping. Phase 2 sediments overlie a sharp upper surface on Phase 1, which can be mapped across the Nohut section (Fig. 10) and is marked by a sharp colour change from blue-grey to yellow-buff. This surface has an irregular geometry that appears to be determined by the locally irregular geometry of the upper surface on Phase 1. The colour change also marks the introduction of siliciclastic material into the section. Medium to fine-grained sandstones occur in packages up to 35 m thick, which have a broad lenticular geometry. These bodies are found towards the base of Phase 2 and towards the top, separated by thick sections of monotonous calcarenites, marls, siltstones and thin-bedded sandstones. The sand-

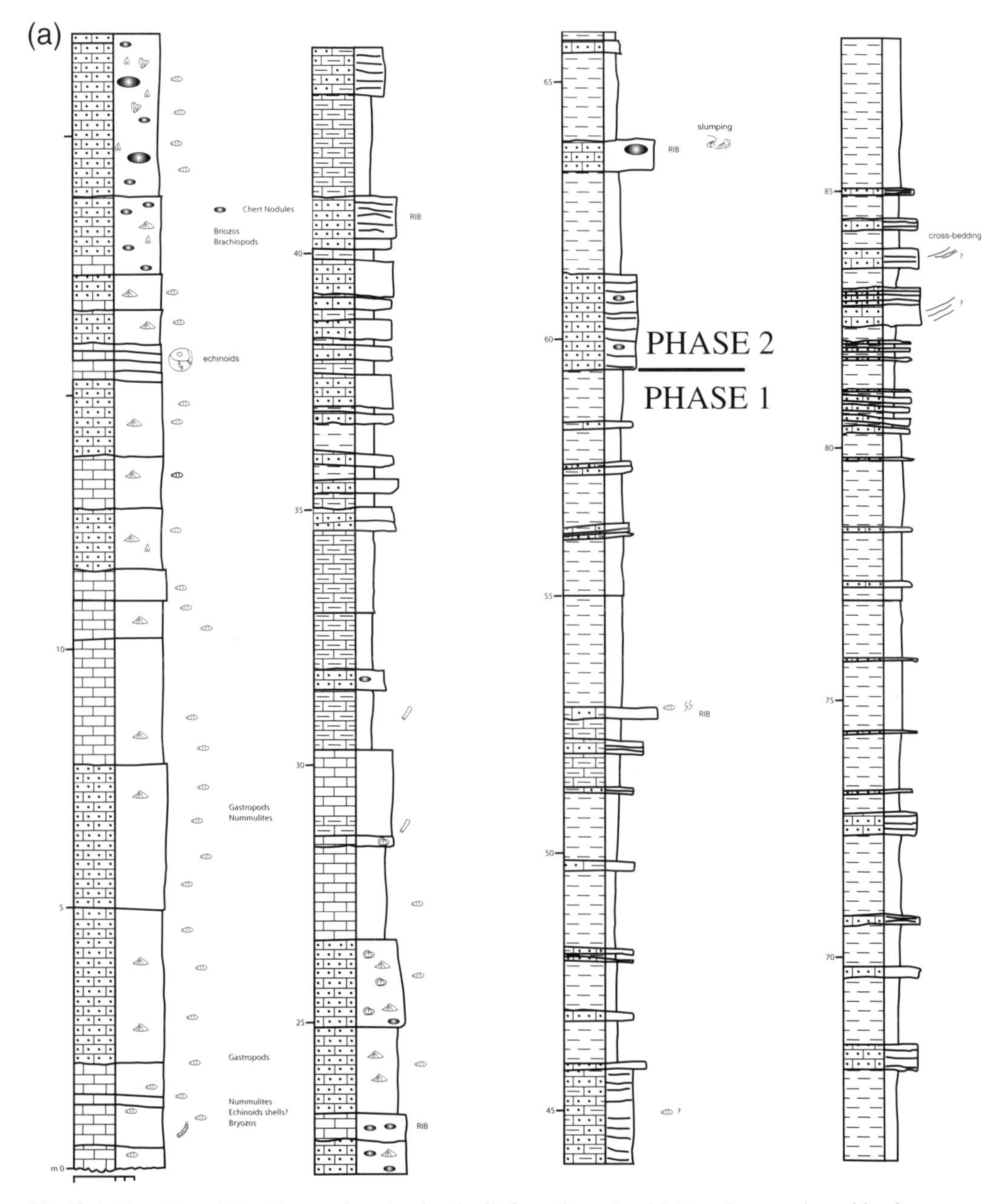

Fig. 10. (**a**) Log 2 from Nohut Tepe section, showing details from Phases 1 and 2. Note the general transition from limestones with reworked shelf bioclastic material to slope marls and calcarenites, some of which are cross-bedded;

stones are usually calcarenites within the lenticular bodies and beds are 0.15–0.35 m thick, normally graded (sometimes with coarse or granular bases), and have laminated tops (Fig. 12). They are characterized by intense bioturbation, a combination of horizontal and vertical burrows, with *Chondrites* and *Sabularia* being particularly common. Locally, oysters and other reworked bioclastic material are recognized, in graded beds. Many calcarenites have chert nodules, are usually well bedded, and contain an abundance of mixed benthonic foraminifera. Most beds are graded. Many of the marls contain abundant plant debris. Some of these lenticular bodies are shown in more detail in Figure 11b. Close

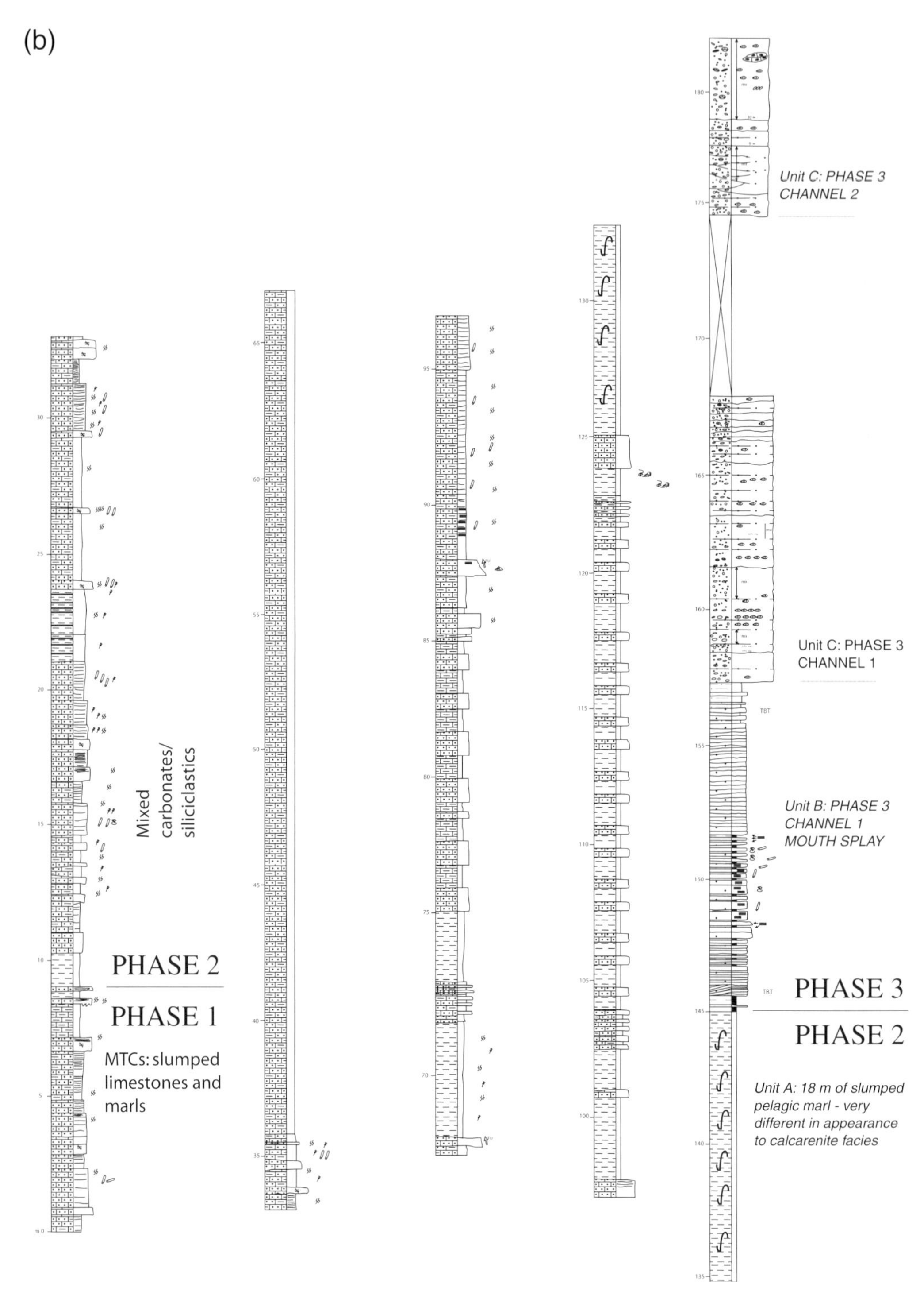

Fig. 10 ***continued*****.** (**b**) Log 3 from Nohut Tepe section, showing the Phase1/2 and Phase 2/3 transitions. The separation into units A, B and C are seen in the latter (sub-channel slumps; channel mouth splay; channel). See text for details;

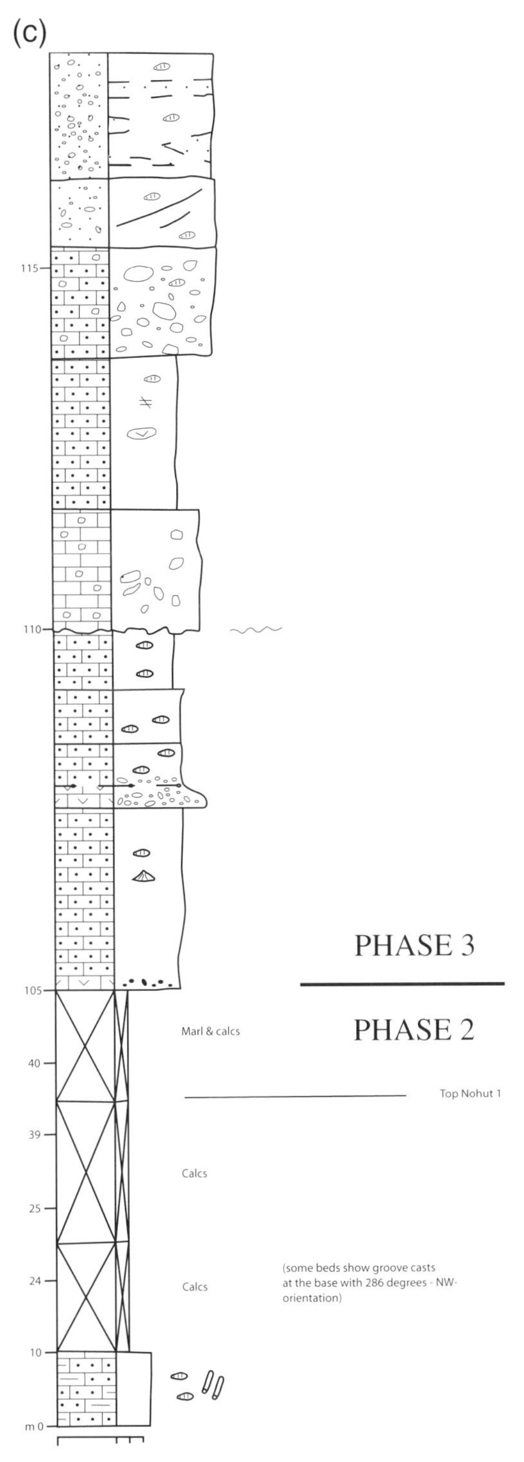

Fig. 10 ***continued.*** (**c**) Log 5 from Nohut Tepe, showing the thickness of the underlying fine-grained facies and a close-up of the stratigraphy of a Phase 3 channel.

inspection of Figure 10 shows these bodies to be offset stacked towards the east against the contact between Phases 1 and 2. Within the fills, many beds are turbidites, with graded tops (usually T_a–T_b). There is no obvious down cutting recognized at the bases of the channels — the calcarenites and other facies passively infill topographic lows, stacking towards the eastern margin of the overall channel complex. They have an average geometry of 150+ m width and 13–15 m thickness (aspect ratio of 10:1).

Phase 3: Clastic sediments

The third and upper major package of the Nohut Complex corresponds to a major influx of coarse-grained clastic sediments. The package is ordered into four units:

1 Unit A: an 18–22 m thick slumped pelagic interval (Figure 10c).
2 Unit B: a package of interbedded thinly-bedded, normally graded sandstones and siltstones which are commonly current-rippled and contain abundant deep-water ichnofauna (e.g. *Sabularia*, *Chondrites*, *Palaeodictyon*). Some of the sandstones are locally coarse, with detrital material (e.g. black Elaziğ Magmatic Complex basalts). These packages of tabular thin-bedded sediments are over 500 m in width, about 25 m thick; they thin towards the edges and have a lenticular or hemi-lenticular geometry. They are thickest under the axes of the overlying erosive gravel bodies. Their flat bases are sharply discordant with Phase 2 sediments.
3 Unit C: gravel lenses, which are best seen at the top of Nohut Tepe, where a series of landscape-forming bluffs cap the crest of the hill (Fig. 10). These small bluffs comprise discontinuous bodies of coarse-grained sediment (also seen on the top left of Fig. 11) on a sharply discordant contact with the calcarenites and marls of the higher parts of Phase 2 mixed siliciclastics/carbonates. The gravelly sandstones of Phase 3 are strongly imbricated and comprised mainly of stratified sediments with a high proportion of reworked shelfal *Nummulites*. Palaeocurrents and clast composition indicate a southerly provenance. These gravel bodies are highly lenticular in geometry, typically 25 m thick and 300 m wide (Fig. 12). The gravel bodies are isolated and encased within deep-water slope mudstones (which contain benthic foraminifera typical of upper slopes from Middle Eocene; Dellamonica 2004). These channels do not have an offset

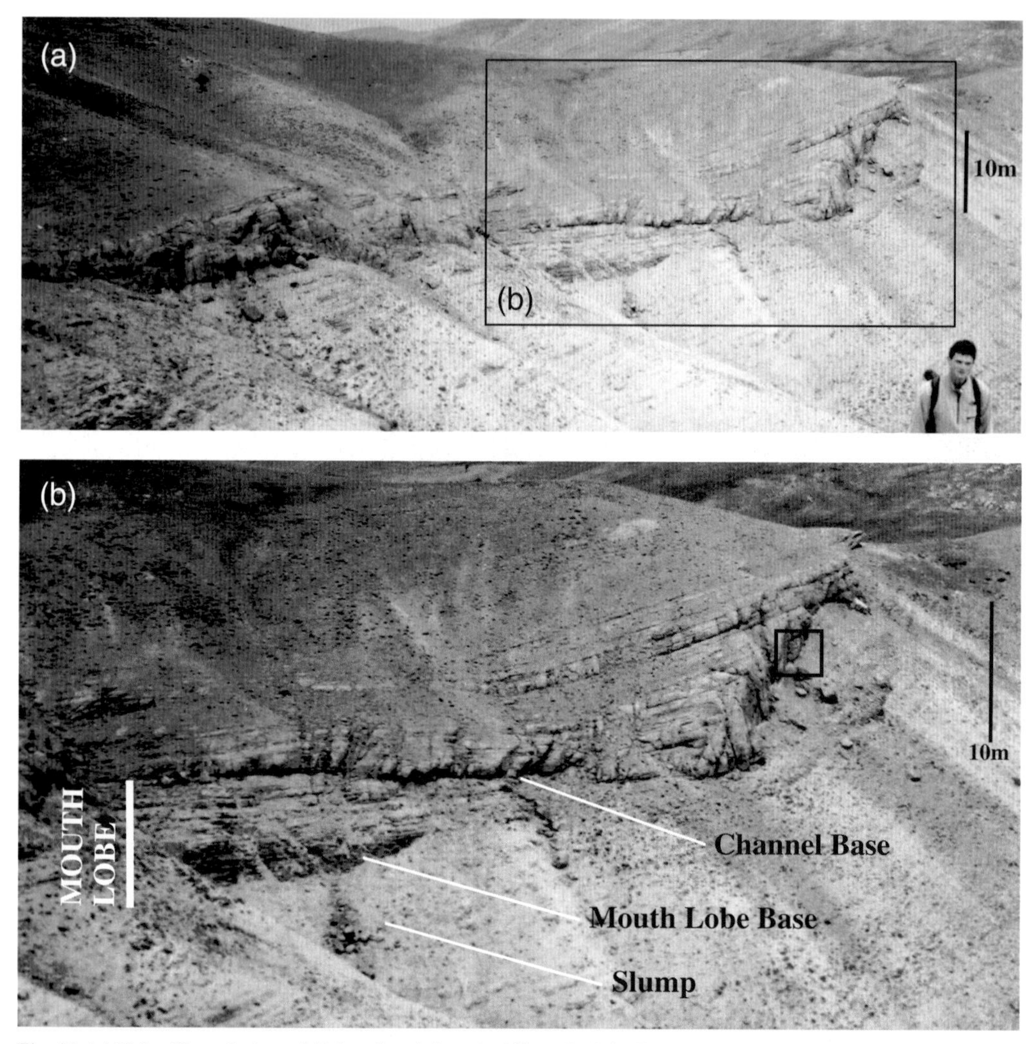

Fig. 11. (**a**) Nohut Phase 3 channel. Palaeoflow is into the hill, to the left; (**b**) Detail from Nohut Phase 3 channel. The deeply incisional nature of the base of the channel is seen, eroding into its own mouth splay. The mouth splay is underlain by an 18 m thick mud slump. See text for details.

Fig. 12. (**a**) Detail from the eastern margin of Nohut Phase 3 channel, showing the steeply incisional base; (**b**) Nohut Phase 3 channels have tabular pebbly sandstone bed fills, with very marked imbrication of the pebbles. Clasts are of Elaziğ Magmatic Complex origin, with local Seske Limestone clasts. *Nummulites* are common in the matrix. See text for details and implications.

Fig. 13. Margin of Gir Tepe, the youngest of the channel elements in the Nohut Channel Complex.

stacked geometry in Phase 3. The bases of these lenses are strongly erosive (Fig. 12). Two of the four channel fills that make up the isolated pods of coarse-grained material at Nohut are shown in Figure 10c (Log N-5), and one is shown at the top of N-3 (Fig. 10b). In N-3 the pebbles are often imbricated with palaeoflow to the NW and WNW. Most are matrix supported pebbly sandstones, locally clast-supported, and commonly full of *Nummulites* (themselves often imbricated) and bivalve fragments. Seske Limestone and Elaziğ Magmatic Complex clasts are common (Fig. 2). In N-3 the base of the channel complex (105–108 m) is characterized by cross-bedded *Nummulites*-rich bioclastic calcarenites, with abundant mud chips towards the base; the middle (108–115 m) by coarser clastic facies, including matrix-supported pebbly sandstones, and the upper part (114–118 m) by low-angle cross bedded pebbly sandstones with large *Nummulites*.

4 Unit D: mudstones and rare siltstones.

Overall, the weathering profile across Units A–D is: recessed and poorly exposed fine-grained interval (D), prominent bluffs of coarse-grained sediments (C) erosive into slightly less prominent thin beds (B), overlying a recessed series of marly sediments (A). The thickness of these packages is irregular, due to the topography on top of the slumps below and erosion on the bases of the gravels above.

On Figure 9b, a hill is seen behind Nohut Tepe, called Gir Tepe, which marks a channel body towards the top of the Nohut entrenched channel complex. This channel body is 100 m thick and 400 m wide and nested entirely within a mixed mudstone and marl envelope. The body has a strongly erosive base (Fig. 13). It is preceded by a thick slumped marl section, as in the Phase 3 Nohut Channels. Below this slumped interval are local coarse-grained sandstones with floating pebbles and cobbles of Elaziğ Magmatic Complex and Keban Metamorphic Complex. The fill comprises bedded gravelly sandstones and pebbly conglomerates, which thicken upwards (0.5–2.5 m thick beds, Fig. 14). The gravels are almost entirely comprised of Keban metamorphic clasts, derived entirely from the south, with lesser proportions of Elaziğ Magmatic Complex, Seske Limestone and intraformational Kirkgeçit Formation (each $<5\%$). The upper sections of the Gir Tepe Channel contain local blocks of Kuşçular Formation conglomerate, up to 20% locally. Strong pebble imbrication fabrics are seen throughout the Gir Tepe section. Bed dips increase progressively through the Gir Tepe section, reaching 20° at the top of the exposure.

Nohut Complex interpretation

The Nohut Complex is interpreted as an entrenched deep-water slope channel complex, derived from the south, which has a three-fold division fill. The channel complex is incised through Paleocene and

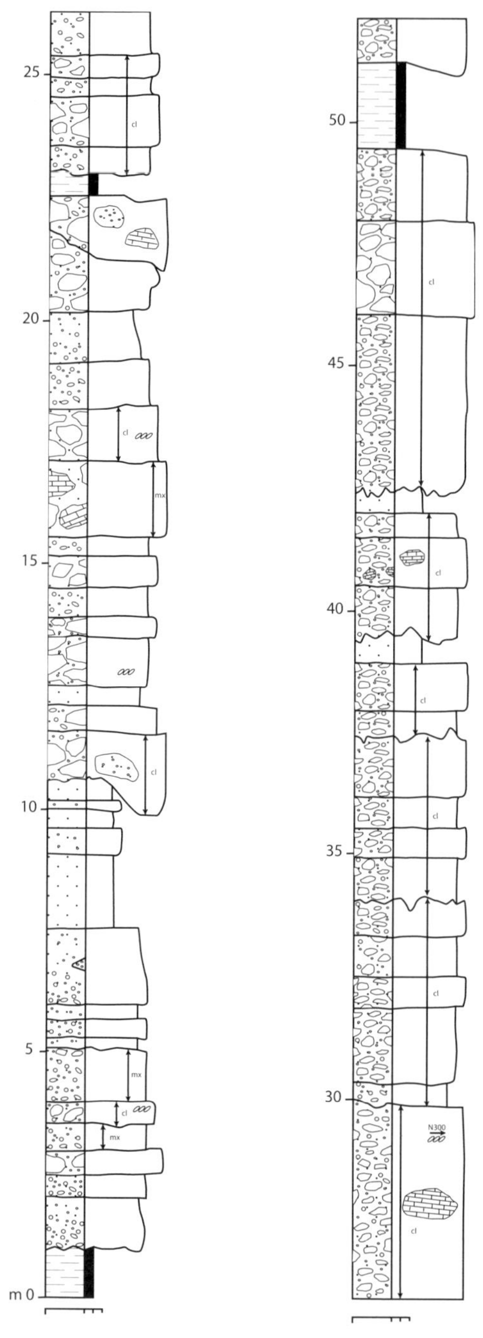

Fig. 14. Gir Tepe Channel. This log shows the lower 50 m of the 150 m thick Gir Tepe Channel fill. Note the predominance of clast-supported conglomerates towards the top. The lowermost sections of Gir Tepe Channel are matrix-supported pebbly sandstones. Almost all of the fill of this channel is made up of Keban metamorphic clasts.

Lower Eocene bedrock. This surface is interpreted as a sequence boundary, probably related to the earliest phases of opening and bypass of sediment from the northern margin of the basin (Cronin *et al.* 2000*b*). A schematic diagram of the architecture of the Nohut Channel Complex is shown in Figure 15.

Phase 1 is interpreted as a phase of passive slope behaviour subsequent to erosion, with periodic wasting of slope sediments into the confined Nohut area, probably from the south though this is not clear. Some of these slumps are substantial in volume and are probably mass-transport complexes, as they include rafts of bedded carbonate slope material as well as slumped marl. Sediment from the shelf area is only in the form of reworked *Nummulites*, implying the presence of *Nummulites* shoals in the outer shelf area, and almost no siliciclastic input.

Phase 2 is interpreted as a phase of slope progradation with the introduction of siliciclastic sediments and the development of deep-water slope channels with mixed siliciclastic-carbonate fills. The upper part of Phase 2 sees reactivation of channels after a period of relative quiescence, with localized slumping. The base of this phase is not thought to be as stratigraphically significant as the base of Phase 1.

Phase 3 is interpreted as a phase of clastic input, primarily by gravity currents, into the Nohut Complex. It was initiated by large-scale slumping of deep-water mudstones that accumulated on a slope after Phase 2 when the basin in the area deepened. The punctuated development of gravel-filled deep-water channels with sandy and silty channel mouth splays of limited lateral extent followed. The gravelly channels migrated over and incised into the channel mouth splays. The mixture of shelf-derived benthonic foraminifera (large *Nummulites*) with rounded pebbles and gravels indicates proximity to a shelf environment (Dellamonica 2004), though the channels themselves are located in the upper deep-water slope area. These gravel channel/sandy channel mouth splay 'couplets' are succeeded by the incisional base of the Gir Tepe gravel and conglomerate-filled incised channel complex, which is interpreted as a fan delta-fed complex that prograded rapidly towards the north.

Overall the Nohut Channel Complex reflects a progressive increase in clastic input, and deepening, throughout its fill history. The body is 3600 m wide and 300 m deep, with a low net:gross fill, apart from focused channelized elements with coarse fills. The southerly provenance of the complex reflects the narrow width of the Kirkgeçit Basin at this locality. The Hor Thrust shown in Figure 6, which is Miocene in age, has dislocated the Eocene sediments of this study from their concordant southern margin.

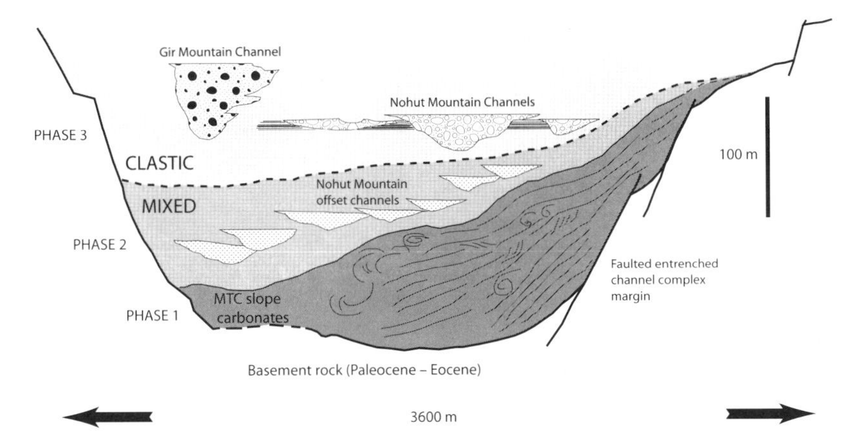

Fig. 15. Schematic of the Nohut Channel Complex, showing the principal fill packages: (i) MTC (mass transport complex) carbonates; (ii) mixed carbonates- siliciclastic sediments; (iii) clastic sediments. The channelized elements are most common in Phases 2 and 3. Note the overall low net:gross of the entire entrenched channel complex.

Aydinlar section

The Aydinlar section is a hillside section through the same stratigraphic interval as the Nohut section. It is located 4 km towards the north (Fig. 4), nearer to the northern shelf break. The section location is shown in Figure 6 and in sections A and B in Figure 9. The Aydinlar Road section is characterized by channelized elements at two stratigraphic intervals, a lower interval of isolated, slumped, sand-filled erosional channels, and an upper interval of larger offset stacked channels. These intervals do not appear to be contained within a larger entrenched channel complex, as at Nohut. The regional palaeocurrent directions are all from the north, in contrast to the Nohut Channel Complex, where palaeocurrents were from the south and SE (Fig. 6). Two cross-sections located on Figure 6 (sections A and B), show the interpreted stratigraphic relationship between the Aydinlar and Nohut sections (Fig. 7). In section B, the Main Channel shown on the left in the Aydinlar Road section is at a similar stratigraphic level as the coarse-grained gravel channels of the Nohut Section. On section B, it can be seen that a number of small thrusts, related to the Miocene Hor Thrust (Fig. 6) have made mapped correlation between the two sections difficult, and this remains an area of uncertainty. It is not yet known whether the middle and upper sections in the Nohut Channel Complex and at Aydinlar are stratigraphically equivalent. The channel elements in both sections are documented as examples of different styles of slope channel fill architecture within the same overall stratigraphic interval. It was suspected that the lower channel interval of Phase 2 at Nohut Tepe was equivalent to the lower slumped channel interval of Aydinlar Road, and that the Phase 3 channels of Nohut were equivalent to the higher Main Channel at Aydinlar Road, and detailed biostratigraphic work (Dellamonica, *pers. comm.*) supports the correlation. Further biostratigraphic and geochemical work is underway to confirm these correlations.

The Aydinlar Road section is shown in Figure 16. The section is divided into three intervals. The base of the complex is not seen at Aydinlar Road, though to the SE at Marik (Fig. 6) the lower part of the interval contains the thick Marik Member, which is interpreted as a fan delta that prograded from the east (Ozkul 1988). The Marik Member terminates rapidly against an intraslope syn-sedimentary fault (Fig. 6) and, further to the west, the same interval comprises slumped marls and limestones. In this paper we focus on the upper two intervals.

Phase 1: Slumped carbonates

The slumped carbonates are identical to those seen in Phase 1 of the Nohut Complex although they do not appear to overlie an erosional surface. They are at least 150 m thick and comprise a mixture of limestones, calcarenites and marls, all in large slide blocks with low angle discordant surfaces. Figure 16a shows the undisturbed continuous stratigraphic section from a series of olistoliths in the SW of the area (Fig. 6), to the Aydinlar Road section. Examination of the carbonate interval reveals a series of channelized elements, filled with limestones, localized intervals of calcarenite, and thick massive sandy beds composed entirely of *Nummulites*. Many of these intervals have been disturbed locally. Biostratigraphic work indicates outer shelf water depths (<80 m; Dellamonica 2004).

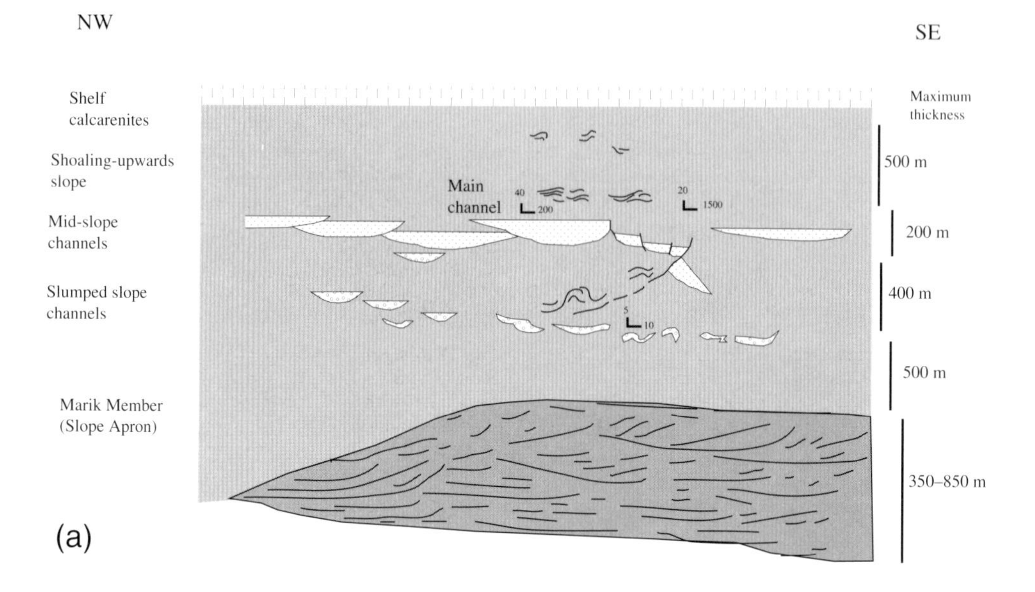

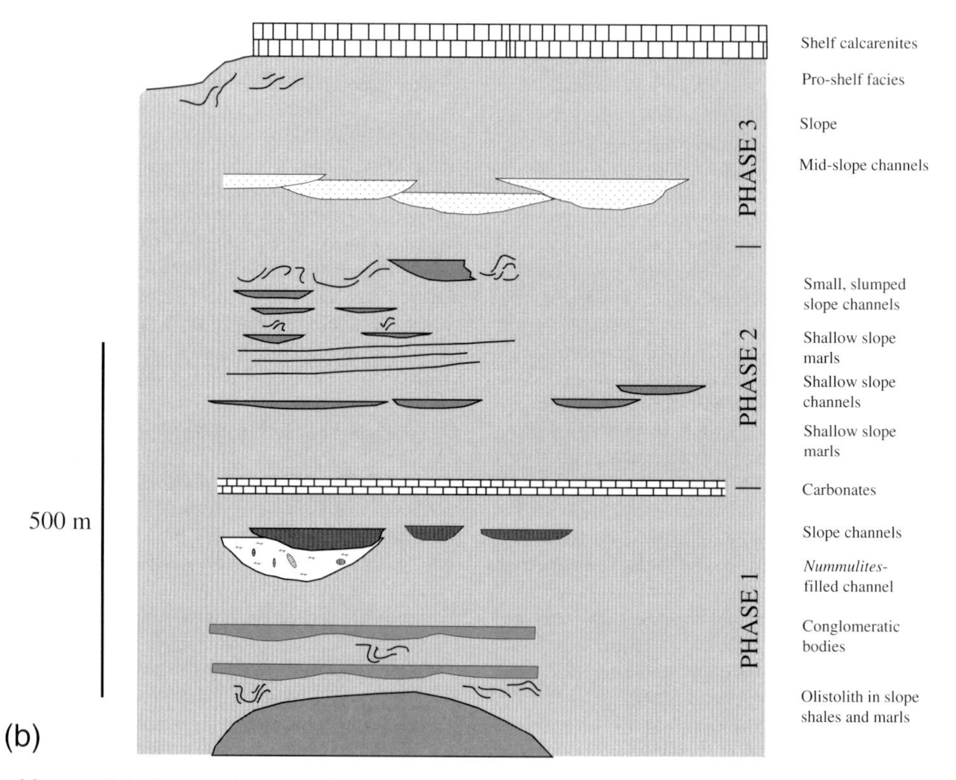

Fig. 16. (**a**) Aydinlar Road section – east. This section is a composite schematic figure, equivalent to part of a structural cross-section between B'–B and C'–C sections shown in Figures 6 & 7, showing both the Marik Member at the base and the Aydinlar Road channels towards the top of the interval; (**b**) Aydinlar Road section – west. This section is a composite schematic figure, equivalent to A'–A on Figure 6 (Fig. 7a), showing the olistoliths and all of the channel elements to Aydinlar Road.

Fig. 17. Foundered channel element from the Aydinlar Road channel complex Phase 2. These channels are characterized by mixed siliciclastic-carbonate fills, and are nested in a slumped muddy/marly background, with no evidence for levees.

Fig. 18. Margin of the Main Channel exposed at Aydinlar Road. The fill is characterized by tabular pebbly sandstones with mud chip breccias, interbedded with graded turbidite sandstones. The margin on the left is strongly affected by clastic injection features.

Phase 2: Mixed carbonates – siliciclastic sediments

Phase 2 comprises interbedded marls and calcarenites, which have a higher proportion of syn-sedimentary disturbance than Phase 2 in the Nohut section. Lenticular bodies of mixed sandstone and calcarenite are found throughout Phase 2 (Fig. 17). These bodies have erosive bases, are 3–7 m thick and 50–200 m wide, and their fills are characterized by 0.7–1.2 m thick coarse-grained sandstones. Most of these channel bodies are slumped, primarily foundered completely within enveloping muddy and marly sediments.

Phase 3: Clastic sediments

Phase 3 comprises coarse grained gravelly sandstones and conglomerates within an erosive channel complex, called the Main Channel in Figure 7b. One margin of this channel is shown in Figure 18. This Channel complex is 35 m thick, and up to 700 m wide, with a number of smaller scale associated channel fills located at the same level (Fig. 16a, b). The channel sediments fine and thin upwards and interbedded fine-grained sediments are full of deep-water ichnofacies and benthic foraminifera, indicating deep-water (*c.* 600 m or more; Dellamonica 2004). Two logged sections through the Main Channel are shown in Figures 19 and 20.

Figure 19 is through the axis of the main channel. The base of the Main Channel is at 0 m. Above the base are three 0.2–0.4 m thick sandstones beds, with prominent cross-bedding. The beds themselves are lenticular with flat bases and mounded tops. The beds thicken and thin laterally due to this lenticularity, with crest-to-crest distances of up to 4 m. The beds may be graded locally, and many have granule or pebble layers. They are separated by thin mudstone beds that contain deep-water benthic foraminifera. At 2 m above the channel base, the channel fill is characterized by thick clast and matrix-supported conglomerates, with strong pebble imbrication fabrics. In Figure 20, these conglomerates thin towards the channel margins. Some thinner sandstone beds within the channel fill are trough cross-stratified. One thick pebble sandstone contains an interval of mud chip breccia (Fig. 20, 7 m) nested within the central portion of the bed, which passes laterally into coherent intervals of interbedded heterolithics, suggesting *in-situ* brecciation of the mud chip interbed. The western margin of the Main Channel (Fig. 18) is very sharp, and many of the thin conglomerate beds have been injected into the heterolithic channel margin sediments. Vertical conglomeratic dykes are also seen, and these are graded locally from their margins from pebbly sandstone into a granular sandstone core.

The Main Channel is overlain by a thick succession of thin-bedded sandstones, siltstones and mudstones, with very rare localized pebbly mudstones and minor slumps (Fig. 19, 24.5 m). Complete Bouma sequences are exceptionally common. These sediments pass upwards into shelfal calcarenites, which cap the succession at Aydinlar Road.

Aydinlar Road complex interpretation

The Aydinlar Road section is interpreted as a series of mid-outer shelf and upper slope channels, derived from the north, within an open slope interval that has a three-fold division in fill sedimentation, not dissimilar to the Nohut Section to the south. A schematic diagram of the architecture of the Aydinlar Road section is shown in Figure 16.

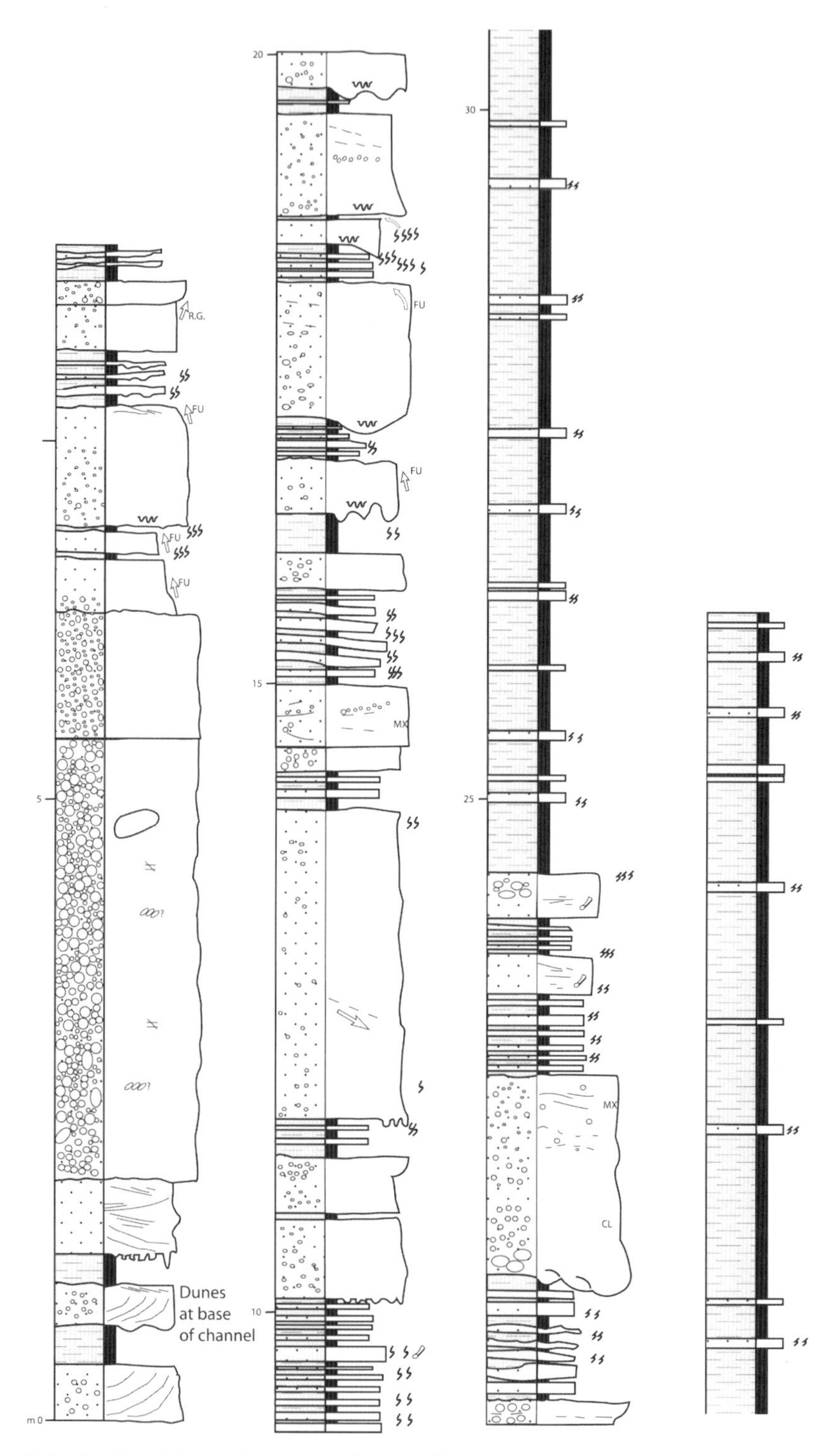

Fig. 19. Aydinlar Road log B-5 through the axis of the Main Channel.

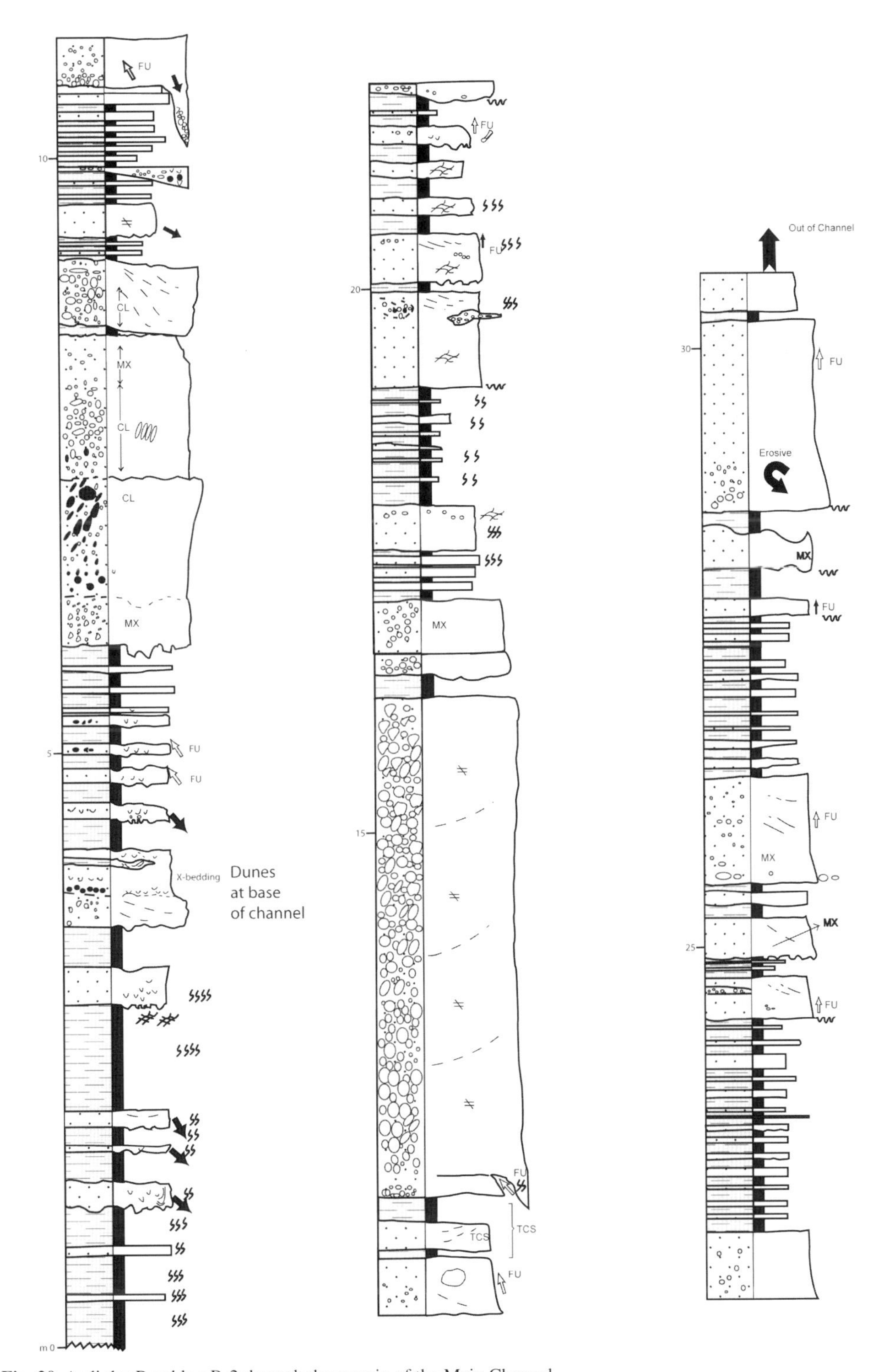

Fig. 20. Aydinlar Road log B-2 through the margin of the Main Channel.

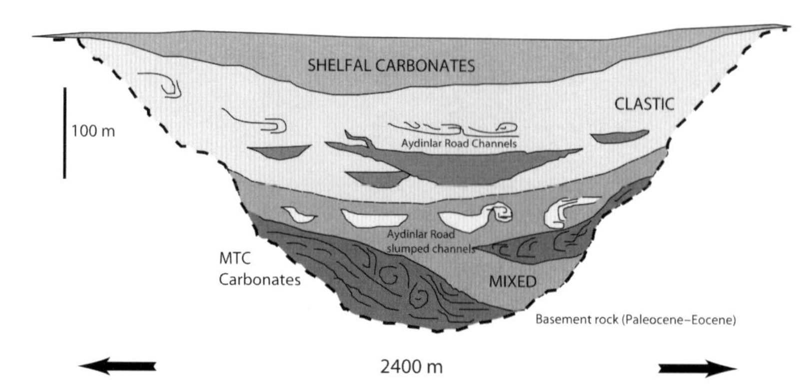

Fig. 21. Schematic of the Aydinlar Road section, showing the principal fill packages. Note how the mixed and clastic phases (2 and 3) have more internal syn-sedimentary deformation than the Nohut section, perhaps indicative of the higher slope at this locality. The section is prograded over by shelfal carbonates (calcarenites).

Phase 1 is interpreted as a phase of widespread mass wasting after basin opening. The complex was incised in a rapidly subsiding basin margin setting due to block faulting off the limbs of prominent anticlines that were oriented sub-parallel to the basin margin. The olistoliths seen at the SW margin of the basin are large (<150 m) blocks of basement Keban metamorphic bedrock, interpreted to have collapsed into the basin from the south-western area during the early phases of basin opening. They are nested within Kirkgeçit Formation sediments and can be mapped to *in-situ* bedrock of the same basement Keban metamorphic rocks to the SW. The olistoliths are found in basin floor deep-water sediments. The slumping and sliding formed mass-transport complexes within locally confined topography, interpreted as having been generated tectonically.

Phase 2 is characterized by small-scale slope channels that foundered within the enveloping mixed shale/marl sediments to give a prominent series of slumped channel bodies. These channels have sharp bases and no associated levee or overbank facies (Fig. 21). The sandy fills are medium–coarse grained sandstones, with sharp tops and bases. They are interpreted as backfilled slope channels, indicating that the channel bases record bypass into deeper parts of the basin to the south and SW. The morphology of the erosional channel bases is simple, and interpreted to reflect single phases of cutting into the enveloping fine grained slope marls.

Phase 3 is dominated by sand and gravel-filled channels in the Aydinlar Road section. This is interpreted to reflect a phase of clastic input from the northern basin margin. The lower part of the Main Channel fill is interpreted as a channel base, characterized by traction-dominated features such as channel bars, channel thalwegs and sand and gravel dunes, reflecting an early phase of sediment bypass. This phase of partial channel filling is succeeded by a major phase of conglomeratic and sandy gravity flows. The transition from bypass axial facies to a major depositional phase within the Main Channel at Aydinlar is interpreted as corresponding to a transition similar to that described by Mutti & Ricci Lucchi (1972) from the Hecho Group in the Spanish Pyrenees at Ainsa. This transition (from 'Type 1' to 'Type 2') marks a change in channel behaviour in a slope setting that has been interpreted to reflect a change in flow efficiency (Mutti & Ricci Lucchi 1972) or a progressive reduction in slope grade (Cronin *et al.* 1998). Phase 3 in Aydinlar is also characterized by clastic injection features and other evidence for syn-sedimentary movement of clastic material due to gravity and loading. This was not seen in the Nohut section to the south. Above the Main Channel, the slope facies include full Bouma sequences in many of the sandstone beds, indicating very low slopes, and many traditionally abyssal depth trace fossils (such as *Palaeodiction*). These sediments are interbedded with mudstones, and locally, pebbly mudstones with extrabasinal clasts. Phase 3 is capped by shelfal facies, which rapidly prograded over the complex from the north. The nature of the contact between the upper slope/ramp environment of the upper part of Phase 3, and the overlying shelfal calcarenites, is not thought to represent a major sequence boundary or change in relative sea level (Cronin *et al.* 2000*b*).

Overall the Aydinlar Road section is interpreted to record rapid incision and filling from the north on a rapidly subsiding basin margin. The sediments coarsen upward and the water depth is thought to have increased up-section, with a rapid increase in clastic input. The section is characterized throughout by syn-sedimentary mass-wasting, principally from slumping and sliding, reflecting the advance of the loading shelfal facies from the north.

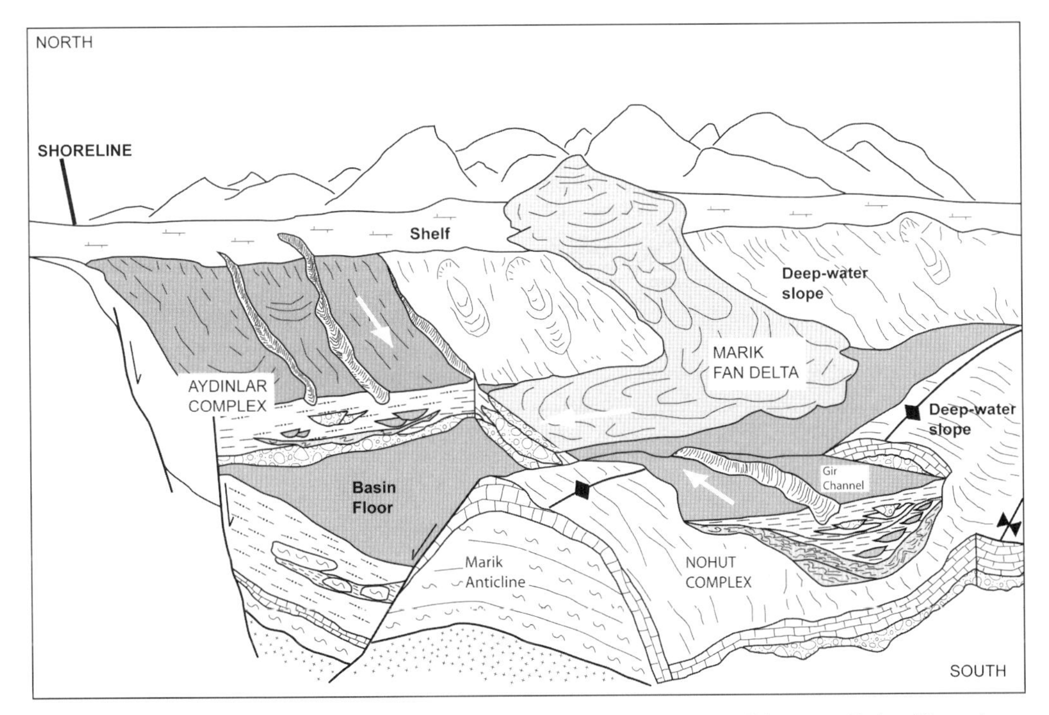

Fig. 22. Block model for the Middle Eocene of the Aydinlar–Nohut area west of Baskil in eastern Turkey. The entire area shown in the block model has been thrust to the south, so the geological story immediately to the south has been obscured. Sediments were being sourced both from the north and the south at this time. The sea floor topography was inherited from an earlier Paleocene phase of thrusting, which led to the growth of low amplitude folds in the area, and an uplifted hinterland to the north (and locally, probably the south). Extension in the Middle Eocene saw the limbs of these earlier folds subsiding very rapidly and the creation of a series of deep basins which filled rapidly with gravity flow deposits after initial mass-wasting from surrounding slopes. Fan delta-fed systems prograded rapidly into low topography, forming large entrenched deep-water channel complexes like those described in the text.

Discussion

A series of deep-water slope channel elements from the Eocene of eastern Turkey reveal a predictable distribution of coarse-grained channel and other architectural element packages within a slope succession that prograded over laterally confined sea floor topography (Fig. 22). The Nohut Channel Complex is almost 3 km wide and over 250 m deep, and is interpreted as an entrenched deep-water slope channel complex that was sourced from the southern basin margin. This has been called the Nohut Channel Complex. The second system at Aydinlar is interpreted as a deep-water slope complex, sourced from the northern margin of the basin. It is at least 2 km wide and several hundred metres thick.

Both sections are floored by MTCs (mass transport complexes), with slumps and slide blocks of intra-basinal sediments and locally of olistoliths derived from bedrock exposed either on the seafloor or at the basin margin to the south or SW. Though there are uncertainties over the lateral extent of the MTCs at the base of the Aydinlar section, those at the base of the Nohut Channel Complex are clearly seen to pinch out against the confining walls of bedrock that mark the edge of the entrenched channel complex.

In both the slope sedimentary systems, a number of coarse-grained deep-water slope channel systems are documented. These are always nested in enveloping muddy slope sediments. The channel elements have different architectural characteristics.

Type 1 slope channels. These channels are typified by the channel elements seen in Phase 2 of the Nohut Complex. Individual channels have width:depth (aspect) ratios of 10:1. The channels have marked bases but the erosion is low angle and not evident on close inspection. The fills passively infill the channels. There is very little fine-grained material in the channel fills, and many beds are amalgamated, indicating limited amounts of bypass during filling. The fills are interpreted as turbidites sourced from the outer shelf and transported into these upper slope channels, probably by storms. These type 1 slope channels have no recognized levees and are usually incised into background slope marls. The channels offset stack towards one of the margins and thus there is physical communication between these channel bodies.

Type 2 slope channels. These channels are typified by the channel elements seen in Phase 2 of the Aydinlar slope section. The channels have been strongly affected by syn-sedimentary sliding and slumping. Many of the channels have foundered on detached rafts of marly slope material, or on slide surfaces or glide planes on the marly slope. Some of the channel bodies have broken up into smaller rafts of sand, and others have even folded over on themselves completely, perhaps being locally bulldozed by other slide elements within these slide packages. The channel elements do not appear to have travelled great distances. The fills are very sandy, with no fine-grained material and there are commonly 5–8 sandstone beds in each channel fill. Aspect ratios are typically 10:1, though this depends on the degree of rafting or slumping of the channel in question.

Type 3 slope channels. These are typified by Phase 3 of the Nohut Channel Complex. The channels have multiphase fills, locally with reworked bioclastic material at the base, and then incised into by several later phases of channel activity. The bases of these slope channels are very abrupt and commonly strongly erosive into a thick series of interbedded massive or rippled fine–medium grained sandstones and siltstones. They are of limited aerial extent, not passing far either side of the overlying channel margins, though possibly winging out in both directions. Below this package, which locally has an irregular base with sandstones and siltstones infilling low relief topography, there is always an associated underlying thick package of muddy slumped slope material. The Type 3 slope channel cuts down into the sandstones and siltstones that overlie the slumped material and has a tabular fill of interbedded pebbly sandstones and conglomerates. Imbrication and other evidence for traction indicate powerful gravity currents and related reworking of sediment in the channels during phases of activity. These channels do not appear to offset stack, though several phases of reactivation appear to relocate over the thalwegs of earlier phases. The examples studied at Nohut were not in physical communication with adjacent channels. This is considered to reflect the topography of the associated underlying sandstone/siltstone packages, which are interpreted as channel mouth splays that have been partly 'cannibalized' by prograding channels. These channel-mouth splay couplets are isolated in the upper parts of the channel complex fill, forming shoestring shaped bodies of coarse clastic material. The intimate association of slumps, with tabular thin sheet sand package of limited lateral extent and then incised gravel and sand-filled channel is strongly reminiscent of the HARPS model of Flood and Damuth (1987).

Type 4 slope channels. These slope channels are typified by the Main Channel of the Aydinlar section. This channel has a width of up to 700 m and is 35 m thick (aspect ratio of 20:1). The fill is very coarse grained above an initial phase of cutting and bypass, represented by cross-bedded dunes and bar forms in the lowest part of the channel, that pass up into very coarse-grained gravity flow deposits. *In-situ* brecciation of heterolithic facies in the axis of the channel, passes laterally into coherent heterolithic packages and indicates dewatering and shallow subsurface liquefaction of sediments with confined high pore pressures. Dewatering and brecciation of heterolithic facies is characteristic of overpressuring in the axis of Type 4 channels. Clastic injection is common at the margins of these channels. Conglomeratic dykes at the margins were injected vertically and deposited pod-like sills that are impossible to distinguish in 1D section from other channel fill sediments. This type of clastic injection has the effect of 'bulking up' the net coarse-grained sediment volume in positions that are off the main coarse-grained channel axis. Similarly, and on a smaller scale, sills have been injected laterally from dykes into enveloping marginal heterolithic facies. Above the coarse-grained fill elements the Type 4 channels progressively shut-down and were abandoned very abruptly and overlain by finer-grained facies. The mechanism of this rapid switching-off is unclear.

Type 5 slope channels. These are characterized by very deep incision and infilling by a mixture of clast-supported and matrix-supported conglomerates. As seen within the Gir Tepe Channel, these Type 5 channel complexes are interpreted as gullies that form down slope of prograding steep-fronted gravel deltas. The upper parts of these gully fills are characterized by higher dipping packages, interpreted to reflect progradation of the fan delta toes directly into the gully itself.

Originally, the Nohut and Aydinlar Road channel complexes were thought to have occurred within two separate slope basins, confined by erosional topography into older basement rocks, until the scale and geometry of the confining erosional surfaces became apparent. The complexes have widths of 3600 m and 2400 m, with thicknesses in excess of 250 m each, respectively. These dimensions are remarkably similar to the large entrenched deep-water slope channel complexes found in the subsurface offshore Gulf of Guinea (e.g. Barrufini *et al.* 2000; Mayall & Stewart 2000). The fill architectures of most of the two mud-prone sections described for the first time in this paper are very similar, despite the fact that the two channel complexes come from different sides of the Elaziğ Basin.

When compared to subsurface examples of multi-phase entrenched deep-water slope channel complexes of comparable size and net:gross, in particular examples seen on 3D seismic offshore West Africa (e.g. Barrufini *et al.* 2000), the similarities are striking. There are many examples of transparent and highly reflective bundles of seismic reflectors in these channel complexes, with evidence for isolated re-entrenchment in the upper parts of the channel complexes. With the exception of the carbonate facies capping the top of the succession, the lower parts of the channel complexes are very similar, characterized by more connected channel elements overlying very disturbed sediment packages that may have been affected by large-scale synsedimentary slumping within the channel complex.

Comparison ('rock-truthing') using outcrop analogues tests the real lithotype association with geometry interpreted from seismic. Compound master erosional surfaces are often difficult to interpret on seismic with confidence. Down-system changes in successive strike sections through these channel complexes are also easier to understand. Such analogue databases now provide a much more realistic dataset to populate seismic data with lithology information, allowing reservoir bodies to be mapped with more confidence.

The authors wish to thank the sponsoring companies during the various phases of data acquisition in Turkey, 1996–1999: Amoco, Amerada Hess, Conoco, Elf and Enterprise; 2000–2001: ENI Agip S.p.A.; 2002–2004: BP Angola Business Unit, UNOCAL, and ConocoPhillips. Our Turkish colleagues in Firat (Euphrates) University, particularly Prof. Ahmet Sagiroglu, Dr Mehmet Turan and Dr Erjan Aksoy, are thanked for local support and advice, and Prof. Erdal Kerey (Istanbul University) and Prof. Gilbert Kelling (Keele University) are thanked for initially introducing the lead author to the Elaziğ Basin. Patrizia Rocchini and Giacomo Spadini are thanked for access to the subsurface data and discussions on the nature of these. More detailed work on more sand-prone subsurface examples is in progress with Spadini and Rocchini. I wish to thank Nick Drinkwater and Steve Flint for detailed and considered reviews of the first version of this paper.

References

ABREU, V., SULLIVAN, M., PIRMEZ, C. & MOHRIG, D. 2003. Lateral accretion packages (LAPS): an important reservoir element in deep water sinuous channels. *Marine and Petroleum Geology*, **20**, 631–648.

AKSOY, E., TURAN, M., TURKMEN, I. & ÖZKUL, M. 1996. Tertiary evolution of the Elaziğ Basin, E. TURKEY. *In:* Korkmaz, S. & Akcay, M. (eds) *Proceedings of the Symposium on the 30th anniversary of the Geology Department at KTU*, October 1995. Trabzon, Turkey, 293–310.

AVŞAR, N. 1989*a*. Tertiary stratigraphy of the Elaziğ region. *Journal of Faculty of Engineering and Architecture*, Selcuk University, Turkey, **1**, 30–39.

AVŞAR, N. 1989*b*. *Nummulites fabianii* and *Nummulites perforatus* Zones of Kirkgeçit Formation in the Elaziğ region. *Journal of Faculty of Engineering and Architecture*, Selcuk University, Turkey, **2**, 14–25.

BARRUFINI, L., GARCIA, P., MARINI, A.J., MOTA, B. & ROCCHINI, P. 2000. West Africa deep-water sedimentary processes and deposits: the use of advanced imaging techniques in their recognition and classification. *In*: MORAIS, M.L.D., AMARAL, J., PAQUETC, A.A. & BATISTA, C. (eds) *4th Colloquium on the stratigraphy and the palaeogeography on the South Atlantic*, GeoLuanda 2000 International Conference, Luanda, Angola, May 21–24. University Agostinho Neto, Geological Society of Africa.

BINGÖL, F. 1984. Geology of the Elaziğ area in the Eastern Taurus region: Geology of the Taurus Belt, MTA (Ankara), 209–216.

BINGÖL, F. & BEYARSLAN, M. 1996. Geochemistry and petrology of the Elaziğ Magmatics. *In*: KORKMAZ, S. & AKCAY, M. (eds) *Proceedings of the Symposium on the 30th anniversary of the Geology Department at KTU*, October 1995. Trabzon, Turkey, 208–224.

ÇELIK, H. 2003. *Stratigraphic and tectonic features in the vicinity of Mastar Mountain (southeast of Elaziğ)*. PhD Thesis, Euphrates (Firat) University, Graduate School of Science and Technology, Department of Geological Engineering, Elaziğ, Turkey. 95 p.

CRONIN, B.T., HURST, A., ÇELIK, H. & TÜRKMEN, I. 2000*a*. Superb exposure of a channel levee and overbank complex in an ancient deep-water slope environment. *Sedimentary Geology*, **132**, 205–216.

CRONIN, B.T., HARTLEY, A.J., ÇELIK, H., HURST, A., TÜRKMEN, I. & KEREY, E. 2000*b*. Equilibrium profile development in graded deep-water slopes: Eocene, Eastern Turkey. *Journal of the Geological Society, London*, **157**, 943–955.

CRONIN, B.T., HARTLEY, A.J., OWEN, D. & KNELLER, B. 1998. Slumps, debris flows and sandy deep-water channel systems: implications for the application of sequence stratigraphy to deep water clastic sediments. *Journal of the Geological Society*, **155**, 429–432.

DELLAMONICA, X.L.N. 2004. *Biostratigraphic data for reservoir correlation and prediction of basin evolution in sand-rich turbidite successions*. Unpublished PhD Thesis, University of Aberdeen. 255p.

DEPTUCK, M.E., STEFFENS, G.S., BARTON, M. & PIRMEZ, C. 2003. Architecture and evolution of upper fan channel-belts on the Niger Delta slope and in the Arabian Sea. *Marine and Petroleum Geology*, **20**, 649–676.

FLOOD, R.D. & DAMUTH, J.E. 1987. Quantitative characteristics of sinuous distributary channels on the Amazon deep-sea fan. *Geological Society of America Bulletin*, **98**, 728–738.

FONNESU, F. 2003. 3D seismic images of a low-sinuosity slope channel and related depositional lobe (West Africa deep-offshore). *Marine and Petroleum Geology*, **20**, 615–629.

MAYALL, M. & STEWART, I. 2000. The architecture of turbidite slope channels. *In*: WEIMER, P. ET AL. (eds) *Deep-Water Reservoirs of the World.* SEPM special publication (December 2000), 578–586.

MAYALL, M. & STEWART, I. 2001. The architecture of turbidite slope channels. *In*: FRASER, S.I., JOHNSON, H.D. FRASER, A.J. EVANS, A.M. (eds). *Petroleum Geology of Deep-Water Systems: Advances in Understanding 3D architecture.* Abstracts, Geological Society, London, p27.

MUTTI, E. & RICCI LUCCHI, F. 1972. Le torbiditi del l'Apennino sttentrionale: introduzione all'analisi di facies. *Memoir Societa Geologica Italiana*, **11**, 161–199.

ÖZKUL, M. 1988. *Elaziğ Batisinda Kirkegit Formasyonu uzerinde sedimentolojik incelemeler.* Unpublished PhD thesis, Firat (Euphrates) University, Elaziğ, Turkey, pp. 186.

ÖZKUL, M. 1993. Kirkgeçit Formasyonu'da (Eosen, Elaziğ) flis iz fosilleri ve ortamsal dagilimari [Flysch trace fossils from the Kirkgeçit Formation (Eocene, Elaziğ) and environmental distribution]. *Journal of Isparta Engineering Faculty*, Akdeniz (Black Sea) University, Isparta, Turkey, **7**, 15–30.

ÖZKUL, M. & KEREY, I.E. 1996. Deep-sea shelf facies analysis: Kirkgeçit. *Turkish Journal of Earth Science*, **5**, 57–70.

ÖZKUL, M. & USENMEZ, S. 1986. Sedimentological study of Eocene deep-sea conglomerates formed north-east of Elaziğ. *Engineering and Architecture Faculty Journal*, Gazi University, Ankara, Turkey, **1**, 53–73.

ROBERTSON, A.H.F. 2000. Mesozoic-Tertiary tectonic-sedimentary evolution of a south Tethyan oceanic basin and its margins in southern Turkey. *In:* BOZKURT, E. WINCHESTER, J.A. & PIPER, J.D.A. (eds) *Tectonics and Magmatism in Turkey and the surrounding area.* Geological Society, London, Special Publication, **173**, 97–138.

SPRAGUE, A.R., SULLIVAN, M.D., CAMPION, K.M., ET AL. 2002. The physical stratigraphy of deep-water strata: A hierarchical approach to the analysis of genetically-related stratigraphic elements for improved reservoir prediction. *National AAPG/SEPM meeting abstracts*, Houston, Texas, March 10–13.

TURAN, M. & BINGÖL, A. F. 1991. Kovancilar–Baskil area: tectono-stratigraphic aspects. *Ahmet Acar Symposium Proceedings*, Çukurova Universitesi, Adana, 213–227.

Concept of equilibrium profile in deep-water turbidite systems: effects of local physiographic changes on the nature of sedimentary process and the geometries of deposits

J-N. FERRY[1], T. MULDER[2], O. PARIZE[3] & S. RAILLARD[4]

[1] *Groupe Congo Pau, Centre scientifique et technique Jean Feger, Total, av. Larribau, 64018 Pau Cedex, France (e-mail: ferry_jn@yahoo.fr)*

[2] *Département de Géologie et Océanographie, Université de Bordeaux-1, av. des Facultés, 33405 Talence cedex, France*

[3] *CGES (Sédimentologie), Ecole nationale supérieure des Mines de Paris, 35, rue Saint Honoré, 77305 Fontainebleau, France*

[4] *Centre scientifique et technique Jean Feger, Total, av. Larribau, 64018 Pau Cedex, France*

Abstract: In the middle slope section of the Lower Congo Basin a late Miocene channel system was tracked on 3D seismic profiles over more than 350 km. Along its course, between shelf and basin, the system encountered four regional tectonic structures that induced local slope modifications, either by uplift or by subsidence. The turbidite deposits of this channel system were influenced strongly by these structures, in terms of both character and morphology. From the proximal to the distal part of this channel system, variations in parameters such as the sinuosity, the width and depth of basal incision, the presence of splay and levee deposits, the location of vertical aggradation zones and channel avulsion, all correlate with changes in longitudinal slope gradient. Thus, along a conventional sigmoidal slope, the convex regions are subjected to erosional processes whereas the concave regions are depositional. The direct relationship observed between sedimentary deposits and changing slope gradient highlights an important control in deep-water turbidite systems. This apparent response to local gradient changes on the slope suggests the existence of a sedimentary equilibrium profile similar to that defined for fluvial systems.

In recent years the oil industry has shown a keen interest in understanding how major submarine fan systems evolve in deep-water environments. Observation tools such as 3D seismic are well suited to the study of deep-water environments. These data have enabled scientists to understand better the organization and morphology of major recent turbidite systems (Damuth & Kumar 1975; Droz & Bellaiche 1985; Kolla & Coumes 1987; Weimer 1990; Damuth 1994; Rigaut 1997). Although the general development of these systems is now understood, the knowledge of their detailed geometry and depositional processes remains fragmented. The primary aim for industry is to model the reservoir properties of the accumulations; however, for scientists the main goal is to bridge the gaps in knowledge, observation scales and understanding between exposed ancient systems and modern systems, which are observed remotely (Mutti & Normark 1987). In recent works, Peakall *et al.* (2000) stated 'Understanding the morphological evolution and associated depositional histories of submarine channels is crucial for predicting and interpreting the resultant sedimentary architectures'. In this light, the relationships between slope physiography and sedimentation have been studied extensively from basin scale (Menard 1955; Normark 1985) to sedimentary facies scale (Kneller & McCaffrey 1999). The observed downslope variation of sedimentary processes throughout deep-water sediment gravity systems (Beaubouef & Friedmann 2000) led to the introduction of the concept of sedimentary equilibrium profile for density flows in marine environments (Pirmez *et al.* 2000).

The study of one Miocene turbidite channel system in the lower Congo Basin, discussed in this paper, confirms the importance of local slope variations on the behaviour of gravity flows (e.g. levee growth; lobe deposition; spatial and temporal channel sinuosity evolution). After describing the regional geological setting, observations are presented on the distribution and longitudinal evolution of the morphology of gravity flow deposits above four major tectonic structures. These structures lie along 350 km of continuous seismic profile data acquired from the continental shelf to the deep ocean basin, from the extreme proximal to distal parts of the system. Then the notion of equilibrium profile is discussed, as applied to deep-water turbidite channel systems from observations and interpretations performed on 3D seismic data made available by the Total petroleum group.

From: HODGSON, D.M. & FLINT, S.S. (eds) 2005. *Submarine Slope Systems: Processes and Products*. Geological Society, London, Special Publications, **244**, 181–193. 0305–8719/$15.00

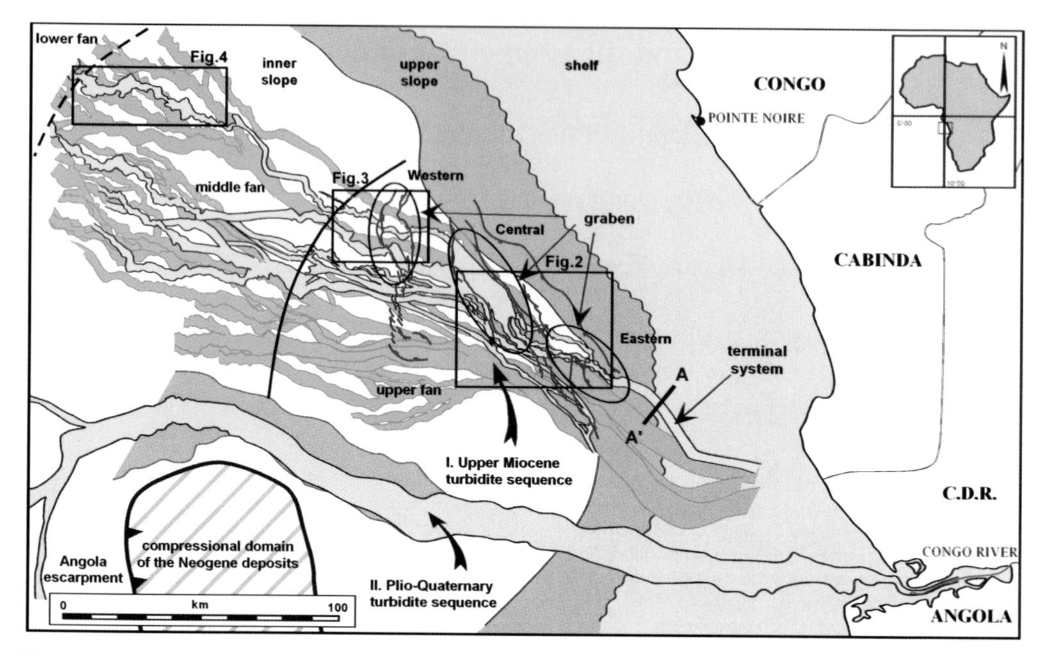

Fig. 1. Map of the Lower Congo basin showing the sequence of the Upper Miocene (yellow) and the present-day Pliocene–Quaternary turbidite sequence (grey), the physiography of the Upper Miocene margin, the tectonic elements and the location of figures.

Geodynamic setting

The turbidite system presented in this paper constitutes the terminal phase in the history of the Upper Miocene major turbidite succession in the Lower Congo basin, central west Africa (Fig. 1). This sedimentary sequence precedes that of the Pliocene–Quaternary system ascribed to the Congo River (Ferry *et al.* 2004). Stratigraphically, therefore, it lies just below the epeirogenic event in the Pliocene that affected the entire West African margin (Cahen 1954; Nze Abeigne 1992; Valle *et al.* 2001).

The Upper Miocene succession is located almost entirely in the northern part of the Congo Basin. The sedimentary transport axes of this system indicate that they were fed from a single point source located very close to the present-day Congo estuary. All of the Upper Miocene studied turbidite deposits are constituents of a single deep-water submarine fan system extending more than 500 km in length and covering a surface area estimated to be at least 100 000 km^2. Morphologically, this Upper Miocene deep-water turbidite fan is comprised, from upstream to downstream, of an upper fan, a middle fan and a lower fan. It is classified as a mud-rich submarine fan (Ferry *et al.* 2005).

The deposits of this fan system were influenced by four tectonic structures between the shelf edge and its distal section, 350 kilometres offshore present day Congo (Fig. 1). These structures are composed of three graben (eastern, central, western) and an area containing many salt intrusions. Deformation of the Tertiary sedimentary pile is the result of gravity tectonics, active at the end of the Upper Miocene (Figs 2, 3 & 4). Figure 2 shows the eastern and central graben in the proximal part of the system. Figure 3 shows the western graben in the middle part of the fan profile and Figure 4 shows the domain of salt intrusions and gravity tectonics. Figures 3 and 4 also comprise a large-scale seismic section that illustrates the effect of the gravity structures generated on the present-day seafloor slope. This effect is presumed to be similar to that which existed at the end of the Upper Miocene because tectonic structures were reactivated by tilting of the West African margin (Cramez & Jackson 2000); the direction of deformation remained the same throughout the Pliocene, as demonstrated by the seismic sections. The Pliocene interval comprises a series of constant thickness hemipelagic units (Wefer *et al.* 1998; Berger *et al.* 2002) and so thickness variations in this series are interpreted as due only to syn-sedimentary deformation rather than any depositional variability. Additionally, the correlation between their position and the morphological changes of the system indicates that these tectonic structures affected the seafloor relief.

Based on the above reasoning, the impact of these structures on the late Miocene seafloor is considered to have been similar to that of the structures present

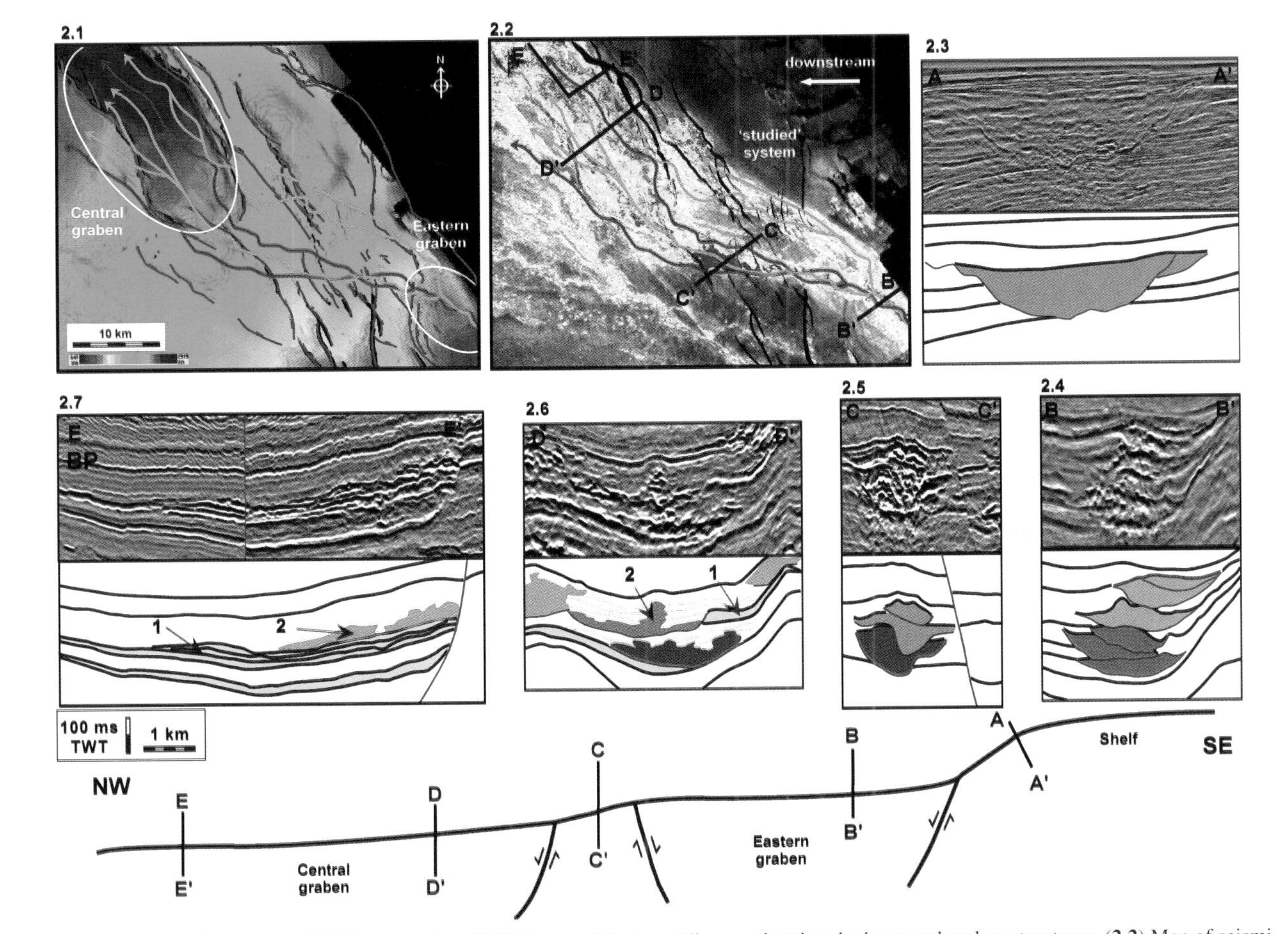

Fig. 2. Proximal section of the turbidite system. (**2.1**) Two-way time (TWT) map of the base Pliocene showing the horst and graben structures. (**2.2**) Map of seismic amplitude values (for an isopach layer, from the base Pliocene horizon, down 100 ms TWT: yellow, high values; grey, low values) displaying location of deposits of the turbidite system (arrows, transport axes). (**2.3–2.7**) Seismic profiles of associated interpretation sections: the canyon in the shelf (AA′); the six channel complexes separated in the eastern graben (BB′); the amalgamated channel complexes in the horst (CC′); the splay deposits (1) and the channel levees (2) in the central graben (DD′ and EE′).

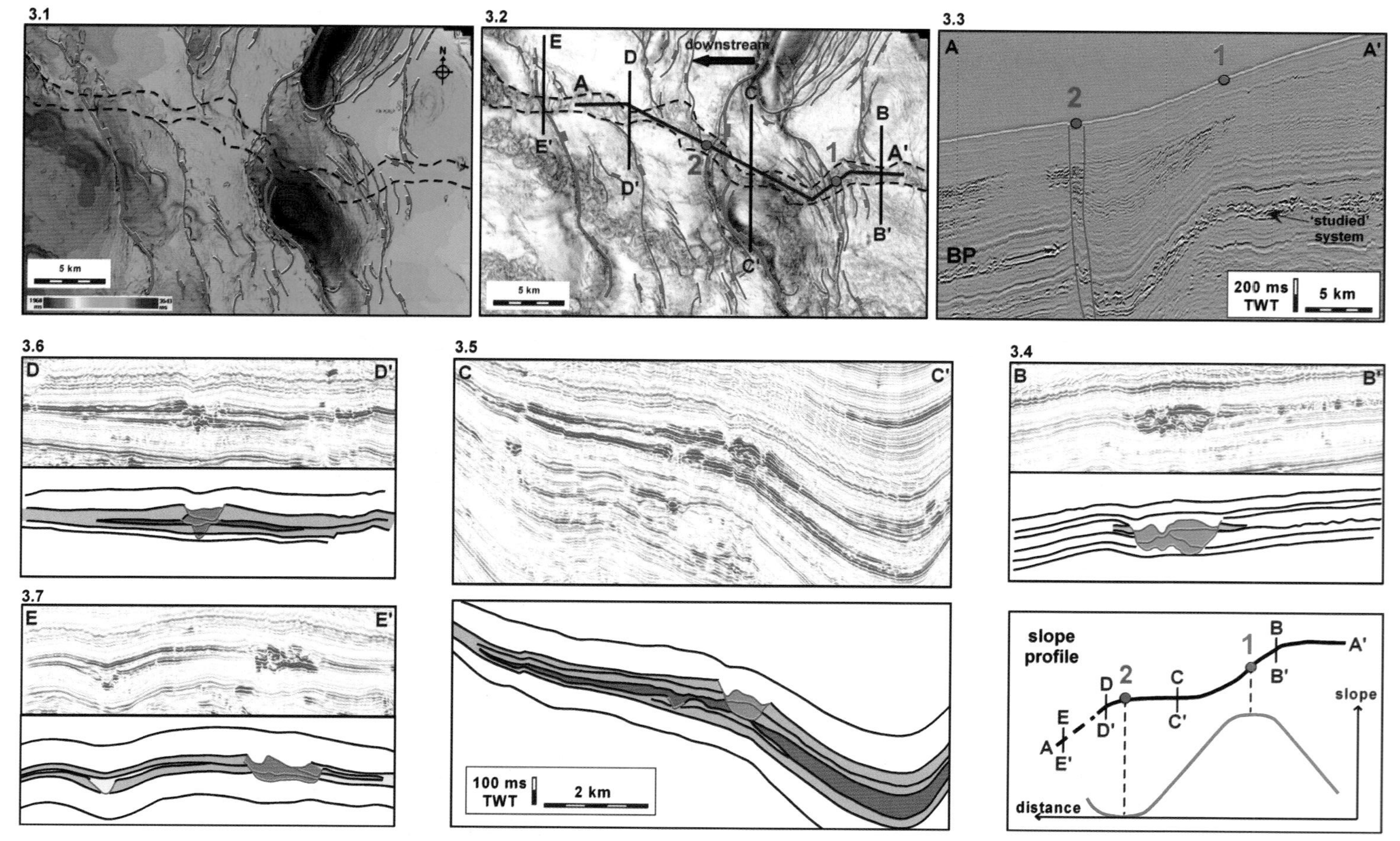

Fig. 3. The turbidite system in the medial profile position. (**3.1**) Two-way-time (TWT) map of the base Pliocene showing the western graben; (**3.2**) seismic amplitude map (for an isopach layer from the BP horizon, 100 ms TWT thick) location of turbidite system deposits (dotted line, transit axis border). (**3.3–3.7**) Seismic profiles and associated interpretation sections: the channel complex downstream of the central graben and upstream of the western graben (BB′); levee deposits (light grey) in the graben (CC′); progressive disappearance of levees from the downstream complex of the structure (DD′ and EE′).

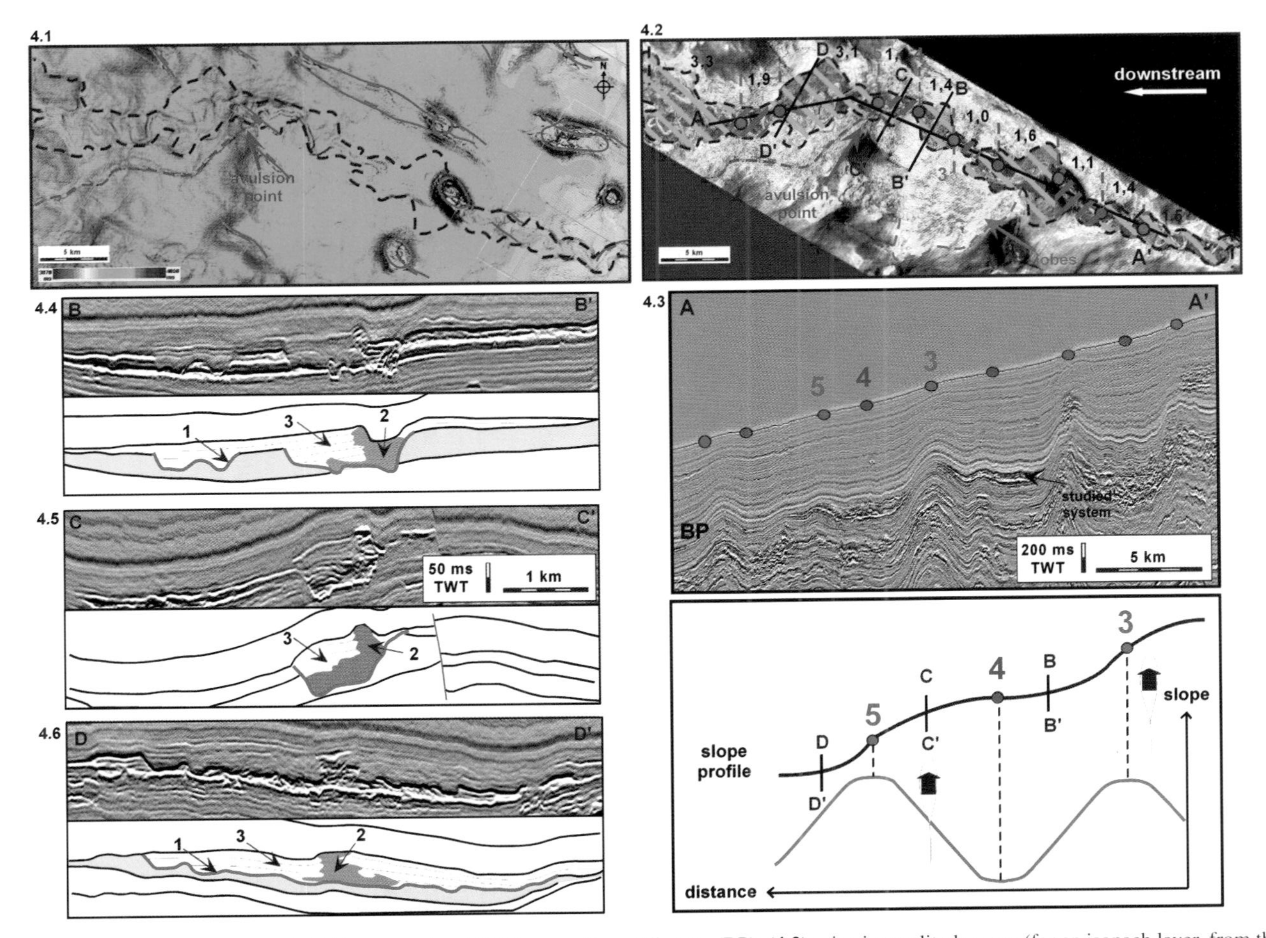

Fig. 4. The distal part of the turbidite system. (**4.1**) Two-way-time (TWT) map of base Pliocene (BP); (**4.2**) seismic amplitudes map (for an isopach layer, from the BP horizon, 100 ms TWT thick: yellow, high values; grey, low values; location of deposits of the turbidite system (arrows, transport axes). (Sinuosity: green hatched, high values; blue hatched, low values; dotted, edge of sedimentary transport axis). (**4.3–4.6**) Seismic profiles and associated interpretation sections of the channel complex: large base, shallow base (BB′); deep narrow base (CC′); large base and very shallow (DD′); (1) basal erosive surface, (2) channel fills, (3) levee deposits.

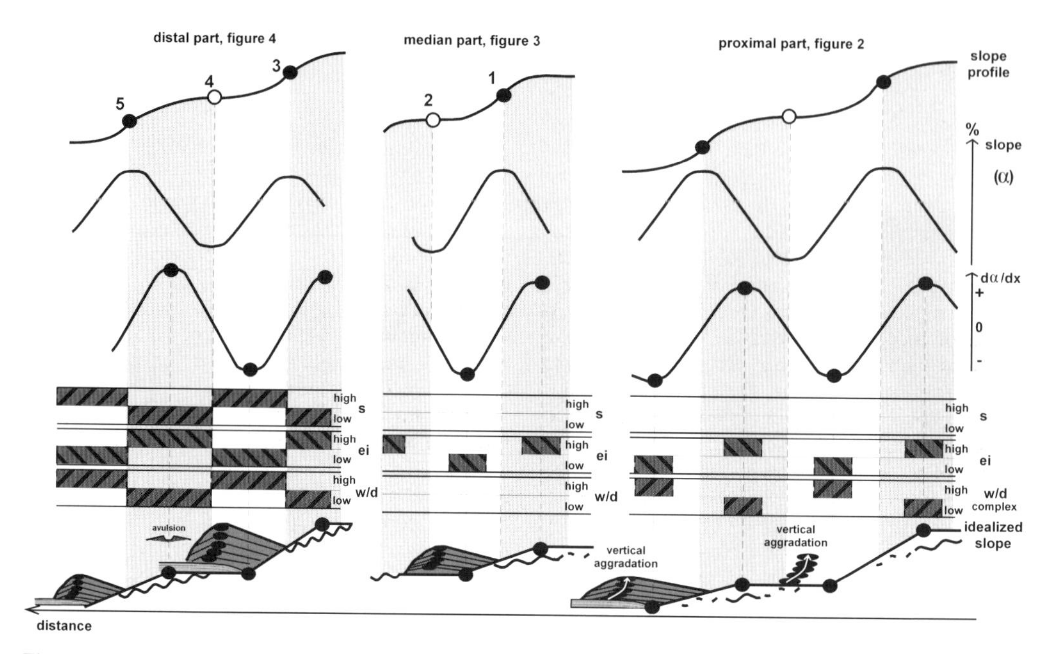

Fig. 5. Reconstitution and correlation of morphological parameters of turbidite deposits for proximal, medial and distal parts of the system, as a function of slope variation profiles. dα/d*x*, slope gradient; s, sinuosity; ei, erosive intensity; w:d, ratio of the system's width to its depth.

on the current seafloor. The Gaussian distribution slope profile (Adams & Schlager 2000) used to construct the diagram in Figure 5 was established on the basis of the physiography of the present-day seafloor. Its sigmoid shape results either from a local decrease in slope gradients by a depression in the seafloor for the graben (subsidence) or an increase in slope gradients due to local swelling of the seafloor above salt intrusions (uplift).

Longitudinal morphological evolution of the turbidite fan system

Proximal section: the eastern and central grabens

The stratigraphic succession within these grabens reflects the response of the depositional systems to the first modifications in slope gradient controlled by structure (Fig. 2). The grabens are located on the 'shelf to basin' profile at the first break in slope (eastern) and at the transition between the upper slope and the lower slope (central). The channelized turbidite system crosses these two structures after bypassing the shelf edge. The reconstructed proximal slope profile (Fig. 2) comprises the knick-point or increasing slope gradient beyond the shelf edge and the sharp slope gradient decrease located at each of the graben entry points, where the normal boundary faults are located. Between these two grabens, the edge of the eastern horst (i.e. the western edge of the eastern graben) generates an increasing slope gradient. The entire upper slope profile is thus marked by a series of three terraces from the shelf to the central graben. The morphology of the turbidite system and the types of deposits evolve considerably along the profile of this irregular slope.

On the shelf, the sedimentary transport system runs through a small canyon with clear-cut basal incision (Fig. 2, section AA′), about 4 km wide and about 150 ms TWT deep. The canyon fill is composed of a chaotic high-amplitude seismic facies at the base and more continuous reflectors at the top. The basal part is interpreted to contain an amalgamation of coarse-grained turbidite deposits (Walker 1967; Luthi 1981; Mutti & Normark 1991). This canyon fill represents the sedimentary sequence in the proximal part of overall system. It begins with initial erosion followed by a development phase associated with transport and deposition of coarse-grained sediment and terminates with a final abandonment phase and filling by muddy deposits.

At the base of the slope, turbidity currents flowing out of the canyon were entirely captured by the rapidly subsiding eastern graben (Fig. 2, section BB′). In the centre of this trough, the sedimentary sequence is stratigraphically subdivided into six separate, aggrading sedimentary bodies. Each of these bodies, or channel complexes (*sensu* Kolla *et al.* 2001) is composed of a 2 km-wide erosional base with a sedimentary fill about 50 ms TWT thick, comprising high amplitude, chaotic seismic facies.

The transition from canyon morphology to channel complex morphology takes place over a very short distance (20 km), omitting an intermediate stage valley morphology (Shepard & Emery 1973; Rigaut 1997). This rapid, incomplete transition is thought to be the consequence of early deceleration of the turbidity currents. The deceleration correlates with the reducing slope gradient at the entry of the eastern graben. The effect of a physiographic threshold induced by the decreasing slope gradient is considerably enhanced by the rapid subsidence of the graben because it contributes to the vertical aggradation of the six channel complexes, limits their amalgamation and eliminates the valley morphology 'stage' entirely.

At the horst, the normal fault bordering the western edge of the eastern graben is marked by an increase in slope gradient. Here, only three of the six channel complexes are still present. The courses of the other complexes are slightly shifted either northward or southward (Fig. 2, section CC′). The remaining three channel complexes are amalgamated and each one is strongly eroded by the overlying complex. Relative to their respective morphologies in the eastern graben, all are narrower (about 150 m) and have more pronounced basal incision, which is concomitant with a twofold increase in fill thickness. Although they are located downstream of the eastern graben, the morphology of the channel complexes on the horst suggest higher energy turbidity currents. These characteristics are correlated with an increase in slope gradient on the eastern border of the horst.

Downstream of the horst, entry into the large central graben (10 km wide) is accompanied by a significant decrease in slope gradient, concomitant with a radical change in the morphology of the channel complexes. In the centre of the graben, two types of turbidite deposits can be observed. Splay (sheet) deposits cover the entire depression and are marked by thick, continuous seismic reflectors with strong amplitude (Fig. 2, section EE′). Channel complexes (Fig. 2, section DD′) are composed of poorly defined, wide (more than 2.5 km) erosional bases and significant filling by vertical aggradation of channel-levee deposits.

Although located in the proximal part of the overall profile, the system shows marked aggradation through the central graben. As for the eastern graben, the physiographic depression is accompanied by a reduced slope gradient, i.e. a deceleration in the velocity of the gravity flows (Kneller & Branney 1995).

Middle section: the western graben

Down profile from the eastern and central graben, the turbidite system is divided into six sequences corresponding to six channel complexes. One of them, described above in the central graben, extends northward and laterally crosses the third collapse structure, the western graben (Fig. 3). This trough produced a decrease in the gradient of the seafloor at its entry (point 1) and an increase in gradient of the seafloor at its exit at point 2 (section AA′, Fig. 3). These combined variations in slope gradient caused changes in the morphology of the channel complex that crosses the structure (Fig. 3).

Upstream of the graben, the channel complex shown in section BB' is the same as that previously described in Figure 2 (section CC′) in the eastern and central graben. About 20 km beyond the structure its morphology returns to the conventional morphology for a complex located in a middle profile position, with a lack of splay deposits and a well marked basal incision about 2 km wide, containing 100 ms TWT of amalgamated channel fill material.

In the centre of the western graben the slope gradient is low (section CC′) and the channel complex exhibits major morphological changes. Levees developed laterally over several kilometres in the channel complex (light grey on the interpretation). Their seismic facies is composed of high-amplitude continuous reflectors. Also, the channel complex is thinner and is stratigraphically divided with a clearly distinct channel and levees in the basal part. Between the channel and the rest of the channel complex body are locally intercalated deposits of even, low-amplitude seismic facies (dark grey on the interpretation).

Downstream of the western trough, where slope gradients increased again, the morphology of the channel complex gradually changes: the body of the channel complex immediately narrows down to a width of 750 m, coincident with decreased channel sinuousity. The levees are still present but they are thinner and less extensive. The deposits intercalated between the channels tend to disappear (section DD′) and finally, about 10 km downstream of point 2 (section EE′), the channel complex regains the aspect it had (width and thickness) upstream of the structure and is marked by the progressive disappearance of the levees.

The western graben clearly affected the slope gradient of the seabed at the time of formation of this channel complex. These local slope value variations had a direct effect on the dynamics of the turbidity currents. This evolution resulted in a decrease in basal erosion of the complex and the local appearance of levees.

Distal section: salt intrusions

The channel complex position now described is located in the distal part of the turbidite system, more than 350 km from the present day coast and 20 km downstream of the western graben. At this location, the seafloor was locally affected by the presence of salt intrusions, which formed due to regional gravity tectonics. The longitudinal variations of the channel complex are associated with a slightly undulating substrate resulting from multiple local breaks in slope (Fig. 4, section AA′). In this distal area, the sedimentary history of the system includes an early depositional stage with frontal splay development, a prograding stage associated with channel erosion and sediment bypass, a depositional stage with vertical aggradation of the channel complex and an abandonment phase with channel avulsion (Ferry *et al.* 2005). On a seismic amplitude map (Fig. 4), the edges of the basal erosion surface are marked by a dotted black line. A hatched area marks the parts of this erosional surface composed of erosional channels with high or low sinuosity (green and blue, respectively), which can be quantified visually. The sinuosity of the constructive channel forming the fill of the complex is mapped, for each delimited part, by an increase or decrease in slope values (Ferry *et al.* 2005).

In this area, the entire course of the complex is subjected to five increases (red points) and decreases (blue points) in slope gradient (Fig. 4, section A-A′). These variations have short wavelengths as they alternate very rapidly, every two or three kilometres. On the seismic amplitude map, increasing slope values can be observed preceding areas where the channel sinuosity is high, regardless of whether they are basal erosional channels of the complex or constructive channels composing the fill. The sinuosity of the latter varies between 1.4 when entering the zone, and 3.3 when leaving the zone. Conversely, channel segments following points of decreasing slope value are characterized by low sinuosity of both the erosional and constructive channels (sinuosity varies between 1.5 and 1.9). The recurrent evolution of channel sinuosity values as a function of the slope values reveals a direct relationship between these two parameters.

In cross section, the channel complex exhibits very important morphological modifications partly related to variations in channel sinuosity. Seismic sections BB′, CC′ and DD′ (Fig. 4) illustrate examples of these modifications: between points 3 and 4, where the slope decreases, section BB′ shows a large basal incision (almost 3 km wide) attributed to the high degree of sinuosity of the channels, but only 40 ms TWT deep. Conversely between points 4 and 5, where the slope increases, section CC′ exhibits a narrow erosional base for the complex (as narrow as 1 km) but more than 100 ms TWT deep. In section DD', downstream of point 5, the complex returns to the same morphology it had in section BB′, i.e. a large erosional base (almost 5 km wide) and a shallow depth of incision, less than 25 ms TWT. The width of the complex varies as a function of the sinuosity of the erosional channel that formed at its base. Depth variations in the base are directly related to variations in the slope. Thus, the parts of the complex that are wide and shallow are located on parts of the seafloor where the slope values decrease and, conversely, the parts of the complex with a narrow and deep base coincide with parts where slope values increase.

Equilibrium profile and sedimentary processes

Compilation of observations

Regardless of whether it is a result of collapse or uplift, the local sigmoidal curvature of the slope profile directly and locally affects the morphology and nature of the deposits of the turbidite system. Observations made on the channel complex, for each of the cases detailed above, are plotted and correlated to slope value modifications (Fig. 5). The relative slope value variations are added to the slope profiles in Figures 2, 3 and 4, with the maxima and minima indicated on the slope profile by red and blue points. The curve representing the derivative of the slope values (denoted $d\alpha/dx$) has also been added to the slope profiles above. This curve highlights the maxima of slope increase and decrease, i.e. those places where the slope gradient increases and decreases over the shortest distance, and where gravity currents may become unstable. For each case they are used to build the ideal slope profile (Fig. 5). The morphological modifications to the channel complexes are plotted on this profile. Finally, the hatched areas show relative values of channel sinuosity, of maximum basal incision and the width: depth ratio (w/d) of the channel complexes. In the proximal part, this ratio is considered as the consequence of the passage of mostly unconfined gravity currents that had low transport volume. For the medial and distal parts, there appears to be an equivalence in the ratio of channel sinuosity to incision depth.

At abrupt increases in slope gradient, caused by the presence of a shelf edge in the proximal part and the exit points of the eastern and central graben, there is strong basal erosion of the complexes (e.g. at the shelf edge and on the horst separating the two grabens). The eroded areas are localized where slope increase was the most abrupt. Downstream of the steeper slope segments, erosional surfaces are less well pronounced and channel complexes and channels aggrade vertically. In the central graben, the energy of the turbidity currents appears to have been lower than in the more proximal eastern graben. This favoured the development of levees and frontal lobe deposits in the central graben.

In the medial profile position and through the western graben, channel complex morphology also evolved in response to modifications in slope values. At first, decrease in slope is expressed as a decrease in erosional intensity immediately beyond the reduced slope gradient ((dα/dx) max.) and by the appearance of levee deposits. Intensity of basal erosion dropped to very low levels as the complex formed leveed channels with little amalgamation. The decrease in slope gradient at point 1 (Fig. 3) coincides with the appearance of levees associated with the channels. The increase in slope values also leads to the gradual disappearance of levees over tens of kilometres, with a return to significant basal erosion.

In the distal part of the studied succession, changes in sinuosity, depth of basal erosion and the appearance of splays are observed. In areas where slope gradient increased, the sinuosity value of the channels is low, basal incision is deep and the width: depth ratio of the channel complex is low. In areas where the slope gradient decreased, sinuosity values are high, levees associated with channels are well developed, incision is shallow and the width:depth ratio of the channel complex is high.

The final avulsion of the channel complex occurred at point 5 (Fig. 4). Deposition of the frontal splays appears to have been initiated in areas of decreasing slope gradient (Fig. 4).

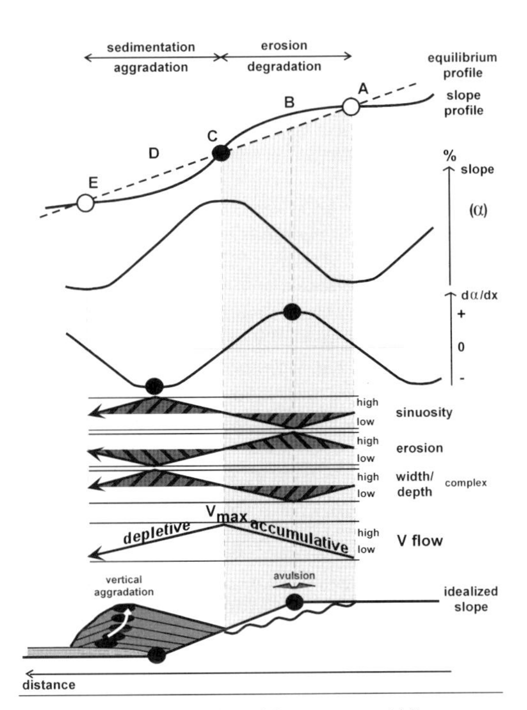

Fig. 6. Equilibrium profile of deep-water turbidite systems: evolution of morphological parameters of the system as a function of slope profile variations. Sedimentary degradation dominant on convex parts of the profile and sedimentary aggravation dominant on concave parts of the profile.

Interpretations

A Gaussian distribution representative of the slope curvatures encountered is presented in support of the interpretation of the observations (Fig. 6). Important points lying along the gradient profile are labelled A to E. These are the increasing, B ((dα/dx) max.) and decreasing D ((dα/dx) min.) slope gradients, the minima A and E and the maxima C of the slope values (dα/dx = 0). Spatial changes in system architecture relative to these points — sinuosity, erosional intensity and width:depth ratio — are indicated by arrows. Variations in gravity flow velocity as a function of slope values are based on the work of Kneller & Branney (1995).

The spatial evolution of sinuosity is interpreted as increasing between the increased slope gradient (B) and the decreased slope gradient (D), and reducing between decreased slope gradient and increased slope gradient. In other words, sinuosity decreases in response to a sharp increase in slope gradient and increases in response to a sharp decrease of slope gradient. The local adjustment of the slope gradient by evolution of channel sinuosity corroborates observations made on the channels of the deep-water Quaternary fans of the Amazon (Flood & Damuth 1987; Damuth *et al.* 1988) and the Congo rivers (Rigaut 1997). This interpretation of the relationship between the sinuosity of the thalweg of the turbidite channels and the regional break in slope in a deep-water environment is similar to that observed in fluvial environments (Schumm 1986, 1992): the local adjustment of the slope gradient (Sc) by evolution of channel sinuosity (s) constitutes one of the main responses of gravity flows to sharp variations in regional slope (Sv): $s = Sv/Sc$.

However, as it is reactional, the morphological adjustment develops downstream of the slope stress (Leopold & Wolman 1957; Ouchi 1985; Schumm 1986, 1992; Wescott 1993). The morphological adaptation of the channel course to stresses on the slope leads to the presence of high sinuosity values in areas where the slope decreases (C to E) and conversely, low sinuosity values in sections where the slope increases (A to C) (Clark *et al.* 1992; Pirmez & Flood 1995).

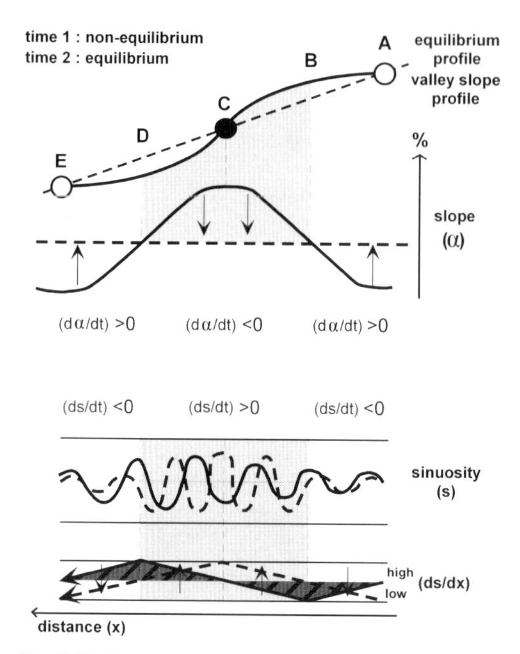

Fig. 7. Evolution, with time, of the channel slope profile to an equilibrium profile, only by the adjustment of sinuosity (t1, unstable initial situation; t2 final equilibrium situation).

If the stress exerted on the slope attenuates or disappears, the natural tendency of the channel is to flatten its slope profile until it reaches its equilibrium profile (Gardner 1983; Pirmez *et al.* 2000). In that case, the slope of segments (AB) and (DE) will increase whereas the slope of segments (BC) and (CD) will decrease over time (Fig. 7). To achieve this, with all other parameters remaining constant (Sv = constant), the sinuosity of the channel must increase (Eqn 1) over time to decrease the slope of the channel (Sc) and conversely, to increase the slope of the channel the sinuosity must decrease (Eqn 2) (Wescott 1993).

$$s+ = \frac{Sv}{Sc-}; \quad \left(\frac{\partial s}{\partial t}\right) > 0 \qquad (1)$$

$$s- = \frac{Sv}{Sc+}; \quad \left(\frac{\partial s}{\partial t}\right) < 0 \qquad (2)$$

The final equilibrium configuration ideally leads to high sinuosity for high regional slope values and low sinuosity values for low regional slope values. The evolution of sinuosity along the slope profile ($d\alpha/dx$) is consistent with this (Fig. 7).

Thus, it is not possible to establish a clear-cut general relationship between the sinuosity measured in the turbidite channels and the slope (Clark *et al.* 1992; Rigaut 1997). This may be because the studied channels have not yet reached their local equilibrium profile. The discrepancy between the sinuosity values and the slope values therefore reflects the equilibrium state of the channel.

Hence, although the evolution of sinuosity as a function of slope variations is similar between marine and continental domains, the relationship is inverted. (Ouchi 1985; Clark *et al.* 1992; Schumm 1992). In the study of turbidite systems, it is essential to make a distinction between the evolution of relative sinuosity in response to slope gradient and sinuosity values. Schumm's diagram (Schumm & Khan 1972), which was only developed for fluvial systems, should not be used without taking into account the notion of equilibrium profile and, of course, it does not provide a tool that allows prediction of the internal pattern of the channels.

Similarly, the appearance of erosional surfaces is independent of slope values but closely related to changes in slope gradient: of the two portions of profile BC and CD (Fig. 6) presenting high slope values, only part of BC was subjected to erosion. Similarly, the flat part, AB is eroded, unlike DE. The eroded profile regions correspond to those with increasing slope gradients (AB and BC) and the greatest erosion occurs at the maximum increase in slope in B (($d\alpha/dx$) max.). Figure 6 shows that the internal energy variations of the currents available for erosion of the substratum (Yoxall 1969), are indicated by a red arrow of the 'erosion' line. It can be seen that this available energy decreases by dissipation of friction at the area where the erosion is the most marked and it accumulates where the erosional intensity is at its lowest.

The width:depth ratio of the channel complex corresponds, in this case, to the sinuosity:erosional intensity ratio. It therefore presents variations that are identical to those of sinuosity but inverted with respect to the erosional tendency. This ratio decreases when the slope gradient increases (AC) and increases when the slope gradient decreases (CE).

In the three cases studied, the frontal or lateral splay deposits start forming where the slope gradient is the lowest (($d\alpha/dx$) min.), defining a decreasing slope at D. The presence of such deposits suggests that the slope break in D creates a hydraulic 'jump' within the turbidity currents, which emphasizes their deceleration (Komar 1971) and enhances deposition (Garcia & Parker 1989; Alexander & Morris 1994). These observations in ancient turbidite deposits corroborate experimental results on the behaviour of turbidity currents subjected to hydraulic jumps. They show that when there is a break in slope, a hydraulic jump within the turbidity current leads to changes in the internal parameters of the current, from supercritical conditions (Froude number, $Fr > 1$) to subcritical conditions (Fr < 1) (Komar 1971). At this time, the velocity of the current drops sharply and its thickness increases, resulting in the surrounding water being incorporated by turbulence into the current, which has the effect of decreasing its density (Komar 1971). Deposition of the coarsest particles transported by the turbidity current, downstream of the hydraulic jump (Carling 1995), is the immediate consequence of the reduction in the internal shear stress of the current (Komar 1971; Garcia 1993). The resulting deposits are called 'slope break deposits' (Mulder & Alexander 2001). Their thickness and extent are relative to the initial velocity of the current and the angle of the slope break (Komar 1971; Mulder & Alexander 2001). Conversely, the turbulence that follows the hydraulic jump contributes to maintaining the sedimentary load in suspension in the current (Komar 1971; Garcia & Parker 1989). In natural environments, this sedimentary mechanism was proposed for debris flow deposits located downstream of an increasing slope, in the San Dimas water reservoir in the United States (Weirich 1988) and for turbidite deposits in the Strava graben of the Corinthian Gulf in Greece (Papatheodorou & Ferentinos 1993).

Levees occur at the highest slope values (in C, V_{max}; Fig. 6); they develop on the part of the profile corresponding to the decreasing slope gradient (CE) and accompany the vertical aggradation of channel fills. Their disappearance, in proximal and medial positions, occurs gradually after the increase in slope values, after point E. The formation of the levees is related to the decreasing erosional confinement, which allows more sediment to spill out of the channel.

Channel avulsion takes place at point C of the profile, where the current velocity is at its maximum (Kneller & Branney 1995). In this particular case, the avulsion of the channel is provoked by the presence of a minor normal fault oriented perpendicularly to the channel axis. It is located exactly 50 m upstream of the bifurcation with the downthrown fault compartment located in the down current direction. This locally generated increasing slope profile was sufficient to induce abandonment by avulsion. At a smaller scale, structural control on the channel very locally disrupts the slope profile induced by the salt intrusions. In the Amazon system, the study of a large number of channel bifurcation points as a function of slope values also appears to show that these occur at the points of maximum slope gradient (Pirmez & Flood 1995; Pirmez *et al.* 2000).

The observation of decreasing width with increasing depth (i.e. decrease in *w*:*d* ratio) of the basal erosion surface confirms the observations conducted under experimental conditions on fluvial currents (Gardner 1983). The increasing slope (nickpoint lip) generates the maximum erosional power of the currents due to the sharp increase at that point of the shear stress between the base of the current and the substratum (Gardner 1983). Observations conducted on the type and morphology of turbidite deposits are conditioned by the natural evolution of turbidity currents between the proximal part of the system and its distal part. Transformations that are generated by local slope variations are therefore expressed differently, depending on whether they occur in the proximal or distal part. The response of the Congo system to hydraulic jumps is more erosional in the eastern graben, whereas it induces deposition of splays in the central graben. Similarly, the forcing of the system by the slope can recreate in the proximal part, sedimentary conditions of the distal part: thus, the expression of the channel-fill in the central graben (slightly erosive into splay deposits and filled with strongly aggrading channel levees) is identical to that observed normally in the distal part of the system. In this case, the occurrence of a hydraulic jump can obviously not be expressed in the same way as in the proximal area.

Conclusions

The depositional behaviour of the late Miocene turbidite system of the Congo Basin exhibits clear responses to local variations in syn-depositional slope gradients. All of these responses show that local slope profile, represented as a sigmoid shape, will generate erosional processes along the convex (increasing slope gradient) segment or depositional processes along the concave (decreasing slope gradient) segment. The line separating these two regions of aggradational versus degradational processes can be defined as the equilibrium profile of the turbiditic system. This virtual limit of the division of sedimentary processes appears nearly identical to that defined by flow in the continental fluvial domain (Wheeler 1964; Schumm 1992). The equilibrium profile is determined locally by the sedimentary response of the currents — erosion or deposition — to irregularities in the slope over which the flow passes. This adjustment correlates perfectly with velocity variations in the flow since the preferential surface area of sedimentation and erosion correspond to the surface area of turbidity current deceleration and acceleration, respectively (Gardner 1983; Kneller & Branney 1995).

Laboratory experiments on fluvial currents show that, regardless of the type of system, they adapt their morphology and erosional tendency in response to local slope stresses generated by uplift or subsidence (Ouchi 1985; Schumm 1986). These morphological changes perpetuate as long as the stress on the slope persists. This observation is particularly well expressed in the area of the salt intrusions in the distal part of the Congo deep-water system (Fig. 4). In the terminal turbidite system, channels were not able to widen at the apex of intrusions, whether due to sinuosity or to erosion, as they were able to do between salt intrusions. The fact that these channels persistently maintain high erosional and low sinuosity values demonstrates that the equilibrium profile was constantly maintained in a state of non-equilibrium by structural growth throughout their depositional history (Yoxall 1969; Schumm 1986; Peakall *et al.* 2000). This demonstrates the persistent tendency for current flow parameters to attempt to reach equilibrium conditions through slope adjustment. In the final stage, this adjustment leads to a regular slope profile, the gradient of which is a function of the cohesion and grain size of the sediments (Wheeler 1964; Schumm & Khan 1972; Gardner 1983; Adams & Schlager 2000). In the observations presented here, the fact that equilibrium is never reached shows that the local stresses on the slope, by uplift or subsidence, dominated over the capacity of the density flows to establish a slope profile close to that of the equilibrium profile.

The authors thank Nicola Mavilla for her critical and constructive proof-reading of this article. We also wish to thank R. Beaubouef, T. Garfield and C. Pirmez for constructive and careful comments that improved the manuscript. This paper is published with the permission of petroleum companies Total, SNPC and Sonangol.

References

ADAMS, E.W. & SCHLAGER, W. 2000. Basic types of submarine slope curvature. *Journal of Sedimentary Research*, **70**, 814–828.

ALEXANDER, J. & MORRIS, S. 1994. Observations on experimental non-channelized turbidites: thickness variations around obstacles. *Journal of Sedimentary Research*, **64**, 899–909.

BEAUBOUEF, R.T. & FRIEDMANN, S.J. 2000. High resolution seismic/sequence stratigraphic framework for the evolution of Pleistocene intra slope basins, western Gulf of Mexico: depositional models and reservoir analogs. *In*: WEIMAR, P., SLATT, R.M., COLEMAN, J., ET AL. (eds) *Deep-water Reservoirs of the World.* Gulf Coast Section SEPM, 40–60.

BERGER, W.H., LANCE, C.B. & WEFER, G. 2002. Upwelling history of the Benguela-Namibia system: a synthesis of Leg 175 results. *Proceedings of the Ocean Drilling Program, Scientific Results*, **175**, 1–103.

CAHEN, L. 1954. *Géologie du Congo Belge.* Masson, Paris. (577).

CARLING, P.A. 1995. Flow-separation berms downstream of a hydraulic jump in a bedrock channel. *Geomorphology*, **11**, 245–253.

CLARK, J.D., KENYON, N.H. & PICKERING, K.T. 1992. Quantitative analysis of the geometry of submarine channels: Implications for the classification of the submarine fans. *Geology*, **20**, 633–636.

CRAMEZ, C. & JACKSON, M.P.A. 2000. Superposed deformation straddling the continental–oceanic transition in deep-water Angola. *Marine and Petroleum Geology*, **17**, 1095–1109.

DAMUTH, J.E. 1994. Neogene gravity tectonics and depositional processes on the deep Niger Delta continental margin. *Marine and Petroleum Geology*, **11**, 320–346.

DAMUTH, J.E. & KUMAR, N. 1975. Amazon Cone: morphology, sediments, age and growth pattern. *Geological Society of America Bulletin*, **87**, 340–346.

DAMUTH, J.E., FLOOD, R.D., KOWSMANN, R.O., BELDERSON, R.H. & GORINI, M.A. 1988. Anatomy and growth pattern of Amazon deep-sea fan as revealed by long-range side-scan sonar (GLORIA) and high-resolution seismic studies. *American Association Petroleum Geologists Bulletin*, **72**, 885–911.

DROZ, L. & BELLAICHE, G. 1985. Rhone deep-sea fan: morphostructure and growth pattern. *American Association of Petroleum Geologists Bulletin*, **69**, 460–479.

FERRY, J.-N., BABONNEAU, N., MULDER, T., PARIZE, O. & RAILLARD, S. 2004. Morphogenesis of Congo Submarine Canyon and Valley; implications about the theories of the canyons formation. *Geodinamica Acta*, **17**, 241–251.

FERRY, J.-N., PARIZE, O., MULDER, T. & RAILLARD, S. 2005. Sedimentary architecture and growth pattern of turbidite systems in distal part, example of the Upper Miocene sedimentary sequence of the Lower Congo basin. *Geodinamica Acta.* (in press).

FLOOD, R.D. & DAMUTH, J.E. 1987. Quantitative characteristics of sinuous distributary channels on the Amazon deep-sea fan. *Geological Society of American Bulletin*, **98**, 728–738.

GARCIA, M.H. 1993. Hydraulic jumps in sediment-driven bottom currents. *Journal of Hydraulic Engineering*, **119**, 1094–1117.

GARCIA, M.H. & PARKER, G. 1989. Experiments on hydraulic jumps in turbidity currents near a canyon-fan transition. *Science*, **245**, 393–396.

GARDNER, T.W. 1983. Experimental study of knickpoint and longitudinal profile evolution in cohesive, homogeneous material. *Geology Society of America Bulletin*, **94**, 664–672.

KNELLER, B.C. & BRANNEY, M. 1995. Sustained high-density turbidity currents and the deposition of thick massive sands. *Sedimentology*, **42**, 1–10.

KNELLER, B.C. & MCCAFFREY, W. 1999. Depositional effects of flow nonunformity and stratification within turbidity currents approaching a bounding slope: deflection, reflection, and facies variation. *Journal of Sedimentary Research*, **69**, 980–991.

KOLLA, V. & COUMES, F. 1987. Morphology, internal structure, seismic stratigraphy, and sedimentation of Indus fan. *American Association of Petroleum Geologists Bulletin*, **71**, 650–677.

KOLLA, V., BOURGES, P., URRUTY, J.-M. & SAFA, P. 2001. Evolution of deep-water Tertiary sinuous channels offshore Angola (west Africa) and implications for reservoir architecture. *American Association of Petroleum Geologists Bulletin*, **85**, 1373–1405.

KOMAR, P.D. 1971. Hydraulic jumps in turbidity currents. *Geology Society of American Bulletin*, **82**, 1477–1488.

LEOPOLD, L.B. & WOLMAN, M.G. 1957. River channel pattern: Braided, meander, and straight. *US Geological Survey Profesional Paper*, **282-B**, 39–84.

LUTHI, S. 1981. Experiments on non-channelized turbidity currents and their deposits. *Marine Geology*, **40**, M59–M68.

MENARD, H.W. 1955. Deep-sea channels, topography and sedimentation. *American Association of Petroleum Geologists Bulletin*, **39**, 236–255.

MULDER, T. & ALEXANDER, J. 2001. Abrupt change in slope causes variation in the deposit thickness of concentrated particle-driven density currents. *Marine Geology*, **17**, 221–235.

MUTTI, E. & NORMARK, W.N. 1987. Comparing examples of modern and ancient turbidite systems: problems and concepts, *In*: LEGGETT, J.K. & ZUFFA, G.G. (eds) *Marine Clastic Sedimentology: Concepts and Case Studies*. Graham & Trotman, London, 1–38.

MUTTI, E. & NORMARK, W.N. 1991. An integrated approach to the study of turbidite systems. *In*: WEIMER, P. & LINK, M.H. (eds) *Seismic Facies and Turbidite Systems*. Springer, New York, 75–106.

NORMARK, W.R. 1985. Local morphologic controls and effects of basin geometry on flow processes in deep marine basins. *In*: ZUFFA, G.G. (ed.) *Provenance of Arenites*, Reidel, Dordrecht, 47–63.

NZE ABEIGNE, C.R. 1992. *Evolution post-rift de la marge continentale Sud Gabon: contrôles tectonique et climatique sur la sédimentation*. Unpublished PhD thesis, University of Montpellier.

OUCHI, S. 1985. Reponse of alluvial rivers to slow active tectonic movement. *American Association of Petroleum Geologists Bulletin*, **96**, 504–515.

PAPATHEODOROU, G. & FERENTINOS, G. 1993. Sedimentation processes and basin-filling depositional architecture in an active asymmetric graben: Strava graben: Gulf of Corinth, Greece. *Basin Research*, **5**, 235–253.

PEAKALL, J., MCCAFFREY, B. & KNELLER, B. 2000. A process model for the evolution, morphology, and architecture of sinuous submarine channels. *Journal of Sedimentary Research*, **70**, 434–448.

PIRMEZ, C. & FLOOD, R.D. 1995. Morphology and structure of Amazon Channel. *Proceedings of the Ocean Drilling Program, Initial Reports*, **155**, 23–45.

PIRMEZ, C., BEAUBOUEF, R.T., FRIEDMANN, S.J. & MOHRIG, D.C. 2000. Equilibrium profile and baselevel in submarine channels: examples from Late Pleistocene systems and implications for the architecture of deepwater reservoir. *In*: WEIMAR, P., SLATT, R.M., COLEMAN, J. ET AL. (eds) *Deep-water reservoirs of the world*. Gulf Coast Section SEPM, 782–805.

RIGAUT, F. 1997. *Analyse et évolution récente d'un système turbiditique méandriforme: l'Eventail profond du Zaïre*. Unpublished PhD Thesis, Université de Bretagne occidentale.

SCHUMM, S.A. 1986. Alluvial river response to active tectonics. *In*: WALLACE, R.E. (ed.) *Studies in Geophysics — Active tectonics*. Washington, D.C., National Academy Press, 80–94.

SCHUMM, S.A. 1992. River response to baselevel change: implication for sequence stratigraphy. *Journal of Geology*, **101**, 279–294.

SCHUMM, S.A. & KHAN, H.R. 1972. Experimental study of channel patterns. *Geological Society of America Bulletin*, **83**, 1755–1770.

SHEPARD, F.P. & EMERY, K.O. 1973. Congo submarine cayon and fan valley. *American Association Petroleum Geologists Bulletin*, **57**, 1679–1691.

VALLE, P.J., GJELBERG, J.G. & HELLAND-HANSEN, W. 2001. Tectonostratigraphic development in the eastern Lower Congo Basin, offshore Angola, West Africa. *Marine and Petroleum Geology*, **18**, 909–927.

WALKER, R.G. 1967. Turbidite sedimentary structures and their relationship to proximal and distal depositional environments. *Journal of Sedimentary Petrology*, **37**, 25–43.

WEFER, G., BERGER, W.H. & RICHTER, C. 1998. Introduction: background, scientific objectives, and principal results for Leg 175 (Benguela current and Angola-Benguela upweilling systems). *Proceedings of the Ocean Drilling Program, Initial Reports*, **175**, 7–25.

WEIMER, P. 1990. Sequence stratigraphy, facies geometries, and depositional history of the Mississippi Fan, Gulf of Mexico. *American Association of Petroleum Geologists Bulletin*, **74**, 425–453.

WEIRICH, F.H. 1988. Field evidence for hydraulic jumps in subaqueous sediment gravity flows. *Nature*, **332**, 626–629.

WESCOTT, W.A. 1993. Geomorphic thresholds and complex response of fluvial systems — some implications for sequence stratigraphy. *American Association of Petroleum Geologists Bulletin*, **77**, 1208–1218.

WHEELER, H.E. 1964. Baselevel, lithosphere surface, and time-stratigraphy. *Geological Society of American Bulletin*, **75**, 599–610.

YOXALL, W.H. 1969. The relationship between falling baselevel and lateral erosion in experimental streams. *Geology Society American Bulletin*, **80**, 1379–1384.

Deformation and submarine landsliding caused by seamount subduction beneath the Costa Rica continental margin — new insights from high-resolution sidescan sonar data

V. HÜHNERBACH[1], D.G. MASSON[1], G. BOHRMANN[2,3], J.M. BULL[1] & W. WEINREBE[2]

[1] *Southampton Oceanography Centre, Waterfront Campus, European Way, Southampton SO14 3ZH, UK (e-mail: vhh@soc.soton.ac.uk)*

[2] *GEOMAR, Wischhofstrasse 1–3, 24148 Kiel, Germany*

[3] *Present address: DFG Forschungszentrum Ozeanränder, Universität Bremen, Postfach 33 04 40, 28334 Bremen, Germany*

Abstract: Subduction of seamounts at destructive sedimented plate margins results in spectacular deformation of the overriding plate. High-resolution sidescan sonar imagery from the Costa Rica margin show the tracks of five individual seamounts, of which four are described in this paper. These were subducted at various times during the last 690 ka and each represents a different stage in the subduction process. Each subducted seamount leaves a parallel-sided depression in its wake, that can be traced for up to 55 km landward of the deformation front. This wake is created by deformation and uplift of the continental slope as the seamount passes beneath it, followed by collapse due to landsliding as support for the uplifted area is withdrawn. Areas of uplift above seamounts are characterized by complex normal and strike–slip fault patterns. Collapse of the uplift along the trailing edge of the seamount creates a zone of slope failure (landsliding) that migrates upslope (or landward) with the seamount. Landslide processes are dominated by debris flow, but also include sliding of coherent blocks and debris avalanche. Erosion occurs by repeated landslides, which produce a series of overlapping debris flows. Downslope sediment transport typically extends over limited distances, resulting in partial 'backfilling' of the scar as its headwall moves up slope. The amount of margin material disrupted by seamount subduction is four to five times the volume of the subducting seamount, of which about three quarters seems to be recycled downslope, backfilling the scar, and nearly one quarter is subducted with the seamount.

Subduction of seamounts and aseismic ridges at destructive plate margins and the resulting deformation of the overriding plate have been described from several places around the Pacific Ocean (Lallemand & Le Pichon 1987; von Huene *et al.* 1989; Masson *et al.* 1990; Collot & Fisher 1991; Kolarsky *et al.* 1995; Kodaira *et al.* 2000; Laursen *et al.* 2002). In many cases gravitational mass wasting is associated with these collision processes (Cadet *et al.* 1987; Fisher *et al.* 1998; von Huene *et al.* 2004). At the convergent continental margin of Costa Rica, the Cocos plate carries a number of seamounts beneath the Central American Plate (Barckhausen *et al.* 1998; von Huene *et al.* 2000). Several deformation traces relating to the subduction of seamounts can be identified on the Costa Rican continental slope (Fig. 1). During RV SONNE cruise 144-2 (Bialas *et al.* 1999) a sidescan sonar survey of nearly 5000 km^2 of the Costa Rica margin was carried out using the 30 kHz TOBI sidescan sonar (Murton *et al.* 1992; Flewellen *et al.* 1993) covering this particular part of ocean floor. This paper presents and describes many of the tectonic and sedimentological processes involved during subduction by using the detailed high-resolution sidescan sonar imagery. Finally, we attempt to estimate the volume of material involved in backfilling the seamount scar and lost in subduction.

Regional setting

On the Pacific margin of Costa Rica, the Cocos Plate subducts beneath the Central American Plate with a relative convergence rate of about 8 cm a^{-1} (DeMets *et al.* 1990, 1994). Subduction is close to orthogonal to the margin, at an azimuth of 27°. Volcanic seamounts on the Cocos Plate, which typically rise 1.5–2.5 km above the adjacent seafloor, are subducted with the oceanic plate along the Middle America Trench. Underthrusting of seamounts has left distinct morphological traces in the slope of the overriding Central American Plate. These traces can be followed up to 55 km landward of the trench, where the over-riding plate is up to 10 km thick (von Huene *et al.* 2000). Swath bathymetry maps of the Costa Rican slope show six major scars related to seamount subduction, each exhibiting different stages of the seamount subduction process (Fig. 1). The various scars extend to between 12 and 55 km landward of the trench, corresponding to seamounts

From: HODGSON, D.M. & FLINT, S.S. (eds) 2005. *Submarine Slope Systems: Processes and Products*. Geological Society, London, Special Publications, **244**, 195–205. 0305–8719/$15.00

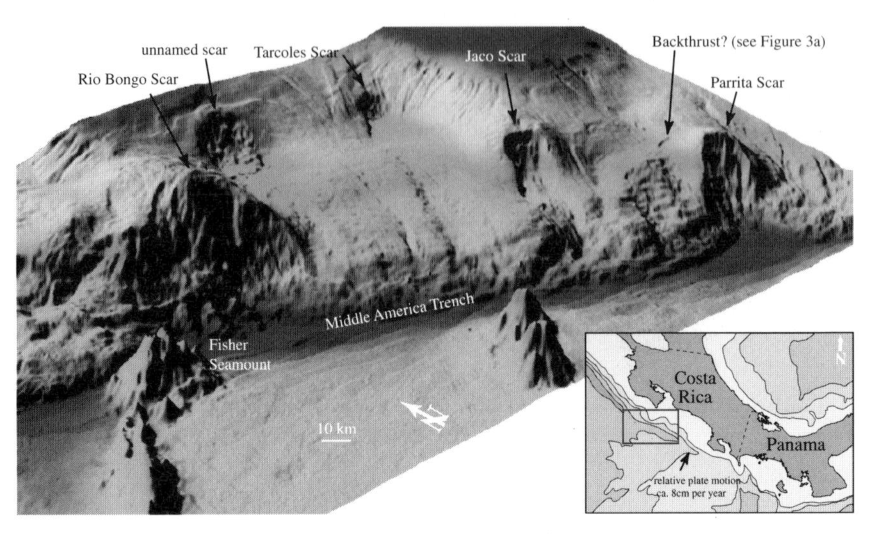

Fig. 1. Shaded relief map of the Pacific Costa Rica margin showing the main seamount subduction scars. Depths range from 250 m near the shelf edge to 3750 m in the deeper part of the trench. Inset shows location of the working area.

that entered the collision zone between 150 and 690 ka (calculated from the NUVEL-1 plate motion data; DeMets *et al.* 1990, 1994). Scars towards the south of the study area (e.g. Tarcoles, Jaco and Parrita scars, Fig. 1) appear to be related to the subduction of discrete seamounts. Further north, other scars (e.g. Rio Bongo, see Fig. 1) appear to be related to subduction of seamounts along a northeasterly extension of the Fisher Ridge, an aseismic volcanic ridge formed along a fracture in the ocean plate (Werner *et al.* 1999).

Datasets

The datasets presented were collected with TOBI (towed ocean bottom instrument), a deep-towed instrument platform with 30 kHz sidescan sonar and 7 kHz profiler (Flewellen *et al.* 1993; Murton *et al.* 1992). The sidescan imagery was processed with PRISM software (LeBas & Hühnerbach 1999) correcting the sidescan imagery radiometrically and geometrically (Blondel & Murton 1997). The multibeam data (Fig.1) was collected with the shipboard HYDROSWEEP system on RV SONNE during several cruises and processed by colleagues from GEOMAR (Bialas *et al.* 1999).

Morphology of scars related to subducting seamounts

The progressive development of scars in the overriding plate, as seamounts are subducted to greater depths, is analysed on the basis of three seamount re-entrants; the Parrita, Jaco and Tarcoles scars (Fig. 1). These scars were formed by seamounts, which now lie 12, 33, and 55 km landward of the Middle America Trench (Fig. 1).

Parrita Scar

The Parrita Scar extends for some 12–15 km landward of the trench axis (Figs 1 & 2). The scar is an elongate depression averaging 6 km in width and up to 500 m in depth. At its seaward end, a re-entrant in the deformation front marks the landward edge of the Middle America Trench. The re-entrant is about 8 km wide and partially filled with blocky debris derived from slope failures within the scar (Fig. 3a, b). There is no evidence that, subsequent to the subduction of the seamount, renewed deformation and accretion of trench sediments have begun to 'repair' the re-entrant in the deformation front. A pronounced area of uplift, up to 600–800 m above the level of the adjacent seafloor, occurs immediately landward of the scar headwall (Figs 1 & 2), immediately above the current position of the subducted seamount (von Huene *et al.* 1995). On its seaward (downslope) side, this uplifted area is characterized by a zone of extensive normal faults and fractures oriented parallel to the margin (Fig. 3a). This extensional fault zone extends alongslope about twice the width of the scar (10–12 km) and is 1–2 km across. Individual faults downthrow mainly in a downslope direction (westwards) and are interpreted to be a result of the collapse of slope sediments and rocks along the trailing edge of the subducting seamount. However, some faults also

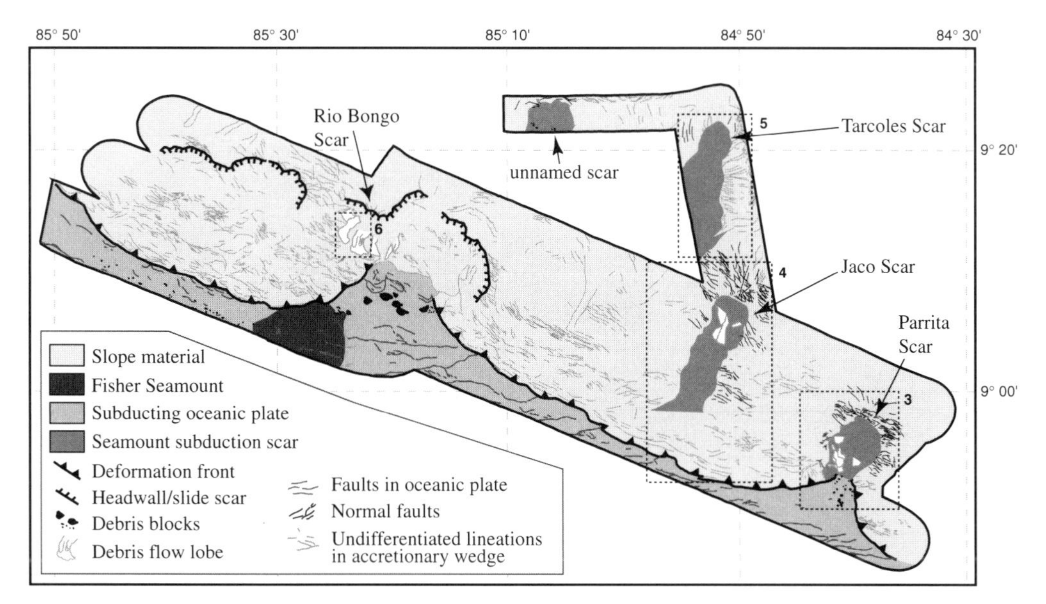

Fig. 2. Simplified interpretation of TOBI sidescan sonar. Numbered boxes show sidescan sonar figure locations.

downthrow in an upslope (or landward) direction; these occur mainly on the downslope edge of the fault zone and remnants of similar faults seem to be preserved along the flanks of the scar (Fig. 3a). Deep-tow video, also collected during SONNE cruise 144-2 (Bialas *et al.* 1999), and seismic profiles show that fault throws can be up to 80 m.

Upslope from the fault zone, the central part of the uplifted seafloor shows few surficial features, with only a few weak radial lineations visible on the sidescan images that are interpreted as a radial pattern of fractures above the crest of the uplift (Fig. 3a). Dominguez *et al.* (1998) reproduced this radial fracture pattern using sandbox models, showing that the fractures accommodate the deformation induced by the seamount by a combination of extensional and strike–slip motion. A bathymetric depression (see Fig. 1) along part of the leading (upslope) edge of the uplift may be evidence of thrust faulting ahead of the subducting seamount (Fig. 3a). However, this feature can be traced for less than 5 km and does not appear to be continuous around all of the leading edge.

Jaco Scar

The headwall of the Jaco Scar is 33 km from the present deformation front (Figs 1, 2 & 4a). The scar forms a parallel-sided depression about 8 km wide which can be traced downslope to the deformation front, although its topographic expression decreases downslope from over 600 m across the headwall to about 200 m mid-way between the headwall and the deformation front (Fig. 4b). Further downslope again, the original re-entrant in the deformation front has been completely infilled by subsequent accretion (Fig. 4a; von Huene *et al.* 2000). Upslope from the headwall, the area of pronounced uplift seen on bathymetric data (Fig. 1) appears as an intensely fractured area on the sidescan data (Fig. 4a). Fractures extend over an area more than twice the width of the scar. The fault pattern appears to be a combination of radial fractures and normal faults which downthrow towards the NE, parallel to the regional slope but oblique to the local slope (Fig. 4a). The normal faults are best developed on the NW side of the headwall scar adjacent to the relict flank of the Tarcoles Scar (Fig. 1) and it is possible that they represent re-activated faults originally associated with this scar. Relicts of similar normal faults are also preserved along the sides of the Jaco Scar downslope from the headwall. In contrast to the Parrita Scar, faults on the trailing edge of the uplift that throw downslope, indicating fracturing and collapse of the headwall, are absent, although a single large slide block fills the headwall area (Fig. 4a).

Tarcoles Scar

The headwall of the Tarcoles Scar is as far as 55 km landward of the deformation front, but a clear parallel-sided depression about 8 km wide can still be traced downslope from the headwall almost to the toe of the margin (Fig. 1). However, there is no evidence for either an uplifted area above the headwall or any

(a)

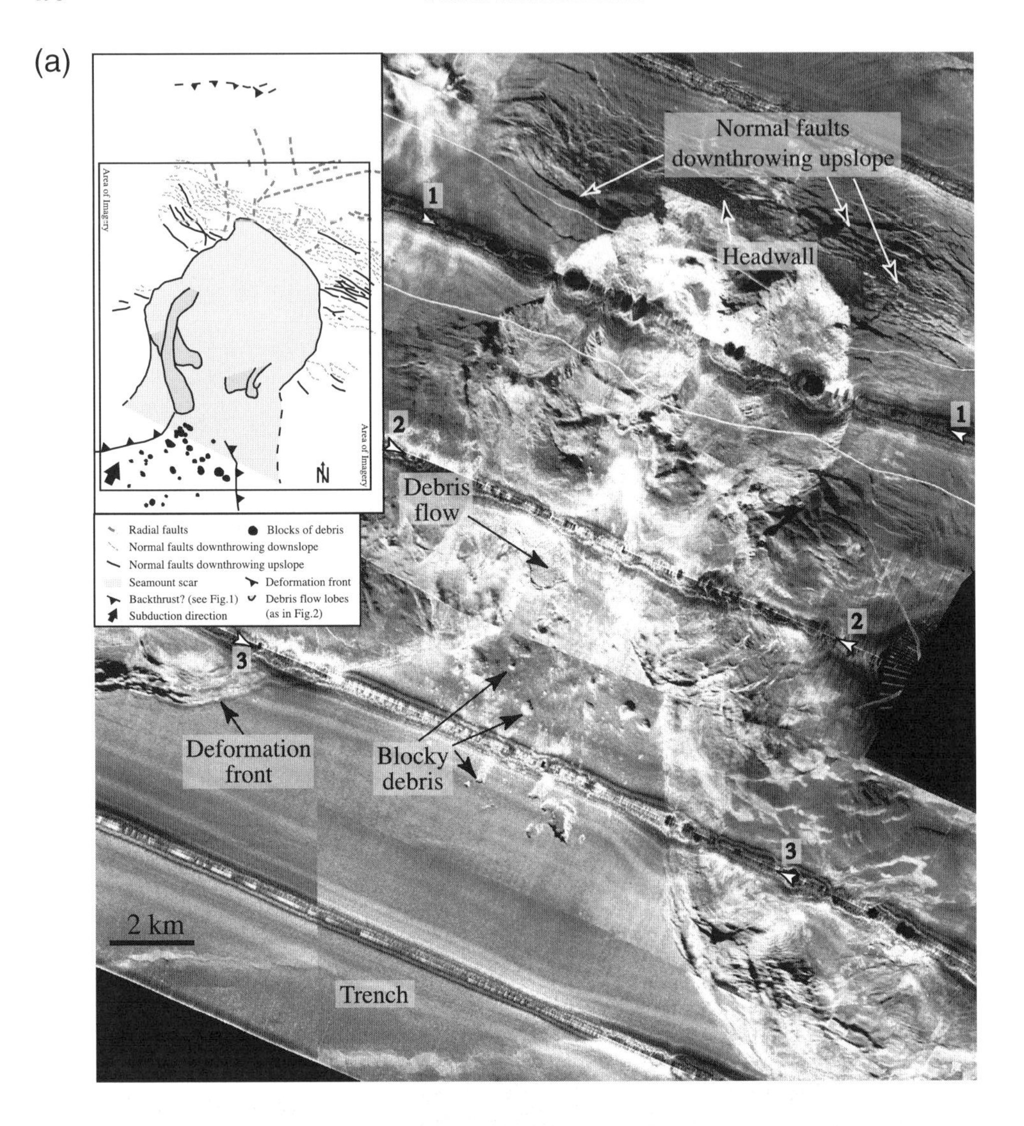

(b)

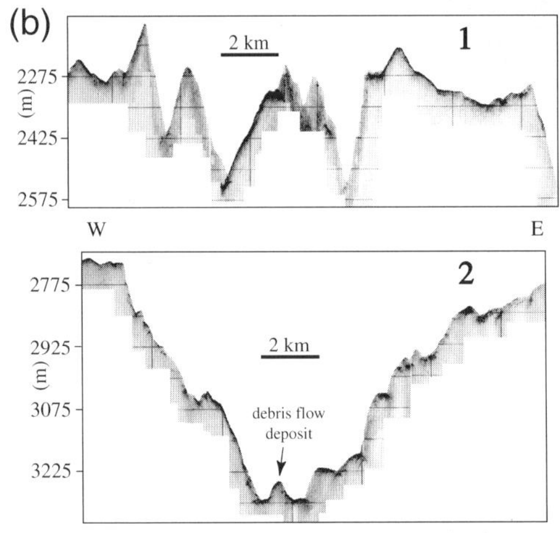

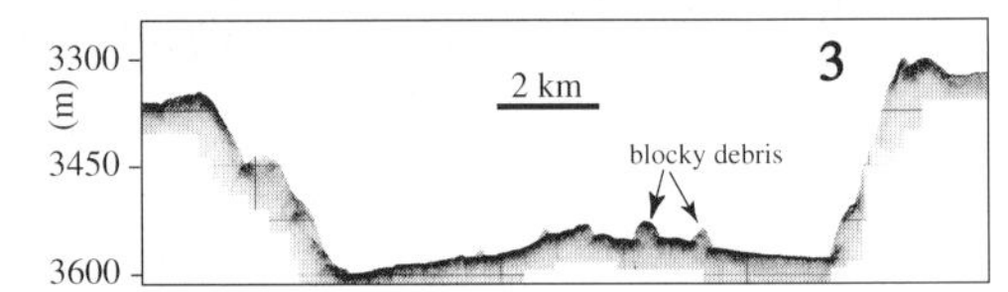

Fig. 3. (**a**) 30 kHz TOBI sidescan sonar image of Parrita Scar showing extensive faulting, debris flow lobes and blocky debris in the trench. High backscatter is bright, low backscatter is dark. Inset shows interpretation, covering a slightly larger area than the sonograph. Numbered arrows indicate 7 kHz profiler records shown in Figure 3b. PRISM software (LeBas & Hühnerbach 1999) was used to process the TOBI data; (**b**) 7 kHz TOBI profiler records across Parrita Scar showing the morphological expression of the seamount subduction scar. Scar is up to 500 m deep and up to 8 km wide. Depth is in metres below sea level.

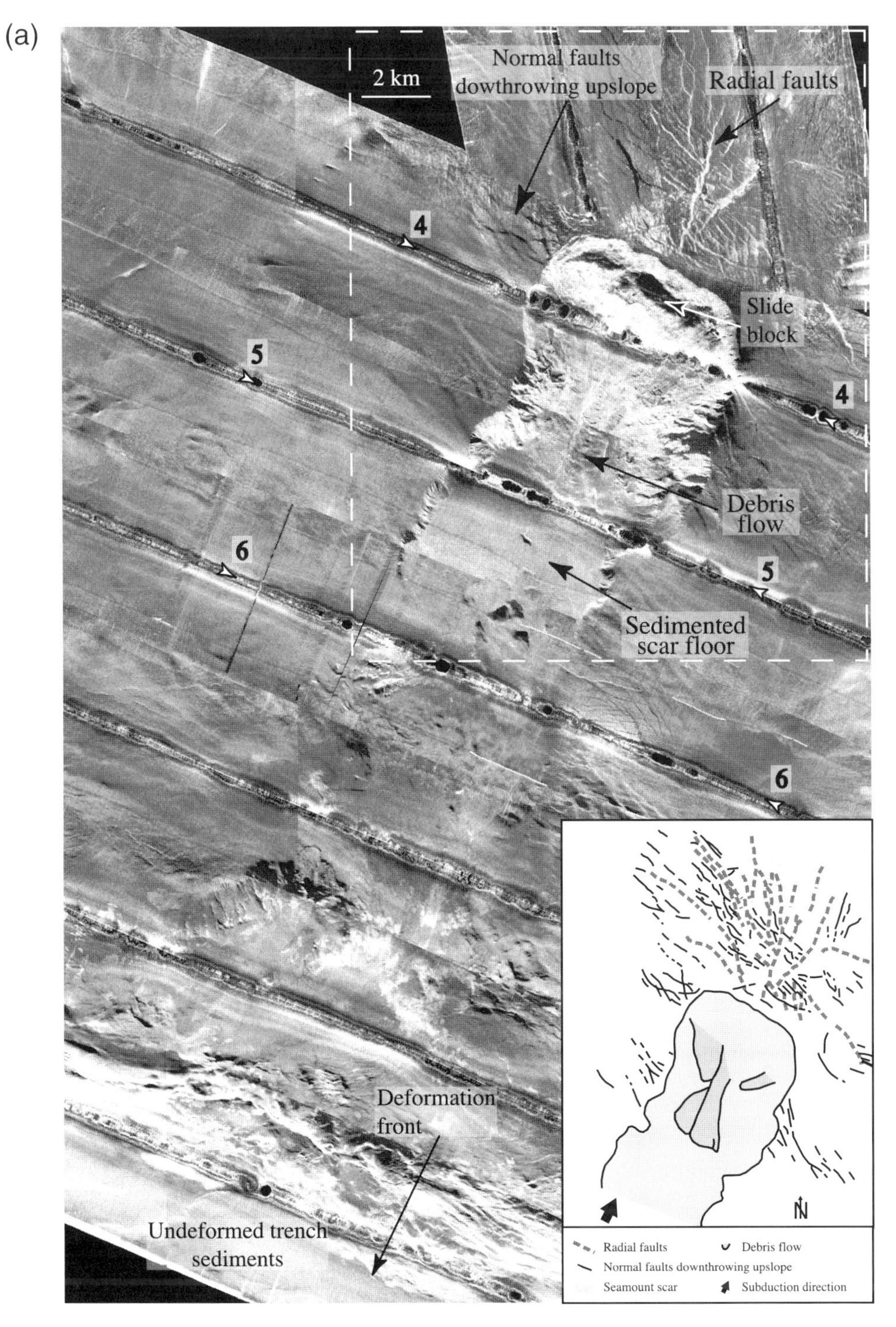

Fig. 4. (**a**) 30 kHz TOBI sidescan sonar image of Jaco Scar showing a seamount subduction scar extending more than 30 km landward of the trench, the fault pattern developed in the uplifted area above the seamount, and a debris flow pathway in the landward part of the scar. High backscatter is bright, low backscatter is dark. White box in sidescan sonar image indicates area of interpretation on inset figure. Numbered arrows indicate 7 kHz profiler records shown in Figure 4b. PRISM software (LeBas & Hühnerbach 1999) was used to process the TOBI data;

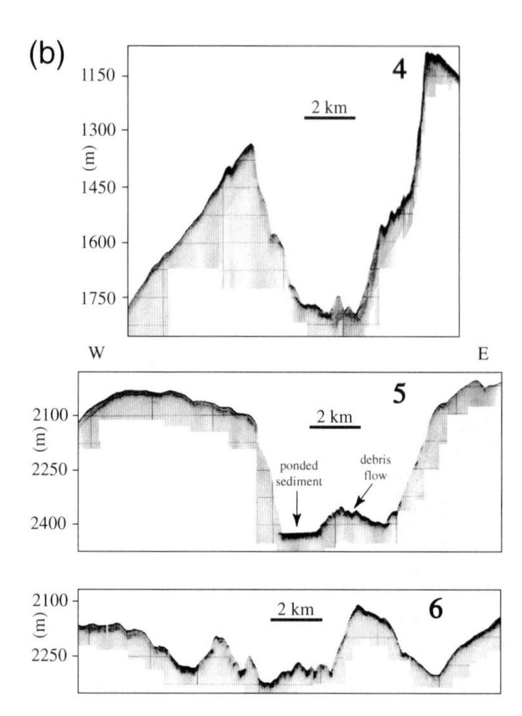

Fig. 4 *continued.* (**b**) 7 kHz TOBI profiler records across Jaco Scar. Note the downslope decrease in the depth of the scar. Depth is in metres below sea level.

significant active fault activity (Fig. 5a). Instead, a network of gullies, some up to 70 m deep and 160 m wide, incises the headwall and sidewalls of the depression (Fig. 5b). Some gullies originate upslope of the headwall and continue across it. The origin of these gullies is unknown but they may have been eroded as relatively unconsolidated sediment was transported downslope by turbulent currents. This type of gully was also observed on oversteepened slopes off Puerto Rico (Scanlon & Masson 1996) and off California (Lee *et al.* 2002). Downslope of the headwall, the floor of the depression is a flat sedimented basin. Overall, it is clear that the Tarcoles Scar is no longer an active tectonic feature, and is now being modified only by sedimentary processes.

Landsliding and seamount subduction scars

All of the active seamount subduction scars in the present study show widespread evidence of landsliding in the area of the headwall and landslide deposits within the scar. Mass wasting processes appear to include sliding of large coherent blocks, debris avalanches and debris flows.

Evidence for large coherent slide blocks is most clearly seen in the Jaco Scar, where a single block, 5 km long by 1.5 km wide, occurs parallel to and just downslope of the main headwall scarp (Fig. 4). This block was crossed by a seafloor video transect which shows the top of the block to be a talus covered bench downthrown about 500 m relative to the top of the headwall. Sediment blocks from previous slope failures within the Jaco Scar are visible protruding through the relatively smooth sedimented scar floor up to 10 km downslope from the headwall. The upper part of the Parrita Scar is also characterized by rough blocky terrain, but here the degree of fragmentation of the failed material appears to be greater, and it is difficult to recognize individual coherent downfaulted blocks (Fig. 3a). The greatest degree of block fragmentation is seen in the re-entrant at the mouth of the Parrita Scar, where the seafloor is covered by randomly scattered blocky debris, with individual blocks up to 1 km across (Fig. 3a, b). This debris field suggests a debris avalanche emplacement mechanism, presumably originating from a catastrophic headwall collapse.

Evidence of debris flow activity can be seen in the Parrita, Jaco and Rio Bongo scars (Figs 3a, 4a & 6). Individual debris flow lobes are typically 1–2 km wide and can be followed for up to 10 km downslope. Profiles crossing debris flow lobes suggest thicknesses of 20–60 m. Flows are parallel sided or broaden slightly downslope with typical blunt terminations (Iverson 1997; Major 1997). In the Rio Bongo scar, seaward of where a subducted seamount of similar dimensions to Fisher Seamount has been imaged using seismic profiles (Roump 1985; von Huene *et al.* 2000), the surface morphology of flows is characterized by longitudinal flow lineations in the upper part and well-pronounced pressure ridges in the distal part (Fig. 6). A series of overlapping debris flows clearly illustrates that failure in the headwall region is a continuous ongoing process characterized by many small events rather than occasional large failures. Debris flows originate mainly from the scars' headwalls but also from their sidewalls (e.g. Fig. 3a). Failure along the sidewalls gives the scars their characteristic scalloped appearance.

A model for seamount subduction stages and the processes described above is presented in Fig. 7 (after von Huene *et al.* 2004). The first stage shows the margin prior to the collision with a seamount. The next stage (similar to Parrita Scar, Fig. 3a) represents a seamount in the early phase of subduction, destroying the frontal prism, uplifting the slope sediments and creating an area of extensive faulting and fracturing ahead of it. Landsliding slowly begins to close the re-entrant and rebuild the frontal prism. As the seamount progresses (stage 3, similar to Jaco Scar, Fig. 4a) a seamount progresses further into the margin. Uplifting continues with the creation of a dense radial fault and fracture network and landsliding backfills the scar. Stage 4 (comparable to

Tarcoles Scar, Fig. 5a) shows a phase in which the seamount has no further surface expression in the form of faults; either because it is destroyed or is too deep to have any impact on the overlying sediments. The prism and parts of the slope are nearly fully rebuilt. Gullies cut through the old head- and side-walls and sediment from the upper slope slowly fills the scar.

Discussion

Our sidescan images show the fault patterns and deformation associated with individual seamount subduction scars in great detail, allowing comparisons with previous observations and modelling (e.g. Dominguez *et al.* 1998). The images show structures that are active during the transient uplift above a subducting seamount, as well as some relict structures, which are preserved along the older flanks of each subduction scar. However, within the scars our data reveal few structural features, because all of the material in these areas has been reworked by landsliding, destroying or overprinting the tectonic fabric. This leads us to conclude that slope failure leading to a variety of landslide types is the most important process in shaping the scars that are observed in the wake of subducted seamounts.

Structure of seamount subduction scars

The radial pattern of fractures seen in the uplifted area above each subducted seamount is thought to accommodate the underthrusting of the seamount through a combination of extensional and strike–slip motion, as predicted by the models of Dominguez *et al.* (1998). These fractures are best developed for the Jaco Scar (Fig. 4a) where the top of the seamount is buried to a depth of approximately 2–2.5 km, but only weakly developed for the Parrita Scar (Fig. 3a), which is at a much shallower depth (*c.* 1 km below the seabed, von Huene *et al.* 1995). Normal faults parallel to the slope, and downthrowing upslope (or landward), occur in the headwall areas of both the Jaco and Parrita Scars along the trailing edge of the uplifted area, again as predicted by the models of Dominguez *et al.* (1998). Our data indicates that the normal faulting associated with uplift occurs before the formation of the radial strike–slip faults seen above the seamount.

Our data show no clear evidence for the occurrence of backthrusts on the leading edge of the uplifted area, as predicted by models and tentatively identified on the slope of the Japan trench in the area of the Daiichi-Kashima Seamount (Dominguez *et al.* 1998). A thrust may define the northwestern margin of the uplifted area associated with the

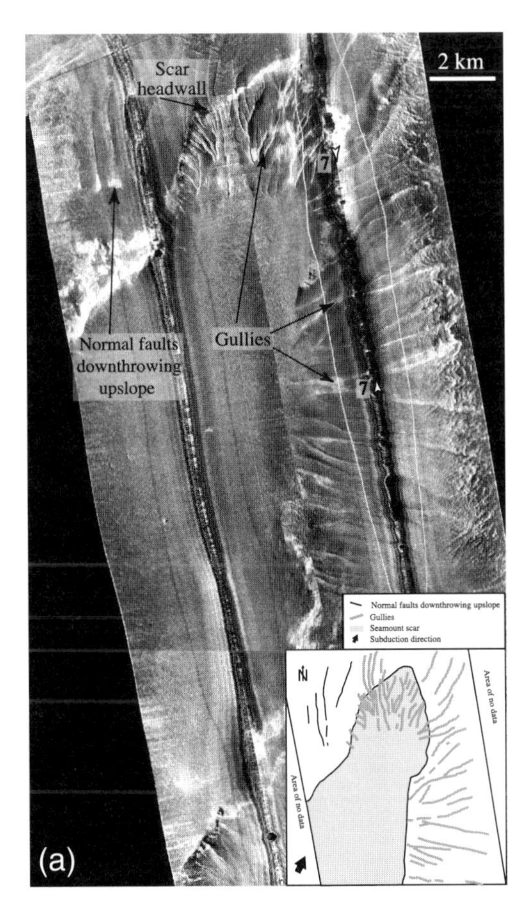

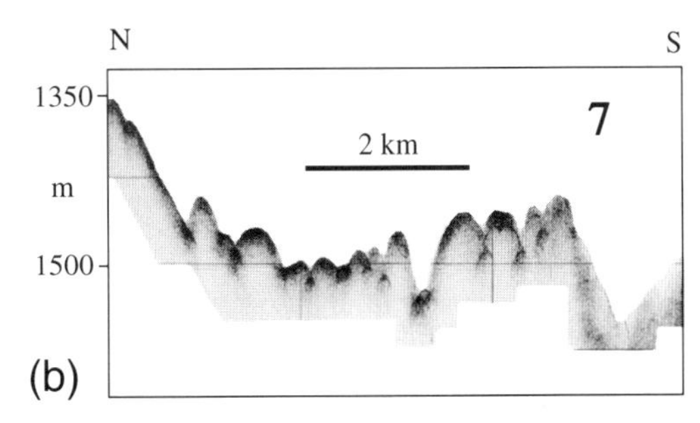

Fig. 5. (**a**) 30 kHz TOBI sidescan sonar image of Tarcoles Scar showing an absence of active faulting and the degradation of the seamount subduction scar due to gullying of its walls and sedimentation in the topographic depression. High backscatter is bright, low backscatter is dark. Inset shows interpretation. PRISM software (LeBas & Hühnerbach 1999) was used to process the TOBI data; (**b**) 7 kHz TOBI profiler record along the sidewall of Tarcoles Scar showing numerous gullies up to 70 m deep and 150 m wide. Depth is in metres below sea level. Arrows in Figure 5a show position of profile.

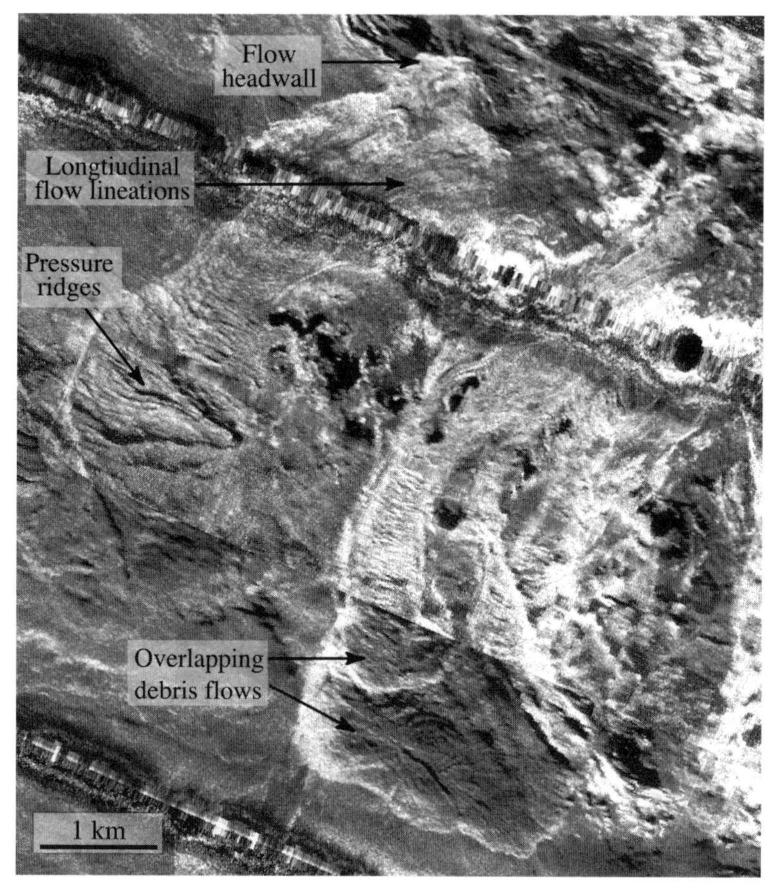

Fig. 6. 30 kHz TOBI sidescan sonar imagery showing overlapping debris flows in the Rio Bongo Scar, north of Fisher Seamount. Note the longitudinal flow fabric in the upper part of debris flows and more distal pressure ridges. PRISM software (LeBas & Hühnerbach 1999) was used to process the TOBI data.

Parrita Scar (Figs 1 & 3a), but no evidence of thrusts is seen around the Jaco Scar uplift (Fig. 4a).

With the increasing distance from the deformation front from the Parrita to the Jaco Scar we observe a decrease in the amount of uplift over the seamount, but an increase in the degree of fracturing and faulting. This may reflect the greater consolidation of the slope sediments with increasing distance from the deformation front. Within 50 km of the deformation front, in the Tarcoles Scar (Fig. 5), active uplift, fracturing and landsliding appear to have ceased, and the remaining topography associated with the scar is being degraded by sedimentary processes. This suggests that the seamount has become detached from the subducting plate either through accretion to the upper plate or mechanical destruction during the subduction process (Barckhausen 1996; Barckhausen *et al.* 1998). As the seamount is subducted to greater depth, the associated uplift of the continental slope becomes progressively lower and broader until the seamount no longer has a topographic trace. The potential for gravity sliding thus gradually decreases. This might explain why the scar narrows landward to form an 'arrow' shaped scar (Fig. 5).

Landsliding in seamount subduction scars

The erosional scars that form in the wake of subducting seamounts are primarily the result of repeated landsliding along the trailing edge of the uplifted area above the seamount. As the seamount advances landward, slope deposits are oversteepened and destabilized by rapid subsidence in its wake. Thus, a short section of oversteepened slope moves landward with time creating a migrating zone of slope failure that results in the parallel-sided scars seen cutting into the slope. Although oversteepening is the primary cause of landsliding, the intense fracturing of the uplifted material, the frequent shallow earthquakes which affect the area (Arroyo 1999; Ranero & von Huene 2000) and the presence of high

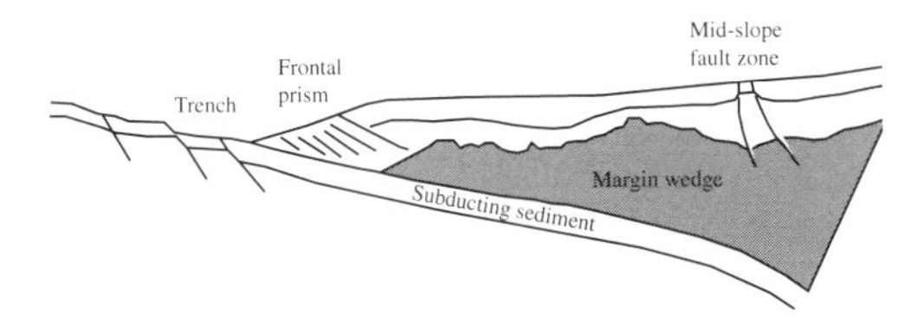

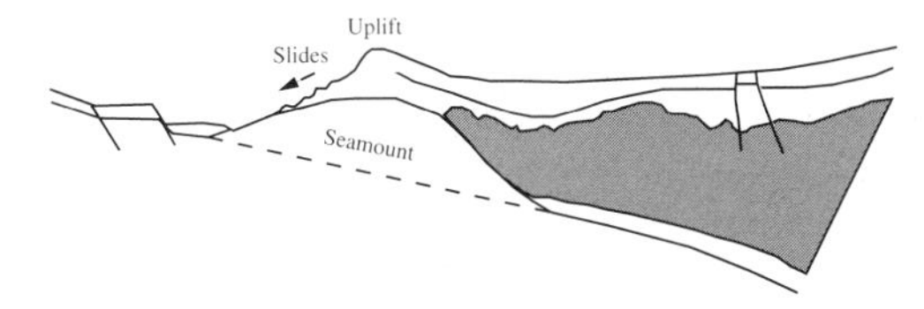

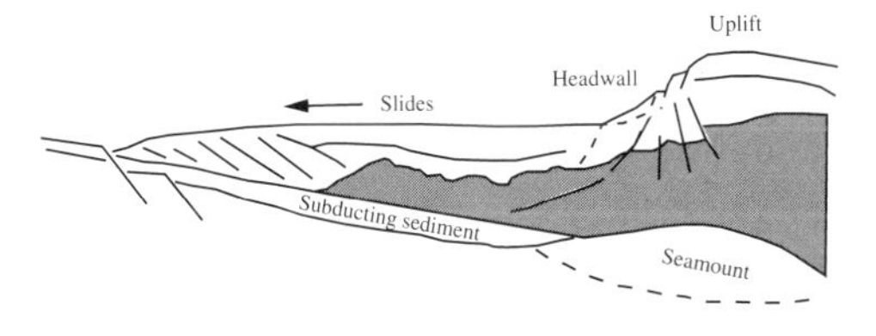

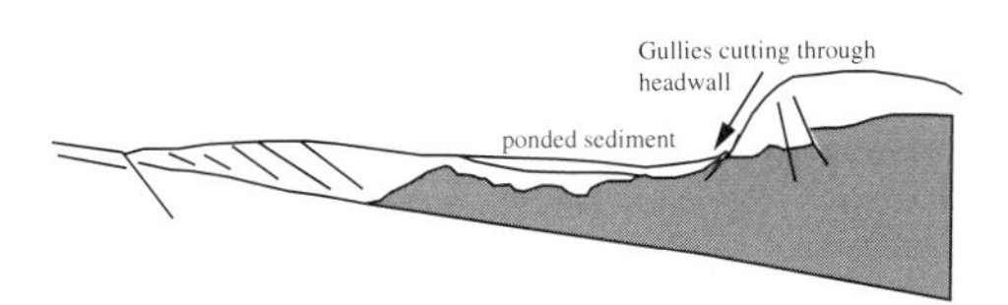

Fig. 7. Two-dimensional model of different seamount subduction stages as described in the text (after von Huene *et al.* 2004).

fluid pressures in the subsurface (as indicated by abundant cold seeps, seen on video data collected during the cruise) are all likely contributors to the initiation of individual failure events.

Our data show that the high relief (up to 600 m deep) erosional scars formed immediately in the wake of subducting seamounts are rapidly filled by sediment deposition. The relief of the Jaco Scar decreases by some 300 m over a distance of 15 km downslope from the active scar, corresponding to an average 'filling' rate of $2\,m\,ka^{-1}$. Since, overall, this part of the continental slope is not characterized by high sedimentation rates, most of this material must be derived from erosion of the scar immediately upslope. This is supported by our observation of debris flow runout, which shows that most flows extend only a short distance (less than 10 km) downslope (Figs 2, 3a, 4a & 6). Clearly these are not highly fluid and mobile debris flows, since they only occur on very steep slopes (an average of 10–12°, measured from the top of the lobes to the distal part with the pressure ridges) and movement stops as soon as the flow encounters a decrease in slope.

Sediment recycling in the subduction process

We have attempted to estimate the volume of material disrupted by the subduction of the Jaco seamount, as an example, to assess how much slope material is eroded by and subducted with the seamount, and how much prism material is eroded by landsliding and accumulated immediately downslope of the seamount backfilling the scar.

For this purpose we used the actual multibeam bathymetry of the Jaco Scar (Fig. 1) and created a contour plot (Fig. 8a) outlining the area affected by the seamount subduction. In a next step, a synthetic contour plot (Fig. 8b) was calculated reconstructing the slope to a stage as if no seamount would have collided with the margin by extrapolating contours using a downslope profile nearby, unaffected by any seamount collision. Nevertheless, a slight difference in the shape of the deformation front between the synthetic plot (Fig. 8b) and Figure 4a remains. This is caused by the indentation of the Tarcoles seamount, that occurred prior to the Jaco subduction, and therefore prevents accurate reconstruction of the Jaco Scar on its western side. But it does not notably affect the overall volume estimate.

The amount of material 'missing' from the Jaco Scar (Fig. 8a) at this stage was estimated by subtracting the actual bathymetry of the scar from the synthetic contour plot. The amount of 'missing' material, assumed to represent the volume of slope material subducted with Jaco seamount, is $20–23\,km^3$. This is roughly the same volume as the seamount itself, based on the models by Barckhausen (1996). The volume agrees with Dominguez *et al.* (2000) who suggested that a volume of frontal margin material comparable to that of the subducting seamount itself is underplated beneath the rear part of the accretionary wedge or subducted.

The total amount of slope material involved in the subduction process at this stage was estimated by multiplying the dimensions for the Jaco Scar (33 km length × 8 km width and 400 m average relief depth), equalling just over $100\,km^3$. Comparing the estimates of the subducted material and the total amount about 20–25% is subducted with the seamount whereas the remaining 75–80% is recycled as backfill through landsliding. Sandbox models from Dominguez *et al.* (2000) suggest that other seamounts along the margin show similar percentages of backfill and subduction volumes.

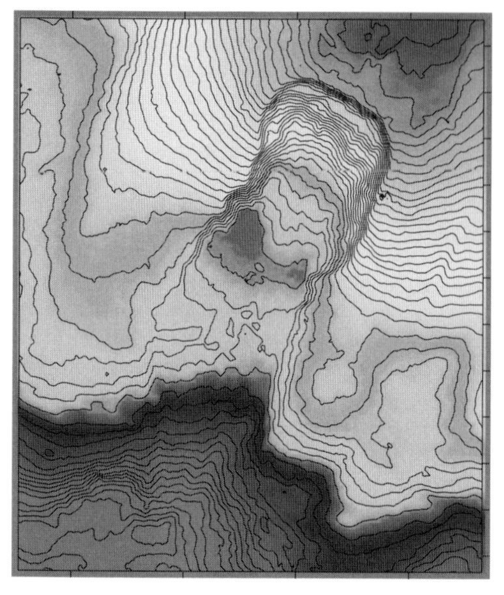

a) b)

Fig. 8. (**a**) Contour plot of Jaco Scar derived from multibeam bathymetry. Depth range from 900 m (medium grey; top right) to 3400 m (dark grey; bottom left). Contour interval is 100 m; (**b**) Synthetic contour plot of Jaco Scar area with extrapolated contours using a downslope profile nearby that is unaffected by any seamount collision. Depth range from 900 m (medium grey; top right) to 3400 m (dark grey; bottom left). Contour interval is 100 m.

Conclusions

Seamounts subducted at active margins leave distinct scars where they deform the overriding plate. The scars form by uplift and fracturing of the slope material above the seamount followed by gravitational collapse of the deformed and fractured material over the seamount's trailing edge. Oversteepening occurs as the support of the uplifted area is withdrawn due to continuing subduction of the seamount. This creates a zone of slope failure that migrates upslope. Erosion occurs by repeated moderate-scale landsliding, which produces a series of overlapping debris flows. Downslope sediment transport is typically over limited distances, resulting in partial 'backfilling' of the scar as its headwall moves upslope. The amount of margin material disrupted by seamount subduction is 4 to 5 times the volume of the subducting seamount, of which about 75–80% seems to be recycled downslope, backfilling the scar, and the remaining 20–25% is subducted along with the seamount.

The authors thank I. Rouse, D. Matthew and R. Wallace for their excellent support during the TOBI operations. Thanks also to master and crew of RV SONNE for their perfect support while using TOBI on their vessel for the first time. D. Hodgson and J. Laursen are thanked for their constructive reviews, which helped to improve the paper.

References

ARROYO, I. 1999. The seismicity in Costa Rica. *In*: BIALAS, J., FLUEH, E.R. & BOHRMANN, G. (eds) FS SONNE Cruise Report SO144/1&2, Paganini. GEOMAR Report **94**, Kiel, 16–22.

BARCKHAUSEN, U. 1996. *Bearbeitung und Interpretation seemagnetischer Messdaten aus dem Pazifik vor der Küste von Costa Rica*. Cuvillier Verlag, Göttingen.

BARCKHAUSEN, U., ROESER, H.A. & VON HUENE, R. 1998. Magnetic signature of upper plate structures and subducting seamounts at the convergent margin off Costa Rica. *Journal of Geophysical Research*, **B103**, 7079–7093.

BIALAS, J., FLUEH, E.R. & BOHRMANN, G. 1999. FS SONNE Cruise Report SO144/1&2, Paganini. GEOMAR Report **94**, Kiel.

BLONDEL, P.H. & MURTON, B.J. 1997. *Handbook of Seafloor Sonar Imagery*. Wiley-Praxis, London.

CADET, J.P., KOBAYASHI, K., AUBOUIN, J., ET AL. 1987. The Japan trench and its juncture with the Kuril trench: Cruise results of the Kaiko project, Leg3. *Earth and Planetary Science Letters*, **83**, 267–285.

COLLOT, J.-Y. & FISHER, M.A. 1991. The collision zone between the north d'Entrecasteaux Ridge and the New Hebrides island arc. 1. Seabeam morphology and shallow structure. *Journal of Geophysical Research*, **96**, 4457–4478.

DEMETS, C., GORDON, R.G., ARGUS, D.F. & STEIN, S. 1990. Current plate motions. *Geophysical Journal International*, **101**, 425–478.

DEMETS, C., GORDON, R.G., ARGUS, D.F. & STEIN, S. 1994. Effect of recent revisions to the geomagnetic reversal time scale on estimates of current plate motions. *Geophysical Research Letters*, **21**, 2191–2194.

DOMINGUEZ, S., LALLEMAND, S.E., MALAVIEILLE, J. & VON HUENE, R. 1998. Upper plate deformation associated with seamount subduction. *Tectonophysics*, **293**, 207–224.

DOMINGUEZ, S., MALAVIEILLE, J. & LALLEMAND, S.E. 2000. Deformation of accretionary wedges in response to seamount subduction: insights from sandbox experiments. *Tectonics*, **19**, 182–196.

FISHER, D.M., GARDNER, T.W., MARSHALL, J.S., SAK, P.B. & PROTTI, M. 1998. Effect of subducting sea-floor roughness on fore-arc kinematics, Pacific coast, Costa Rica. *Geology*, **26**, 467–470.

FLEWELLEN, C.G., MILLARD, N.W. & ROUSE, I.P. 1993. TOBI – A vehicle for deep-ocean survey. *Electronics and Communications Engineering Journal*, **5**, 85–93.

IVERSON, R.M. 1997. The physics of debris flows. *Reviews of Geophysics*, **35**, 245–296.

KODAIRA, S., TAKAHASHI, N., NAKANSHI, A., MIURA, S. & KANEDA, Y. 2000. Subducted seamount imaged in rupture zone of the 1946 Nankaido earthquake. *Science*, **289**, 104–106.

KOLARSKY, R.A., MANN, P. & MONTERO, W. 1995. Island arc response to shallow subduction of the Cocos Ridge, Costa Rica. *In*: MANN, P. (ed.) *Geologic and tectonic development of the Caribbean plate boundary in southern Central America*. Geological Society of America Special Paper **295**, 235–262.

LALLEMAND, S. & LE PICHON, X. 1987. Coulomb wedge model applied to the subduction of seamounts in the Japan Trench. *Geology*, **15**, 1065–1069.

LAURSEN, J., SCHOLL, D.W. & VON HUENE, R. 2002. Neotectonic deformation of the central Chile margin: deepwater forearc basin formation in response to hot spot ridge and seamount subduction. *Tectonics*, **21**, 1038–1064.

LE BAS, T.P. & HÜHNERBACH, V. 1999. *PRISM processing of remotely-sensed imagery for seafloor mapping, version 3.1*. Internal Report. Southampton Oceanography Centre.

LEE, S.E., TALLING, P.T., ERNST, G.G.J. & HOGG, A.J. 2002. Occurrence and origin of submarine plunge pools at the base of the US continental slope. *Marine Geology*, **185**, 363–377.

MAJOR, J.J. 1997. Depositional processes in large-scale debris-flow experiments. *Journal of Geology*, **105**, 345–366.

MASSON, D., PARSON, L.M., MILSOM, J., NICHOLS, G., SIKUMBANG, N., DWIYANTO, B. & KALLAGHER, H. 1990. Subduction of seamounts at the Java trench: a view with long-range sidescan sonar. *Tectonophysics*, **185**, 51–65.

MURTON, B.J., ROUSE, I.P., MILLARD, N.W. & FLEWELLEN, C.G. 1992. Multisensor, deep-towed instrument explores ocean floor. *EOS Transactions, AGU*, **73**, 225–228.

RANERO, C.R. & VON HUENE, R. 2000. Subduction erosion along the Middle America convergent margin. *Nature*, **404**, 748–752.

ROUMP, J. 1985. *Le Fossé d'Amérique Centrale: subduction de seamounts au large du Costa Rica: morphologie de la plaque Cocos dans le fossé et le plan de subduction*. Thèse de Doctorat de 3ème Cycle, University of Brest, France.

SCANLON, K.M. & MASSON, D.G. 1996. Sedimentary processes in a tectonically active region: Puerto Rico north insular slope. *In*: GARDNER, J.V., FIELD, M.E. & TWICHELL, D.C. (eds) *Geology of the United States Seafloor. The View from GLORIA*. Cambridge University Press, Cambridge, 123–134.

VON HUENE, R., BOURGOIS, J., MILLER, J. & PAUTOT, G. 1989. A large tsunamogenic landslide and debris flow along the Peru trench. *Journal of Geophysical Research*, **94**, 1703–1714.

VON HUENE, R., BIALAS, J., FLUEH, E., ET AL. 1995. Morphotectonics of the Pacific convergent margin of Costa Rica. *In*: MANN, P. (ed.) *Geologic and tectonic development of the Caribbean plate boundary in southern Central America*. Geological Society of America Special Paper **295**, 291–307.

VON HUENE, R., RANERO, C.R., WEINREBE, W. & HINZ, K. 2000. Quaternary convergent margin tectonics of Costa Rica, segmentation of the Cocos Plate, and Central American volcanism. *Tectonics*, **19**, 314–334.

VON HUENE, R., RANERO, C.R. & WATTS, P. 2004. Tsunamogenic slope failure along the Middle America Trench in two tectonic settings. *Marine Geology*, **203**, 303–317.

WERNER, R., HOERNLE, K., VAN DEN BOGAARD, P., RANERO, C., VON HUENE, R. & KORICH, D. 1999. Drowned 14-m.y.-old Galapagos Archipelago off the coast of Costa Rica: implications for tectonic and evolutionary models. *Geology*, **27**, 499–502.

Calcareous turbidity current emplacement as an initiation mechanism for substrate brecciation and deformation

B. SAVARY

UMR 5125 CNRS, Paléoenvironnements et Paléobiosphère, UFR Sciences de la Terre, Université Claude Bernard, Lyon 1, 69622 Villeurbanne cedex, France (e-mail: savary@univ-lyon1.fr)

Abstract: The Barremian–Aptian Baronnies syncline, located in SE France, provides the opportunity to study a calcareous turbidite lobe with intercalated breccias and slumps. These features are formed *in-situ* by the emplacement of turbidity currents that distorted the underlying semi-consolidated substrate. The brecciation occurs in three stages. The first stage is represented by the penetration of calcarenitic sediment into the underlying unlithified calcisiltic sediment due to the hydraulic pressure of an overriding turbidity current. In the next stage, a pseudo-breccia forms where the brecciated clasts are still attached to the substrate. Finally, these breccia clasts are separated entirely from the seabed and locally entrained into the flow. In addition, the penetration of the flow into the underlying semi-consolidated sediment can induce destabilization, down slope movement and folding. Similar Tithonian-aged (Late Jurassic) breccias have been interpreted previously as *in-situ* wave-induced features in this region; however, this study testifies that this deformation is not diagnostic of storms but can also be induced by turbidity current deposition.

The mechanisms that induce brecciation have to be identified correctly in order to consider them within a sequence stratigraphic context. Calcareous turbidites and their associated breccias, however, are not strongly diagnostic of relative sea-level.

Breccias and conglomerates are common in the sedimentary record and are a ubiquitous component of modern and ancient marine settings (Demicco & Hardie 1994). These two fabrics are classified either by their compositional characteristics (Morrow 1982) or by the processes responsible for their genesis (Twenhofel 1947; Fairbridge 1978; Spence & Tucker 1997). Typically, breccias are related to tectonic (cataclastic breccias) and magmatic (pyroclastic breccias) events but sedimentary breccias also occur. Sedimentary breccias record rare, intense events (Demicco & Hardie 1994), and are generally considered to be the result of major episodes of gravitational instability. Previous mechanisms invoked for the genesis of the submarine calcareous breccias are: (1) collapse of high-angle metastable carbonate seabed slopes (Cook *et al.* 1972); (2) deformation through overpressure due to earthquakes, water loading, gravitational compaction and gas in solution or as hydrates (Spence & Tucker 1997); (3) loading by waves, storms and tides (Spence & Tucker 1997); and (4) subaerial exposure (Demicco & Hardie 1994). As discussed in Bouchette *et al.* (2001), there is little evidence for extensive *in-situ* brecciation processes in the marine environment; however, they proposed a wave-induced *in-situ* brecciation for the formation of the Tithonian (Late Jurassic) breccias exposed in SE France. In the same region, continuous Barremian–Aptian (Cretaceous) outcrops provide the evidence to propose an alternative mechanism for *in-situ* brecciation and slumping in a deep-water (below storm-wave base) environment. The objectives of this paper are to illustrate the field characteristics of calcareous breccias and slumps, propose a mechanism for their generation, and discuss the formation of Tithonian breccias and consider the temporal and spatial distribution of the breccias position with a sequence stratigraphic framework.

Geological setting

In SE France, Jurassic and Cretaceous marine deposits are widely exposed. They record the development of a sedimentary basin, commonly named the 'Vocontian Trough'. From Oxfordian (upper Jurassic) to Aptian (lower Cretaceous) time, carbonate material was remobilized and transported into the deep basin. Basin floor water depth estimates vary from a few hundred metres (Wilpshaar & Leereveld 1994) to a thousand metres deep (Ferry & Rubino 1989). The remobilized carbonate material was intercalated with a very thick succession (>1000 m thick on average; Wilpshaar & Leereveld 1994) of alternating deep-water marlstones and mudstones (Debrand-Passard *et al.* 1984). These resedimented carbonates correspond to breccias of Tithonian age (Remane 1970; Beaudoin 1977), huge slump and debris flow deposits of upper Oxfordian (Raja Gabaglia 1995) and Lower Cretaceous age (Le Hegarat 1974; Ferry & Flandrin 1979; Fries 1986; Arnaud-Vanneau &

From: HODGSON, D.M. & FLINT, S.S. (eds) 2005. *Submarine Slope Systems: Processes and Products*. Geological Society, London, Special Publications, **244**, 207–220. 0305–8719/$15.00

Arnaud 1990), and calcarenitic turbidites predominantly deposited during the Barremian (Ferry 1978, 1984). It is generally thought that these are gravity deposits (Beaudoin 1977) although a controversial alternative hypothesis has recently been proposed for the Tithonian breccias suggesting that they are the result of a wave-induced mechanism (Seguret *et al.* 2001; Bouchette *et al.* 2001).

During the Barremian–Aptian interval, the Urgonian platforms (rudist-rich facies) surrounding the Vocontian Trough reached their maximum extension (Arnaud-Vanneau *et al.* 1982). The prolific production of shallow-water carbonates induced the transport of large volumes of carbonate material into the deep basin. The calcarenitic sediment was transported via narrow channels and deposited within a submarine lobe environment (Fig. 1a). The Baronnies syncline (Drôme, France) provides a 15 km long exposure along a Barremian–Aptian lobe of a carbonate submarine fan fed from the Bas Vivarais Platform in the west (Ferry 1976).

Characteristics of the Baronnies carbonate submarine lobe

In this region, the Barremian–Aptian outcrops are continuous and mainly oriented parallel to the palaeoflow direction (west–east, Fig. 1b). The turbidites are composed primarily of fine-grained bioclastic calcarenites or calcisiltites. Along the proximal to distal transect grain-size decreases and sedimentary features evolve. In these calcareous turbidites, secondary silicification is frequent.

The proximal part of the lobe (near Vercoiran, Fig. 1b) is 32 m thick and contains poorly sorted turbidite sequences that are amalgamated to form thick (metre-scale) structureless units. Channel forms (Fig 2a) are present but narrow (metre-scale) and shallow (metre to decimetre-scale). In this proximal region of the lobe, the sequences are mainly represented by Bouma a–e and ab–e intervals. Typically, bed bases are erosive and bed tops are highly bioturbated (their mottled structure prevents interpretation of the type of burrows).

The medial part of the lobe (near St Auban, Fig. 1b) is 39 m thick and mainly represented by decimetre to centimetre thick, erosive and amalgamated turbidites that contain numerous sedimentary features. Among these features, flute casts (Fig. 2b), which are generally scarce in the calcareous turbidites (Eberli 1991), indicate an eastward direction of the palaeoflows (Fig. 1). It is possible to find complete Bouma sequences and planar lamination is common (Fig. 2c). In addition, calcareous monogenic breccias are rare but present and well exposed, allowing an understanding of their genetic mechanism.

The most distal part of the exposure (in La Combe, Fig. 1b) is 12 m thick and displays well sorted sequences separated by marls at the base and top of the turbidite succession. However, some sequences are amalgamated and are represented mainly by Bouma a–e intervals with some ab–e and b–e intervals (Fig. 2d). Bed tops are bioturbated. There is also a thick slump deposit (reaching 5 m) and calcareous monogenic breccias in the distal part of the lobe.

Description of the monogenic breccias

The Barremian–Aptian lobe is largely dominated by calcarenitic and calcisiltic turbidites but also contains some monogenic breccias, laterally variable in thickness (centimetre to metre thick). These breccias are represented by calcisiltic clasts, variable in size (millimetre to decimetre in length), smooth-shaped, sometimes elongated and oriented parallel to the stratification, and surrounded by a bioclastic calcarenitic matrix (Fig. 3a, b). Contact between clasts and calcarenitic matrix is sharp. Sometimes, within the breccia, a process of separation of a clast can be observed (Fig. 3c). Matrix-supported and clast-supported breccias can be distinguished, although clast-supported breccias are rare. Pseudo-breccias are genetically related to the breccias. They are represented by pseudo-clasts that are surrounded by a calcarenitic matrix but still physically linked to their underlying calcisiltic succession. These pseudo-clasts are diverse in shape but their edge is always rounded and the contact between calcarenitic and calcisiltic sediment is sharp (Fig. 3d). The calcisiltic underlying sediment contains veins filled by bioclastic calcarenite and some millimetre-scale calcisiltic clasts. Generally, these veins are horizontal and the contact between calcarenitic veins and calcisiltic succession is sharp (Fig. 3e). They are centimetres in length and millimetres in width. Vertical veins are less frequent, but more commonly trend downwards. Upward oblique veins are smaller and their contact with the calcisiltic sediment is less sharp (Fig. 3f). The physical relationship between the calcisiltic succession, calcarenitic turbidite, the breccia, pseudo-breccia and veins is illustrated in Figure 3g.

In the medial part of the lobe (near St Auban, Fig. 1b), an individual brecciated bed can be followed for 25 m sub-parallel to the direction of palaeoflow (Fig. 4). The most proximal part of the bed comprises a breccia composed of calcisiltite fragments and surrounded by a calcarenitic matrix (Fig. 4a). The size of the smooth-shaped fragments can reach several decimetres at the base and decreases upwards although overall the breccia elements are poorly sorted. Towards the distal part of the bed (eastward), the calcarenite:calcisiltite ratio decreases (Fig. 4b–e). The basal part of the bed becomes less deformed

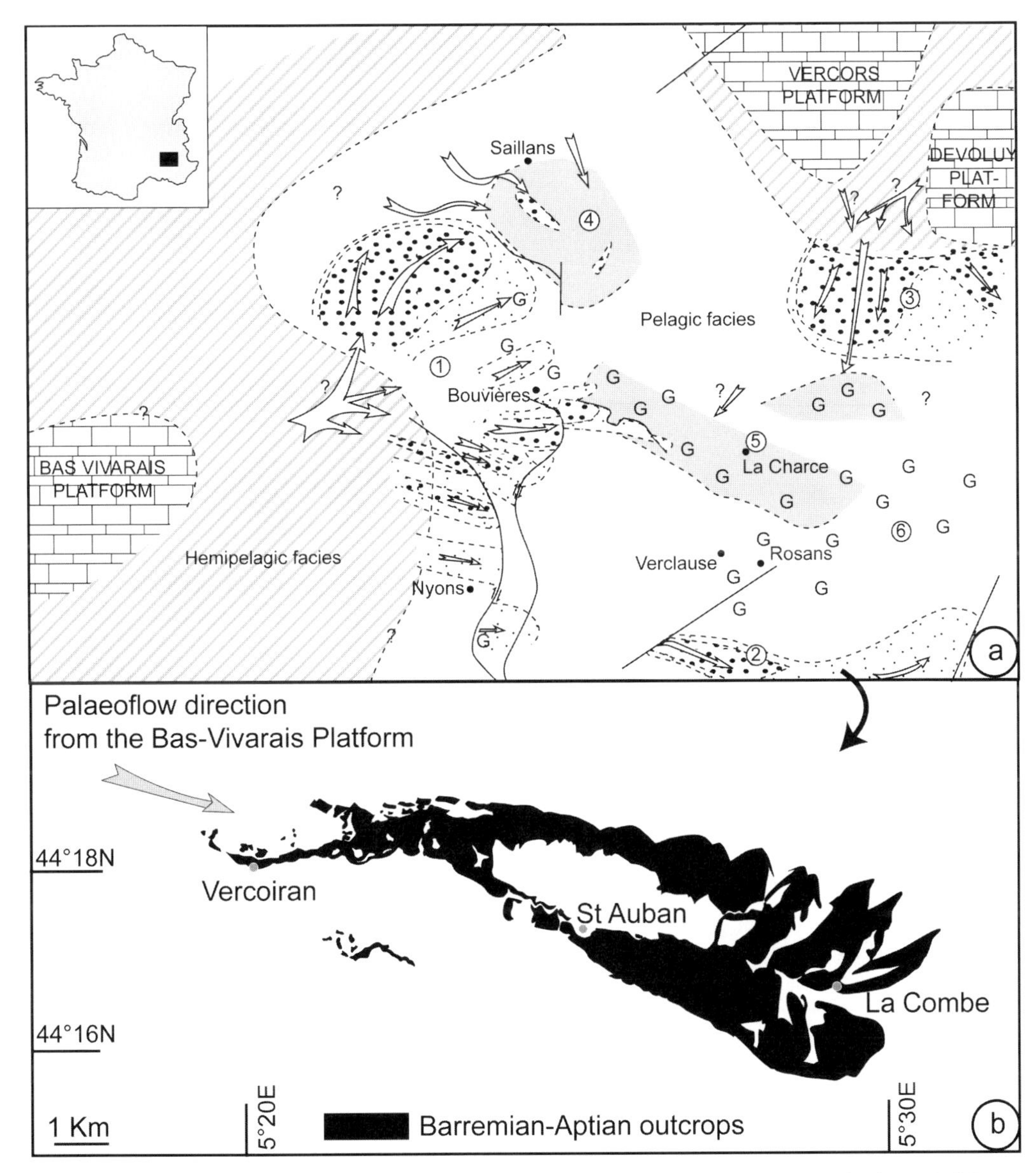

Fig. 1. (**a**) Palaeogeography and distribution of the resedimented carbonates in the Barremian–Aptian interval of the Vocontian Trough (Ferry 1976 modified). Dots, calcarenitic to calcisiltic turbidites; grey zones, muddy flow deposits; G, slumps; arrows, palaeoflow directions; 1, Pays de Bourdeaux Submarine Fan; 2, Baronnies Submarine Fan (studied in this paper); 3, Oriental Diois and Bochaine Submarine Fan; 4, La Chaudière muddy flow deposits; 5, Central muddy flow deposits; 6, Central slumped region. (**b**) Barremian–Aptian outcrops of the Baronnies lobe fed from the west by the Bas Vivarais Platform (Urgonian facies).

revealing a calcisiltic succession (Fig. 4b) to which some fragments of the breccia are still physically linked (Fig. 4c). Finally, at its most distal part, the bed is composed entirely of calcisiltic material cross-cut by a network of calcarenitic veins (Fig. 4d, e).

In the distal part of the lobe, at the La Combe locality (Fig. 1b), a panorama shows the lateral evolution (along 100 m) from a 40 cm turbidite bed in the south to a 5 m thick slump in the north (Fig. 5). This outcrop is oblique–perpendicular to the direction of palaeoflow. In the southern part of the outcrop (near the lobe axis), the base of the succession is marked by a 40 cm thick graded turbidite mostly composed of medium-grained calcarenites.

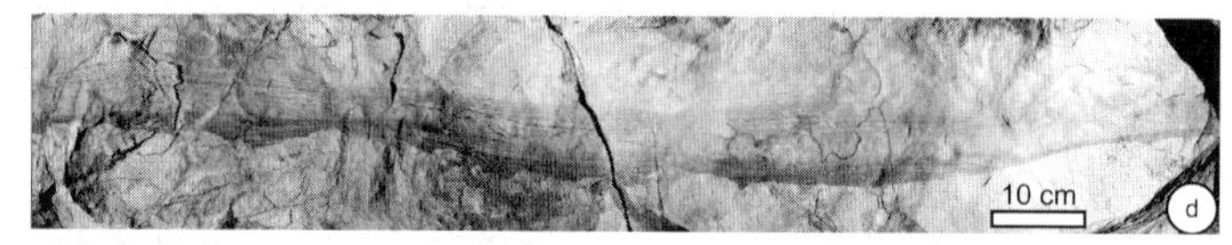

Fig. 2. Facies observed from proximal to distal part of the Baronnies submarine lobe. Proximal part: (**a**) narrow and shallow channel forms occur. Medial part: sedimentary features are numerous; among them, (**b**) flute casts indicate an eastward direction of palaeoflow and (**c**) planar laminations are abundant. Distal part: (**d**) locally, sequences can be slightly erosive and marked by planar laminations (T_{b-e} interval is shown).

Northwards, the bed contains fragments of calcisiltic sediment elongated and oriented parallel to the stratification (Fig. 5a). These fragments are centimetre to millimetre in size and poorly sorted but display a weak fining-upward and a coarsening-northward trend. At this location, the breccia is supported by the calcarenitic matrix that shows some parallel laminations in the upper part of the bed (Fig. 5a). Laterally, the elements of the breccia become coarser, smooth-shaped decimetre-scale elements can be observed (Fig. 5b). Northwards, the bed is 1.4 m thick and displays bowl-like features (Fig 6a, b). The bed is dominantly represented by calcisiltic material containing some calcarenitic veins. It is structureless and folded, which indicates deformation by movement (probably down slope) of a viscoplastic calcisiltic sediment. Northwards, the same bed increases to 5 m thickness; it is represented entirely by calcisiltic material and slumped (Fig. 6).

Genesis of the breccias and folding

The excellent exposure of the Barremian–Aptian calcareous lobe of the Baronnies allows a new mechanism to be proposed for the genesis of carbonate

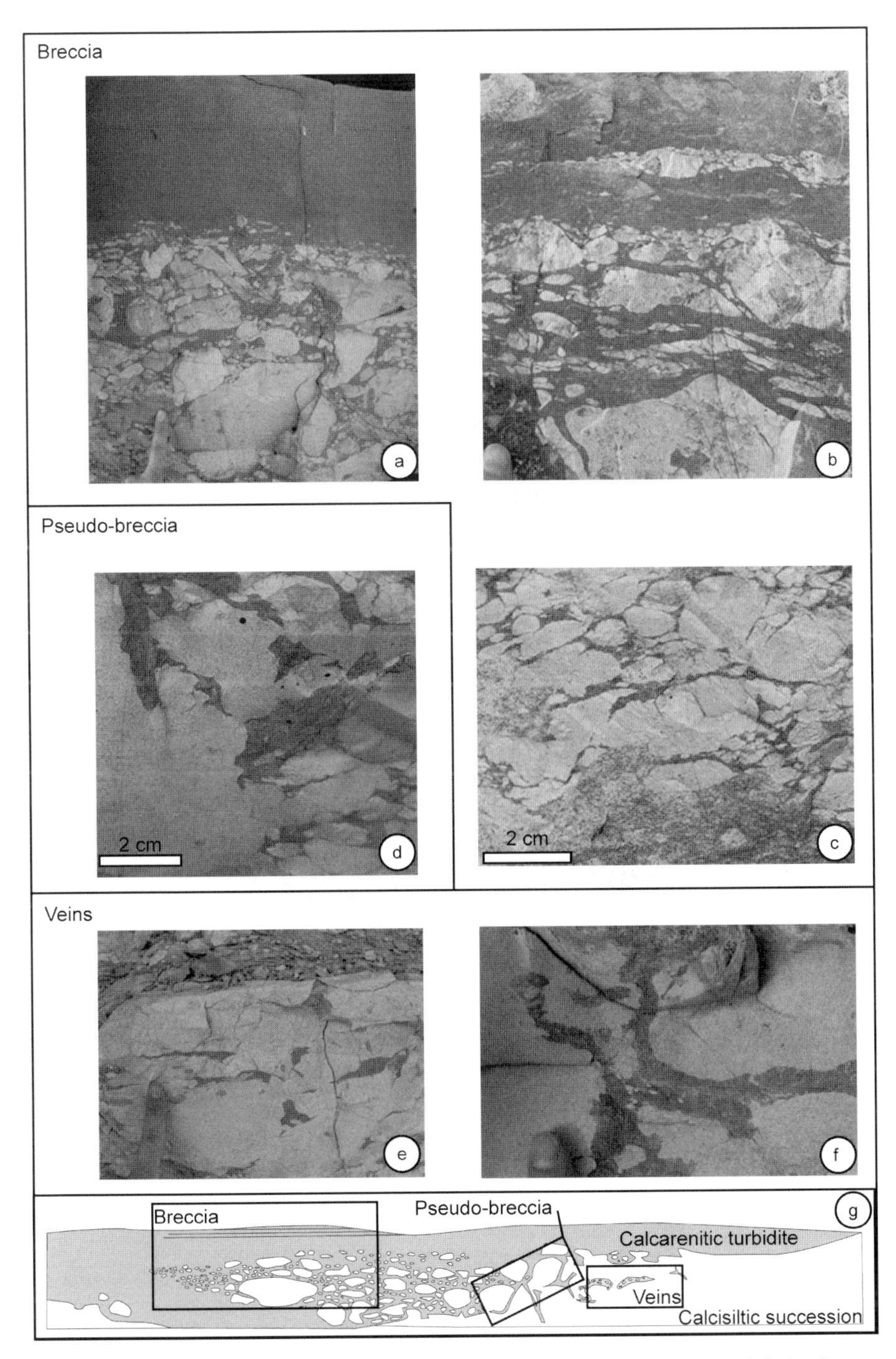

Fig. 3. Photographs showing the characteristics of (**a**, **b**, **c**) the breccias, (**d**) pseudo-breccias and (**f**, **e**) veins. Monogenic breccia: the calcisiltic clasts included in a calcarenitic matrix are (a) variable in size and smooth-shaped; (b) they can be elongated and oriented parallel to the stratification; (c) elongation of clasts can induce their separation. Pseudo-breccia: (d) the upper surface of a calcisiltic succession can be undulated and represented by smooth-shaped and undeformed pseudo-clasts. Calcarenitic veins: the calcisiltic succession is mainly marked by (e) sharp and horizontal calcarenitic veins, whereas (f) vertical and oblique veins are less frequent. (g) Scheme showing the geometrical relations between the calcisiltic succession, calcarenitic turbidite, the breccia, pseudo-breccia and calcarenitic veins.

Fig. 4. Continuous outcrop of the middle part of the lobe illustrating the formation of a breccia (hammer for scale). (**a**) Breccia composed of smooth-shaped calcisiltic fragments surrounded by a calcarenitic matrix (pen for scale). (**b**) The lower part of the bed is a calcisiltic sequence; the middle and upper parts are breccia. (**c**) Low calcarenitic:calcisiltic ratio, some fragments of the breccia are physically linked to the underlying calcisiltic sequence. (**d**) Calcarenitic veins and limited brecciation of the calcisiltic material. (**e**) Calcarenitic veins in the calcisiltic bed.

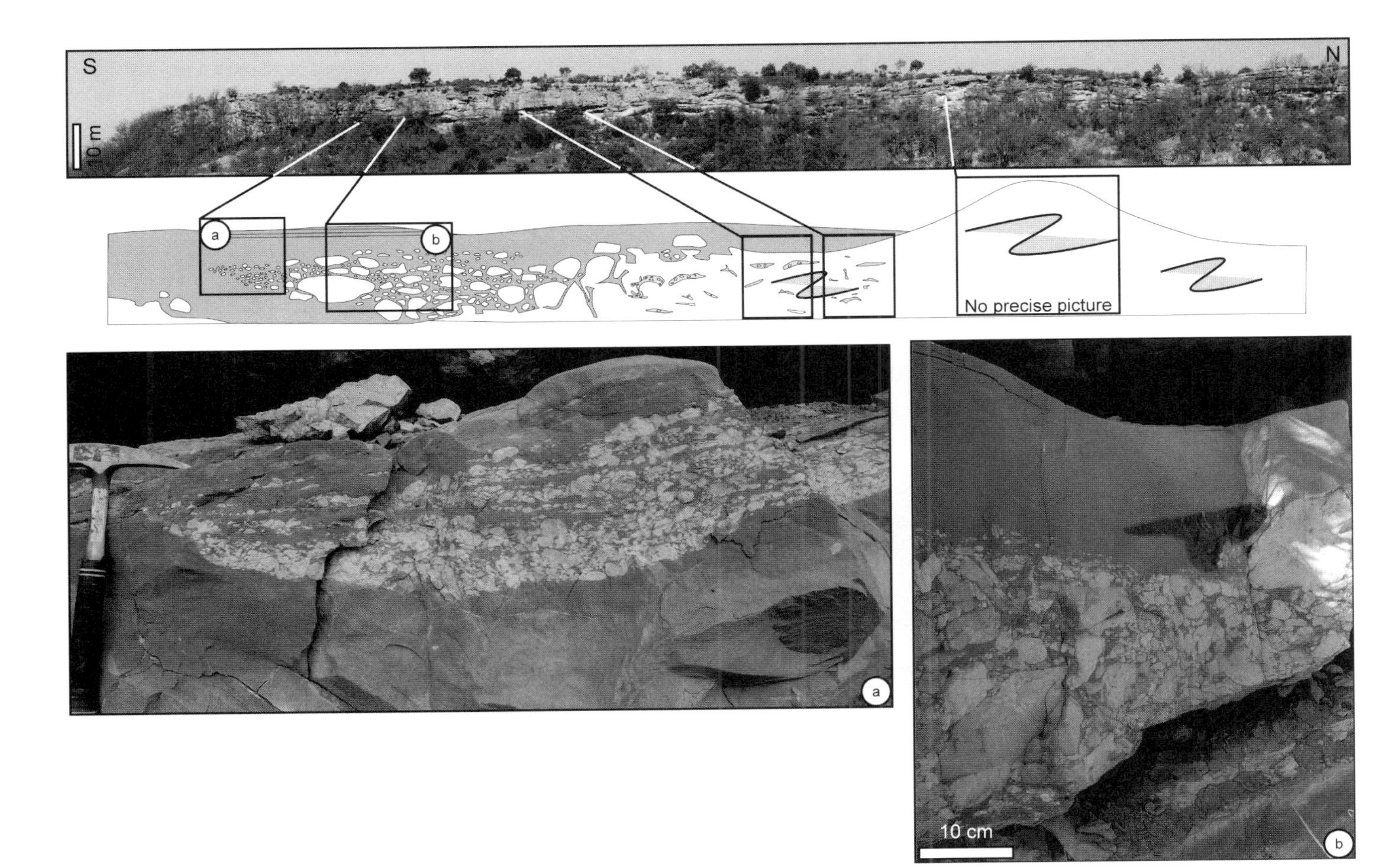

Fig. 5. Southern part of a continuous outcrop in the distal zone of the lobe illustrating the lateral change from a calcarenitic turbidite to a monogenic breccia and a slump. This outcrop is oblique to palaeoflow. (**a**) To the south of the outcrop, near the axis of the lobe, a calcarenitic turbidite contains smooth-shaped calcisiltic fragments and is marked by planar laminations at the top. The photo illustrates the southern termination of a monogenic breccia. (**b**) Northwards, the clasts become coarser; note the presence of silicification of the calcarenitic part of the bed.

Fig. 6. Northern part of a continuous outcrop in the distal zone of the lobe illustrating the lateral change from a calcarenitic turbidite to a monogenic breccia and a slump. This outcrop is oblique to palaeoflow. (**a**) The brecciated bed illustrated in Fig. 5 is represented northwards by an unstructured calcisiltic material that contains calcarenitic veins and bowl-like features. This bed is 1.4 m thick but (**b**) varies laterally in thickness because of its folding.

submarine breccias and slumps (Fig. 7). In the middle part of the lobe, a proximal to distal transect reflects the different stages during the genesis of the breccia. The initiation stage of the brecciation process is preserved in the distal part of the transect whereas the later stages of the process are found more proximally. The first step of the brecciation process is the penetration of calcarenitic sediment into the underlying unlithified calcisiltic sediment through to hydraulic microfracturing induced by the loading of an overriding turbidity current (Fig. 7a, b). This creates centimetre-scale calcarenitic veins that are mainly related to horizontal and downward injections; upward injections are rare. Sustained deformation by the high hydraulic pressure produces a pseudo-breccia in which the pseudo-clasts are still physically linked with the substrate (Fig. 7c). The final stage of the process occurs when the calcisiltic elements become detached from the substrate to create clasts held in the breccia. The elements of the breccia have been pulled up from the underlying bed by the turbidity current and slightly transported by this depositing flow (Fig. 7d). So, this breccia results from *in-situ* reworking (Fig. 7d). During the down slope movement of the flow, the clasts were sometimes stretched and separated. The monogenic pattern of the breccia, the identical nature between the clasts of the breccia and the underlying sediment, the undulated upper surface, the pseudo-clasts and injection veins of this underlying succession, the incohesive rheology of the breccia and the planar laminations in the matrix count against formation through emplacement of a debris flow.

In the distal part of the lobe, the outcrop is oblique to the direction of palaeoflow and shows the same sedimentary features. However, the brecciated bed of this distal zone of the lobe is represented laterally by a slump body. Several hypotheses can be used to explain the formation of these sedimentary features. First, we could propose that folding and slumping of a calcisiltic bed were responsible for the brecciation. Indeed, a break zone occurs between two domains of different remobilization intensity. This zone might be represented by the calcisiltic elements of the breccia. After this brecciation a turbidity current might have remobilized the calcisiltic elements and supplied the calcarenitic matrix of the breccia. This interpretation fails to explain the presence of the calcarenitic veins and the pseudo-breccia. We might also suppose that the emplacement of the slump body drove the brecciation laterally through de-watering processes although no fluid-escape features have been observed. However, another hypothesis is preferred here: the penetration of a turbidity current inside the unlithified seabed produced the breccia (the same mechanism as observed in the middle part of the lobe) and also loaded the bed and induced instability, movement, creeping and folding to form a slump (Fig. 7).

In these outcrops the smoothed shape of the fragments and their occasional elongation, the pseudo-breccia and the slump suggest the semi-consolidation of the calcisiltic seabed when the turbidity current was emplaced. Indeed, these facts imply that the substrate sediment was cohesive but not lithified. These features are probably due to the visco-plastic rheology of the calcisiltic material; in a coarser setting, the sediment (calcareous or silicoclastic) would become fully disseminated. Here, brecciation and slumping were induced by the loading of bypassing flows close to deposition and depositional turbidity currents. These processes occurred in the medial and distal parts of the lobe, where flows are thought to have had less energy than in the proximal part. Indeed, in the distal part of the submarine fan, the energy is mainly low but some higher energy currents can occur. These currents bypassed the proximal parts of the lobe and were probably responsible for the erosion and formation of channel forms. Distally, they generated breccias and slumps. Moreover, the morphology of the lobe might have increased the velocity of the flow towards the fringe because of a lateral increase in steepness. Even if the flow energy was low, the application of a force (deposition) on a fine-grained and semi-consolidated seabed could have generated important deformation structures.

Discussion

Comparison with the Tithonian breccias

The Vocontian Trough contains calcisiltic breccias and calcarenitic deposits of Tithonian age which have been interpreted to form via different mechanisms. Kilian (1888) and Haug (1891) proposed that the breccias resulted from *in-situ* reworking processes but did not invoke a specific mechanism. Later, Kilian (1895) described these rocks as pseudo-breccias including a component of concretionary growth in their formation. Gignoux & Moret (1938) suggested that these breccias were generated by water circulation during shallowing stages of sea level. As the understanding of the palaeogeography and the geodynamics of the Vocontian Trough developed, the formation of the Tithonian breccias was attributed to a debris flow origin and the calcarenites were interpreted as turbidity current deposits (Goguel 1944; Remane 1960, 1966, 1970; Beaudoin 1977). Recently, this interpretation was revised by Bouchette *et al.* (2001) and Séguret *et al.* (2001). They proposed that all the Tithonian breccias were produced *in-situ* by waves and that the calcarenites correspond to *in-situ* sediments produced on a large carbonate ramp. Their process of wave-induced brecciation is characterized on a three-stage mechanism at grain scale: (1) pseudo-cracking; (2) crack

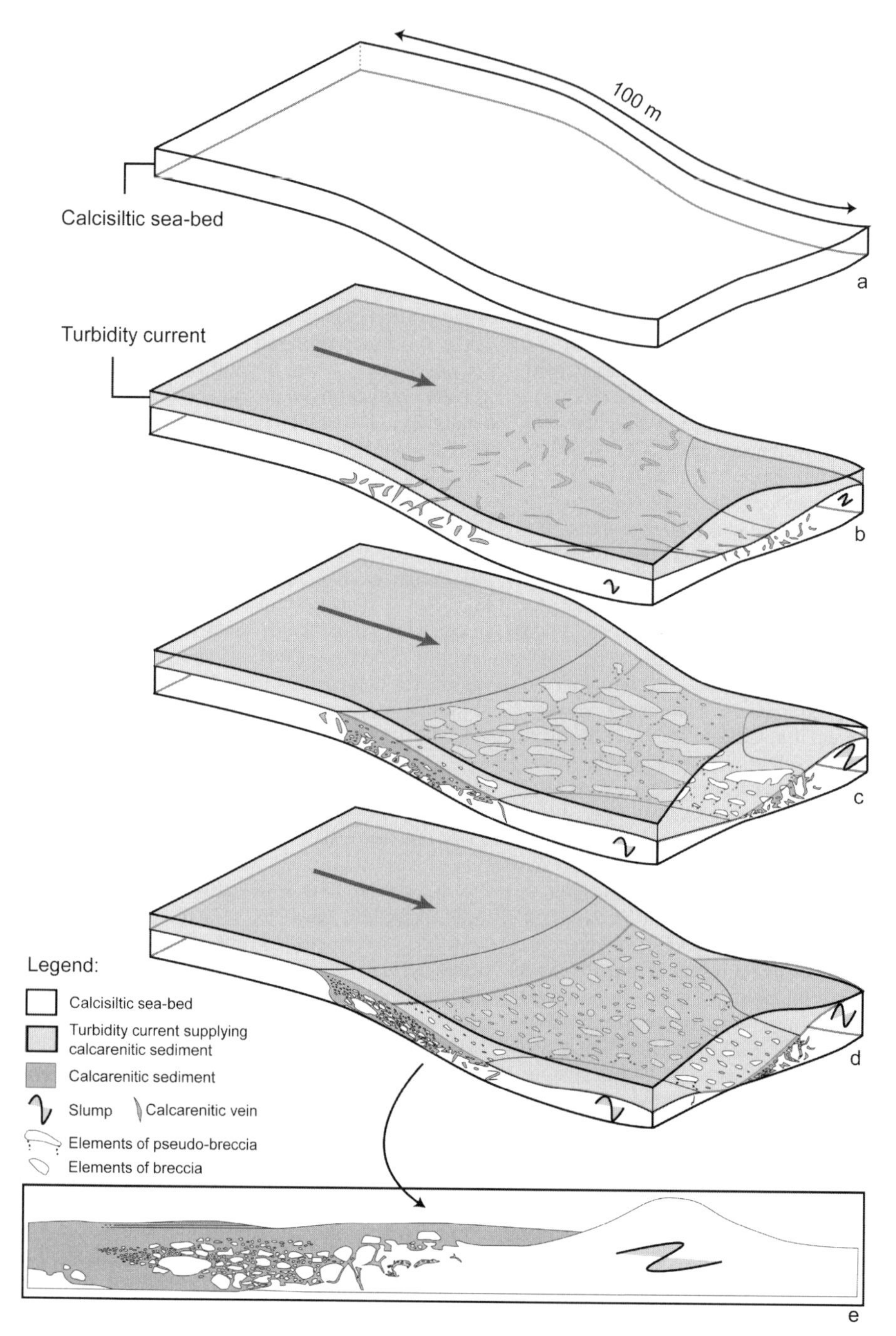

Fig. 7. 3D block diagrams showing the mechanism responsible for the genesis of carbonate brecciation and slumping of a calcisiltic bed in the Barremian–Aptian succession of the Baronnies syncline: a turbidity current. (**a**) Initial situation: seabed is composed of a semi-consolidated calcisiltic sediment. (**b**) Penetration of calcarenitic sediment into the calcisiltic bed due to hydraulic microfracturing induced by loading of an overriding turbidity current. (**c**) Hydraulic pressure produces a pseudo-breccia. (**d**) Calcisiltic elements are separated from the substrate by the turbidity current to create the fragments of the breccia. (**e**) Sedimentary features observed along the outcrops and resulting from the hydraulic pressure of an overriding and depositing turbidity current. Penetration of the current into the semi-consolidated sediment also loads the bed and induces destabilization and folding.

collapse; and (3) heterogeneous liquefaction. They assume that storm events were as strong during the Tithonian as they are today and that the maximal water-depth for a large part of the Vocontian Trough was less than 150 m at that time, which is much shallower than previous seabed depth estimations (Wilpshaar & Leereveld 1994; Ferry & Rubino 1989).

The interpretation of Bouchette *et al.* (2001) and Séguret *et al.* (2001) was based on the recognition of hummocky cross-stratification features (HCS) and rare features named 'dentelles' (Bouchette 2001). First, HCS-like structures are not restricted to storm-influenced environment but are also known in turbiditic settings (e.g. Prave & Duke 1990). Second, the 'dentelles' display the same field characteristics as the monogenic breccias described above from the Barremian–Aptian outcrops, i.e. a calcisiltic bed cross-cut by a network of calcarenitic veins, bounded by an undulated surface (pseudo-breccia) and overlain by a breccia with calcisiltic elements surrounded by a calcarenitic matrix (Séguret *et al.* 2001; see their fig. 14). In consequence, the 'dentelles' features are not diagnostic of storm and/or wave processes.

For the past 60 years, it has been generally accepted that the Tithonian environment of deposition was influenced by gravity currents (Goguel 1944; Remane 1960, 1966, 1970; Beaudoin 1977) rather than wave action. The Tithonian calcarenites, like those in the Barremian–Aptian lobe, might have been transported by turbidity currents. Indeed, the sedimentary features observed in the Tithonian calcarenites are compatible to those from turbiditic settings (e.g. T_{ae}, T_{bc} and T_{bde} intervals are common). These bioclastic calcarenites are graded, typically the beds are coarse to medium-grained at the base and very fine-grained at the top, with common planar laminations. In some cases, these currents could have disrupted the underlying calcisiltic bed *in-situ* to generate: (1) local network of calcarenitic veins; (2) a pseudo-breccia; and (3) a breccia. Among the Tithonian breccias, levels displaying the three stages of the *in-situ* brecciation are rare and not representative of the entire Tithonian succession. Moreover, the turbidites that could have generated the breccias are not dominant in this succession and breccias are generally very thick (metre-scale in thickness). Hence, it is unlikely that most of the Tithonian breccias were related to a turbidity current induced process; rather, they may have been linked to a debris flow mechanism. This alternative proposal for the formation of the Tithonian breccias combines the allochtonous character well illustrated by Goguel (1944), Remane (1960, 1966, 1970) and Beaudoin (1977), with the exceptional process of an *in-situ* brecciation proposed by Kilian (1888), Haug (1891) and Bouchette *et al.* (2001).

Brecciation within a sequence stratigraphic framework

Employing standard sequence stratigraphic models, based on siliciclastic systems, allows the formation and distribution of the breccias to be predicted within a relative sea-level cycle. Maximum resedimentation in the basin is thought to occur during sea-level lowstands (e.g. Haq *et al.* 1987, 1988; Vail 1987; Posamentier *et al.* 1988; Van Wagoner *et al.* 1988; Vail *et al.* 1991). These concepts have been applied to the carbonate depositional system (Sarg 1988; Handford & Loucks 1993). However, the mechanism responsible for the brecciation has to be correctly identified in order to consider the breccias within a sequence stratigraphic context. Indeed, breccias generated by exogenic triggers (*sensu* Spence & Tucker 1997), like gas discharging or seismic shocks, cannot be used directly to interpret the relative sea-level.

This paper demonstrates that breccias can be genetically related to turbidites. Concerning the siliciclastic system, it is thought that turbidites are predominantly deposited during sea-level lowstand (e.g. Vail *et al.* 1987, 1991; Posamentier *et al.* 1988). In theory, the breccias described here could be used as a proxy for the relative sea-level. However, the sequence stratigraphic position of carbonate turbidites is still unclear. Indeed, the standard sequence stratigraphic model applied to the carbonate system involves the lowstand shedding of calcareous turbidites (Biddle 1984; Bosellini 1984; Shanmugam & Moiola 1984; Sarg 1988; Hanford & Loucks 1993). However, during the Pleistocene, sediment production and export from rimmed carbonate platforms peaked during interglacial highstands when platform tops were flooded (Schlager 1992). In the past, when carbonate platforms were affected by low amplitude sea-level fluctuations, the shedding of sediment was certainly less variable between lowstand and highstand periods. Moreover, when the platform exhibits a ramp morphology, turbidites can be triggered during both lowstand and highstand relative sea-level (Schlager 1992; Betzler *et al.* 1999, 2000; Isern & Anselmetti 2001). As the formation of carbonate turbidites is dependent on the amplitudes of the sea-level fluctuations, the palaeoenvironmental variations, the morphology of the platform and tectonic events, the breccias induced by turbidity currents in a carbonate setting cannot be used as a reliable proxy for the relative sea-level.

Conclusion

This study of the Barremian–Aptian succession of the Baronnies syncline suggests that a new mechanism may have been responsible for the formation of submarine calcareous breccias and slumps. Even in the distal part of a 20 km long calcareous lobe, the deposition of turbidity currents may sometimes be powerful enough to cause the *in-situ* brecciation of the underlying unlithified seabed by hydraulic microfracturing. These high energy currents bypass proximal areas of the lobe and are probably responsible for the formation of channel forms. Locally, the penetration of the flow into a semi-consolidated substrate can also induce loading, destabilization and folding. In the sedimentary record, both lateral and longitudinal transects can show an evolution from a turbidite sequence to a breccia and a slump.

Among the Tithonian-aged breccias, widely developed in the Vocontian Trough, some intervals display the same characteristics as observed in the Barremian–Aptian breccias. Although these Tithonian breccias have been interpreted as being wave-induced *in-situ*, they are not diagnostic of a storm process. Some of the Tithonian breccias may have been generated by the emplacement of turbidity currents and debris flows.

This paper demonstrates that breccias may be genetically related to overlying turbidites. These breccias result from an *in-situ* reworking caused by loading of a turbidity current. Because of the complex interplay in variations of relative sea-level, palaeoenvironmental conditions and platform morphologies that control the initiation and deposition of calciturbidites, they are likely to occur during all periods of a relative sea-level cycle. Hence, calcareous turbidites and their associated breccias are not strongly diagnostic of relative sea-level.

Funding came from both TOTAL petroleum company and from the GDR-Marges, a French CNRS-TOTAL joint project. Thanks are due to Serge Ferry of the University of Lyon for fruitful discussions, Yann Merran for his competence and pleasant company in the field, and William Lyons of the MIT for the English improvement. Comments on the manuscript by D. Masson, S. Flint and D. Hodgson are gratefully acknowledged.

References

ARNAUD-VANNEAU, A. & ARNAUD, H. 1990. *Hauterivian to lower Aptian carbonate shelf sedimentation and sequence stratigraphy in the Jura and northern Subalpine chains (southeastern France and Swiss Jura).* International Association of Sedimentologists, Special Publication, **9**, 203–233.

ARNAUD-VANNEAU, A., ARNAUD, H., COTILLON, P., FERRY, S. & MASSE, J.P. 1982. Caractères et évolution des plates-formes carbonatées Périvocontiennes au Crétacé inférieur (France Sud-Est). *Cretaceous Research*, **3**, 3–18.

BEAUDOIN, B. 1977. *Méthodes d'analyse sédimentaire et reconstitution du bassin: Jurassique terminal – Berriasien des chaînes subalpines méridionales.* Thesis, University of Caen, France.

BETZLER, C., REIJMER, J.J.G., BARNET, K., EBERLI, G.P. & ANSELMETTI, F.S. 1999. Sedimentary patterns and geometries of the Bahamian outer carbonate ramp (Miocene–lower Pliocene, Great Bahama Bank). *Sedimentology*, **46**, 1127–1143.

BETZLER, C., PFEIFFER, M. & SAXENA, S. 2000. Carbonate shedding and sedimentary cyclicities of a distally steepened ramp (Miocene, Great Bahama Bank). *International Journal of Earth Sciences*, **89**, 140–153.

BIDDLE, K.T. 1984. Triassic sea level change and the Ladinian–Carnian stage boundary. *Nature*, **308**, 631–633.

BOSELLINI, A. 1984. Progradation geometries of carbonate platforms: examples from the Triassic of the Dolomites, northern Italy. *Sedimentology*, **31**, 1–24.

BOUCHETTE, F., 2001. *Interaction houle/sediments: la rampe carbonatée du Bassin du Sud-Est au Jurassique terminal.* Thesis, University of Montpellier II, France.

BOUCHETTE, F., SÉGURET, M. & MOUSSINE-POUCHKINE, A. 2001. Coarse carbonate breccia as the result of water-wave cyclic loading. *Sedimentology*, **48**, 767–789.

COOK, H.E., MCDANIEL, P.N., MOUNTJOY, E.W. & PRAY, L.C. 1972. Allochthonous carbonate debris flows at Devonian bank ('reef') margins, Alberta, Canada. *Bulletin of Canadian Petroleum Geology*, **20**, 439–486.

DEBRAND-PASSARD, S., COURBOULEIX, S. & LIENHARDT, M.J. (eds) 1984. Synthèse géologique du sud-est de la France. Stratigraphie et paléogéographie. *Mémoire du Bureau de Recherche Géologique et Minière*, **125**.

DEMICCO, R.V. & HARDIE, L.A. 1994. Sedimentary structures and early diagenetic features of shallow marine carbonate deposits. Society of Economic Paleontologists and Mineralogists, Atlas Series, **1**, 265pp.

EBERLI, G.P. 1991. Calcareous turbidite sequences and their relationship to sea-level fluctuations and tectonism. *In*: EINSELE, G., RICKEN, W. & SEILACHER, A. (eds) *Cycles and Events in Stratigraphy*. Springer Verlag, Berlin, 340–359.

FAIRBRIDGE, R.W. 1978. Breccia, sedimentary. *In*: FAIRBRIDGE, R.W. & BOURGEOIS, J. (eds) *Encyclopedia of Sedimentology*. Stroudsburg, Pa.. Dowden, Hutchinson & Ross, New York, **6**, 84–86.

FERRY, S. 1976. Cônes d'epandages bioclastiques en eau profonde et glissements sous-marins dans le Barremien et l'Aptien inférieur vocontiens de la Drôme, implications paléostructurales. Thesis, Université Claude Bernard, Lyon, France.

FERRY, S. 1978. Les 'Calcaires à débris' barrémo-aptiens de la Drôme vocontienne (France SE); des cônes d'épandage bioclastique en eau profonde. *Documents des Laboratoires de Géologie*, Lyon, Hors Série, **4**, 273–303.

FERRY, S. 1984. Apports détritiques dans le Bassin Vocontien. *In*: DEBRAND-PASSARD, S., COURBOULEIX, S. & LIENHARDT, M.J. (eds) Synthèse géologique du sud-est de la France. *Mémoire du Bureau de Recherche Géologique et Minière*, **125**, 332–334.

FERRY, S. & FLANDRIN, J. 1979. Megabrêches de resédimentation, lacunes mécaniques et pseudo-'hard grounds' sur la marge vocontienne au Barrémien et à l'Aptien inférieur (sud-est de la France). *Géologie Alpine*, **55**, 75–92.

FERRY, S. & RUBINO, J.L. 1989. Mesozoic eustacy record on western Tethyan margins. *Livret guide du 2ème congrès de l'Association des Sédimentologistes Français*, **12**, 265–275.

FRIES, G. 1986. *Dynamique du Bassin Subalpin méridional de l'Aptien au Cénomanien*. Thesis, University of Paris 6, France.

GIGNOUX, M. & MORET, J. 1938. Géologie Dauphinoise (1st Edn). Masson, Paris.

GOGUEL, J. 1944. Contribution à l'étude paléogéographique du Crétacé inférieur dans le S.E. de la France. *Bulletin des Services de Cartes Géologiques de France*, **44**, 62–78.

HANDFORD, C.R. & LOUCKS, R.G. 1993. Carbonate depositional sequences and systems tracts: responses of carbonate platforms to relative sea-level changes. *In*: LOUCKS, R.G. & SARG, J.F. (eds) Carbonate sequence stratigraphy — recent developments and applications. *American Association of Petroleum Geologists Memoir*, **57**, 3–41.

HAQ, B.U., HARDENBOL, J. & VAIL, P.R. 1987. The chronology of fluctuating sea level since the Triassic. *Science*, **235**, 1956–1167.

HAQ, B.U., HARDENBOL, J. & VAIL, P.R. 1988. Mesozoic and Cenozoic chronostratigraphy and cycles of sea-level change. *In*: WILGUS, C.K., HASTINGS, B.S., KENDALL, C.G. ST C., POSAMENTIER, H., ROSS, C.A. & VAN WAGONER, J. (eds) *Sea-level changes: an integrated approach*. Society of Economic Paleontologists and Mineralogists, Special Publication, **42**, 71–108.

HAUG, E. 1891. Les chaînes subalpines entre Gaz et Digne. *Bulletin des Services de Cartes Géologiques de France*, **3**, 1–297.

ISERN, A.R. & ANSELMETTI, F.S. 2001. The influence of carbonate platform morphology and sea level on fifth-order petrophysical cyclicity in slope and basin sediments adjacent to the Great Bahama Bank. *Marine Geology*, **177**, 381–394.

KILIAN, W. 1888. *Description géologique de la Montagne de Lure*. Thesis, University of Paris, France.

KILIAN, W. 1895. Notes stratigraphiques sur les environs de Sisteron. *Bulletin de la Société Géologique de France*, **3**, 105–112.

LE HEGARAT, G. 1974. *Le Berriasien du Sud-Est de la France*. Thesis, University of Claude Bernard, Lyon 1, France.

MORROW, D.W. 1982. Descriptive field classification of sedimentary and diagenetic breccia fabrics in carbonate rocks. *Bulletin of Canadian Petroleum Geology*, **30**, 227–229.

POSAMENTIER, H.W., JERVEY, M.T. & VAIL, P.R. 1988. Eustatic controls on clastic deposition: I, Conceptual framework. *In*: WILGUS, C.K., HASTINGS, B.S., KENDALL, C.G. ST C., POSAMENTIER, H., ROSS, C.A. & VAN WAGONER, J. (eds) *Sea-level changes: an integrated approach*. Society of Economic Paleontologists and Mineralogists, Special Publication, **42**, 109–124.

PRAVE, A.R. & DUKE, W.L. 1990. Small-scale hummocky cross-stratification in turbidites: a form of antidune stratification. *Sedimentology*, **37**, 531–539.

RAJA GABAGLIA, G. 1995. *Stratigraphie et facies de tempête de la rampe carbonatée du Jurassique supérieur du bassin du Sud-Est (France): calcarénites, brèches, corps glissés*. Thesis, University of Montpellier II, France.

REMANE, J. 1960. Les formations brèchiques dans le Tithonique du Sud-Est de la France. *Travaux du Laboratoire de Géologie*, Faculté des Sciences de Grenoble, **36**, 75–114.

REMANE, J. 1966. Note préliminaire sur la paléogéographie du tithonique des chaînes subalpines. *Compte Rendu Sommaire des Séances de la Société Géologique de France*, **5**, 201, 1966.

REMANE, J. 1970. Die Entstehung der resedimentären Breccien im Obertithon der subalpinen Ketten Frankreichs. *Eclogae Geologicae Helveticae*, **63**, 685–740.

SARG, J.F. 1988. Carbonate sequence stratigraphy. *In*: WILGUS, C.K., HASTINGS, B.S., KENDALL, C.G. ST C., POSAMENTIER, H., ROSS, C.A. & VAN WAGONER, J. (eds) *Sea-level changes: an integrated approach*. Society of Economic Paleontologists and Mineralogists, Special Publication, **42**, 155–181.

SCHLAGER, W. 1992. *Sedimentology and sequence stratigraphy of reefs and carbonate platforms — a short course*. American Association of Petroleum Geologists, Continuing Education Course Note Series.

SÉGURET, M., MOUSSINE-POUCHKINE, A., RAJA GABAGLIA, G. & BOUCHETTE, F. 2001. Storm deposits and storm-generated coarse carbonate breccias on pelagic outer-shelf (South East Basin, France). *Sedimentology*, **48**, 231–254.

SHANMUGAM, G. & MOIOLA, R.J. 1984. Eustatic control of calciclastic turbidites. *Marine Geology*, **56**, 273–278.

SPENCE, G.H. & TUCKER, M.E. 1997. Genesis of limestone megabreccias and their significance in carbonate sequence stratigraphic models: a review. *Sedimentary Geology*, **112**, 163–193.

TWENHOFEL, W.H. 1947. The environmental significance of conglomerates. *Journal of Sedimentary Petrology*, **17**, 119–128.

VAIL, P.R. 1987. Seismic stratigraphy interpretation using sequence stratigraphy, Part I. Seismic interpretation procedure. *In*: BALLY, A.W. (ed.) *Atlas of Seismic Stratigraphy*, 1. American Association of Petroleum Geologists, Studies in Geology, 27, 1–10.

VAIL, P.R., AUDEMARD, F., BOWMAN, S.A., EISNER, P.N. & PEREZ-CRUZ, G. 1991. The stratigraphic signatures of tectonics, eustacy and sedimentology: an overview. *In*: EINSELE, G., RICKEN, W. & SEILACHER, A. (eds) *Cycles and events in stratigraphy*. Springer Verlag, Berlin, 617–659.

VAIL, P.R., COLIN, J.P., JAN DU CHENE, R., KUCHLY, J., MEDIAVILLA, F. & TRIFILIEFF, V. 1987. La stratigraphie séquentielle et son application aux corrélations chronostratigraphiques dans le Jurassique du bassin de Paris. *Bulletin de la Société Géologique de France*, **3**, 1301–1321.

VAN WAGONER, J.C., POSAMENTIER, H.W., MITCHUM, R.M. JR, *ET AL.* 1988. An overview of the fundamentals of sequence stratigraphy and key definitions. *In*:

WILGUS, C.K., HASTINGS, B.S., KENDALL, C.G. ST C., POSAMENTIER, H., ROSS, C.A. & VAN WAGONER, J. (eds) *Sea-level changes: an integrated approach.* Society of Economic Paleontologists and Mineralogists, Special Publication, **42**, 39–45.

WILPSHAAR, M. & LEEREVELD, H. 1994. Palaeoenvironmental change in the Early Cretaceous Vocontian Trough (SE France) reflected by dinoflagellate cysts. *Review of Palaeobotany and Palynology*, **84**, 121–128.

Index

Page numbers in *italic* denote figures. Page numbers in **bold** denote tables